LITERATURE

For additional information on Intel products in the U.S. or Canada, call Intel's Literature Center at (800) 548-4725 or write to:

INTEL LITERATURE SALES
P.O. Box 7641
Mt. Prospect, IL 60056-7641

To order literature outside of the U.S. and Canada contact your local sales office.

Additional information about Intel products is available on Intel's web site: http://www.intel.com.

CURRENT DATABOOKS

Product line databooks contain datasheets, application notes, article reprints, and other design information. All databooks can be ordered individually, and most are available in a pre-packaged set in the U.S. and Canada. Databooks can be ordered in the U.S. and Canada by calling TAB/McGraw-Hill at 1-800-822-8158; outside of the U.S. and Canada contact your local sales office.

Title	Intel Order Number	ISBN
SET OF NINE DATABOOKS (Available in U.S. and Canada)	231003	N/A
CONTENTS LISTED BELOW FOR INDIVIDUAL ORDERING:		
EMBEDDED MICROCONTROLLERS	270646	1-55512-248-5
EMBEDDED MICROPROCESSORS	272396	1-55512-249-3
FLASH MEMORY (2 volume set)	210830	1-55512-250-7
i960® PROCESSORS AND RELATED PRODUCTS	272084	1-55512-252-3
NETWORKING	297360	1-55512-256-6
OEM BOARDS, SYSTEMS AND SOFTWARE	280407	1-55512-253-1
PACKAGING	240800	1-55512-254-X
PENTIUM® AND PENTIUM PRO PROCESSORS AND RELATED PRODUCTS	241732	1-55512-251-5
PERIPHERAL COMPONENTS	296467	1-55512-255-8
ADDITIONAL LITERATURE: (Not included in databook set)		
AUTOMOTIVE PRODUCTS	231792	1-55512-257-4
COMPONENTS QUALITY/RELIABILITY	210997	1-55512-258-2
EMBEDDED APPLICATIONS (1995/96)	270648	1-55512-179-9
MILITARY	210461	N/A
SYSTEMS QUALITY/RELIABILITY	231762	1-55512-046-6

A complete set of this information is available on CD-ROM through Intel's Data on Demand program, order number 240897. For information about Intel's Data on Demand ask for item number 240952.

January 1996
Order Number: 000900-001

Intel Application Support Services

World Wide Web [URL: http://www.intel.com/]

Intel's Web site now contains technical and product information that is available 24 hours a day! Also visit Intel's site for financials, history, current news and events, job opportunities, educational news and much, much more!

FaxBack*

Technical and product information are available 24 hours a day! Order documents containing:

- Product Announcements
- Product Literature
- Intel Device Characteristics
- Design/Application Recommendations
- Stepping/Change Notifications
- Quality and Reliability Information

Information on the following subjects are available:

- Microcontroller and Flash
- OEM Branded Systems
- Multibus and iRMX Software/BBS listing
- Multimedia
- Development Tools
- Quality and Reliability/Change Notification
- Microprocessor/PCI/Peripheral
- Intel Architecture Labs

To use FaxBack (for Intel components and systems), dial **(800) 628-2283** or 916-356-3105 (U.S./Canada/APAC/Japan) *or +44{0} 1793-496646 (Europe)* and follow the automated voice-prompt. Document orders will be faxed to the fax number you specify. For information on how the Intel Application Support team can help you, order our Customer Service Agreement, document #1201. Catalogs are updated as needed, so call for the latest information!

Bulletin Board System (BBS)

To use the Intel Application BBS (components and systems), dial **(503) 264-7999** or **(916) 356-3600** (U.S./Canada/APAC/Japan) *or +44{0} 1793-432955 (Europe)*. The BBS will support 1200-19200 baud rate modem. *Typical modem configuration: 14.4K baud rate, No Parity, 8 Data Bits, 1 Stop Bit.*

CompuServe *Just type* 'Go Intel'

Intel maintains several forums where people come together to meet their peers, gather information, share discoveries and debate issues. For more information about service fees and access, call CompuServe at 1-800-848-8199 or 614-529-1340 (outside the U.S.). The INTELC forum is set up to support designers using various Intel components.

General Information Help Desk

Dial 1-800-628-8686 or 916-356-7599 (U.S. and Canada) between 5 a.m. and 5 p.m. PST for help with Intel products. For customers not in the U.S. or Canada, please contact your local distributor.

Intel Literature Centers

U.S.	+1-800-548-4725	France	+44{0} 1793 421777
U.S. (from overseas)	+1-708-296-9333	Germany	+44{0} 1793 421333
England	+44{0} 1793 431 155	Japan (fax only)	+81{0} 120 47 88 32

Intel Distributors

Check the back of an Intel data book or request one of the following distributor listing FaxBack documents: #4083 (U.S. Eastern Time Zone), #4084 (U.S. Central Time Zone), #4085 (Mountain Time Zone), #4086 (U.S. Alaska/Pacific Time Zone), #4209 (Europe) or #4403 (Canada).

Other brands and names are the property of their respective owners.

January 1996
Order Number: 000901-001

intel®

Pentium® Pro Family Developer's Manual

Volume 2:
Programmer's Reference Manual

NOTE: The *Pentium® Pro Family Developer's Manual* consists of three books: *Specifications*, Order Number 242690; *Programmer's Reference Manual*, Order Number 242691; and the *Operating System Writer's Guide*, Order Number 242692.
Please refer to all three volumes when evaluating your design needs.

1996

TABLE OF CONTENTS

APPENDIX A
EFLAGS CROSS-REFERENCE

APPENDIX B
EFLAGS CONDITION CODES

APPENDIX C
FLOATING-POINT EXCEPTIONS SUMMARY

TABLE OF FIGURES

TABLE OF TABLES

intel®

1

About This Manual

CHAPTER 1
ABOUT THIS MANUAL

The *Pentium® Pro Family Developer's Manual, Volume 2: Programmer's Reference Manual* (Order Number 242691) is part of a three-volume set that describes the architecture, programming environment, and hardware features of the Pentium® Pro processor. The other two manuals in this set are as follows:

* *Pentium® Pro Family Developer's Manual, Volume 1: Specifications* (Order Number 242690)

* *Pentium® Pro Family Developer's Manual, Volume 3: Operating System Writer's Guide* (Order Number 242692)

The *Pentium® Pro Family Developer's Manual, Volume 2* and the *Pentium® Pro Family Developer's Manual, Volume 3* describe the architecture and programming environment of the processor. The *Pentium® Pro Family Developer's Manual, Volume 2* describes the basic programming environment and the instructions set of the processor. It is aimed at application programmers who are writing programs to run under existing operating systems or executives. The *Pentium® Pro Family Developer's Manual, Volume 3* describes the operating system support environment of the processor, including memory management, protection, task management, interrupt and exception handling, and system management mode. It also describes the opcode structure and requirements for compiler writers. Both manuals provide Intel Architecture processor compatibility information.

1.1. OVERVIEW OF THE PENTIUM® PRO FAMILY DEVELOPER'S MANUAL, VOLUME 2

The contents of this manual are as follows:

Chapter 1 — About the Manual. Gives an overview of this manual and the *Pentium® Pro Family Developer's Manual, Volume 3*. It also describes the notational conventions in these manuals and lists related Intel manuals and documentation of interest to programmers and hardware designers.

Chapter 2 — Introduction to the Intel Pentium® Pro Processor. Introduces the Intel Pentium Pro processor family, gives an overview of the new features found in these processors, and describes the Pentium Pro processor's microarchitecture.

Chapter 3 — Program Execution Environment. Introduces the models of memory organization and describes the register set used by applications.

Chapter 4 — Basic Calls, Interrupts, and Exceptions. Describes the procedure stack and the mechanisms provided for making procedure calls and for servicing interrupts and exceptions.

Chapter 5 — Data Types and Addressing Modes. Describes the data types and addressing modes recognized by the processor.

Chapter 6 — Instruction Set Summary. Gives an overview of all the Pentium Pro processor instructions except those executed by the processor's floating-point unit. The instructions are presented in functionally related groups.

Chapter 7 — Floating-Point Unit. Describes the Pentium Pro processor's floating-point unit, including the floating-point registers and data types; gives an overview of the floating-point instruction set; and describes the processor's floating-point exception conditions.

Chapter 8 — Input/Output. Describes the processor's I/O architecture, including I/O port addressing, the I/O instructions, and the I/O protection mechanism.

Chapter 9 — Processor Identification and Feature Determination. Describes how to determine the CPU type and the features that are available in the processor.

Chapter 10 — Intel Architecture Compatibility. Describes the programming differences between the Intel 286, Intel386™, Intel486™, Pentium, and Pentium Pro processors.

Chapter 11 — Instruction Set Reference. Describes each of the Pentium Pro processor instructions in detail, including an algorithmic description of operations, the effect on flags, the effect of operand- and address-size attributes, and the exceptions that may be generated. The instructions are arranged in alphabetical order.

Appendix A — EFLAGS Cross-Reference. Summaries how the Pentium Pro processor instructions affect the flags in the EFLAGS register.

Appendix B — EFLAGS Condition Codes. Summarizes how the conditional jump, move, and byte set on condition code instructions use the condition code flags (OF, CF, ZF, SF, and PF) in the EFLAGS register.

Appendix C — Floating-Point Exceptions Summary. Summarizes the exceptions that can be raised by floating-point instructions.

1.2. OVERVIEW OF THE PENTIUM® PRO FAMILY DEVELOPER'S MANUAL, VOLUME 3

The contents of the *Pentium® Pro Family Developer's Manual, Volume 3* are as follows:

Chapter 1 — About the Manual. Gives an overview of this manual and the *Pentium® Pro Family Developer's Manual, Volume 2*. It also describes the notational conventions in these manuals and lists related Intel manuals and documentation of interest to programmers and hardware designers.

Chapter 2 — System Architecture Overview. Describes the modes of operation of the Pentium Pro processor and those processor features used to build operating systems and executives, including the system-oriented registers and data structures and the system-oriented instructions. The steps necessary for switching between real-address and protected modes are also identified.

Chapter 3 — Protected-Mode Memory Management. Describes the data structures, registers, and instructions that support segmentation and paging and explains how they can be used to implement a "flat" (unsegmented) memory model or a segmented memory model.

Chapter 4 — Protection. Describes the Pentium Pro processor's support for page and segment protection. This chapter also explains the implementation of privilege rules, stack switching, pointer validation, user and supervisor modes.

Chapter 5 — Interrupt and Exception Handling. Describes the basic interrupt mechanisms of the Pentium Pro processor, shows how interrupts and exceptions relate to protection, and describes how the processor handles each exception type.

Chapter 6 — Task Management. Describes how the Pentium Pro processor supports multi-tasking with context-switching operations and inter-task protection.

Chapter 7 — Multiple Processor Management. Describes the instructions and flags that support multiple processors with shared memory, memory ordering, and the advanced programmable interrupt controller (APIC).

Chapter 8 — Processor Management and Initialization. Defines the state of the processor and floating-point unit after reset initialization. This chapter also explains how to set up the processor for real-address mode operation and protected mode operation, and how to switch between modes.

Chapter 9 — System Management Mode (SMM). Describes the Pentium Pro processor's implementation of system management mode (SMM), which can be used to implement power management functions.

Chapter 10 — Debugging and Performance Monitoring. Describes the debugging registers and other debug features of the Pentium Pro processor. This chapter also describes the time-stamp counter and the performance monitoring counters.

Chapter 11 — Memory Cache Control. Describes the general concept of caching and the specific mechanisms used by the Pentium Pro processor's internal caches. This chapter also describes the memory type range registers (MTRRs) and how they can be used to map memory types of physical memory.

Chapter 12 — 8086 Emulation. Describes the real-address and virtual-8086 modes of the Pentium Pro processor.

Chapter 13 — Mixing 16-Bit and 32-Bit Code. Describes how to mix 16-bit and 32-bit code modules within the same program or task.

Chapter 14 — Code Optimization. Discusses general optimization techniques for programming an Intel Architecture processor.

Chapter 15 — Intel Architecture Compatibility. Describes the differences between 8086, the Intel 286, Intel386, Intel486, Pentium, and Pentium Pro processors. This chapter covers the system architecture of the Intel Architecture processors.

Chapter 16 — Machine Check Architecture. Describes the processor's machine check architecture.

Appendix A — Opcode Map. Gives an opcode map for the Pentium Pro processor instruction set.

Appendix B — Performance-Monitoring Counters. Lists the events that can be counted with the performance-monitoring counters and the codes used to select these events.

Appendix C — Model Specific Registers (MSRs). Lists the MSRs available in the Pentium Pro processor and their functions.

1.3. NOTATIONAL CONVENTIONS

This manual uses special notation for data-structure formats, for symbolic representation of instructions, and for hexadecimal numbers. A review of this notation makes the manual easier to read.

1.3.1. Bit and Byte Order

In illustrations of data structures in memory, smaller addresses appear toward the bottom of the figure; addresses increase toward the top. Bit positions are numbered from right to left. The numerical value of a set bit is equal to two raised to the power of the bit position. The Pentium Pro processor is a "little endian" machine; this means the bytes of a word are numbered starting from the least significant byte. Figure 1-1 illustrates these conventions.

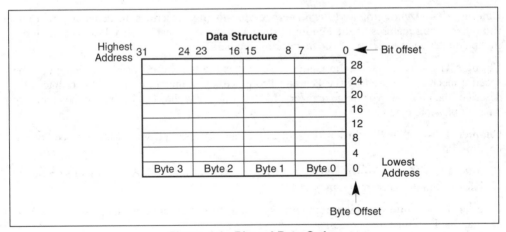

Figure 1-1. Bit and Byte Order

1.3.2. Reserved Bits and Software Compatibility

In many register and memory layout descriptions, certain bits are marked as *reserved*. When bits are marked as reserved, it is essential for compatibility with future processors that software treat these bits as having a future, though unknown, effect. The behavior of reserved bits should be regarded as not only undefined, but unpredictable. Software should follow these guidelines in dealing with reserved bits:

- Do not depend on the states of any reserved bits when testing the values of registers which contain such bits. Mask out the reserved bits before testing.

- Do not depend on the states of any reserved bits when storing to memory or to a register.

- Do not depend on the ability to retain information written into any reserved bits.

- When loading a register, always load the reserved bits with the values indicated in the documentation, if any, or reload them with values previously read from the same register.

NOTE

> Avoid any software dependence upon the state of reserved Pentium Pro processor register bits. Depending upon the values of reserved register bits will make software dependent upon the unspecified manner in which the processor handles these bits. Depending upon reserved values risks incompatibility with future processors.

1.3.3. Instruction Operands

When instructions are represented symbolically, a subset of the assembly language for the Pentium Pro processor is used. In this subset, an instruction has the following format:

```
label: mnemonic argument1, argument2, argument3
```

where:

- A *label* is an identifier which is followed by a colon.

- A *mnemonic* is a reserved name for a class of instruction opcodes which have the same function.

- The operands *argument1*, *argument2*, and *argument3* are optional. There may be from zero to three operands, depending on the opcode. When present, they take the form of either literals or identifiers for data items. Operand identifiers are either reserved names of registers or are assumed to be assigned to data items declared in another part of the program (which may not be shown in the example).

When two operands are present in an arithmetic or logical instruction, the right operand is the source and the left operand is the destination.

For example:

```
LOADREG: MOV EAX, SUBTOTAL
```

In this example LOADREG is a label, MOV is the mnemonic identifier of an opcode, EAX is the destination operand, and SUBTOTAL is the source operand. Some assembly languages put the source and destination in reverse order.

1.3.4.   Hexadecimal and Binary Numbers

Base 16 (hexadecimal) numbers are represented by a string of hexadecimal digits followed by the character H (for example, F82EH). A hexadecimal digit is a character from the following set: 0, 1, 2, 3, 4, 5, 6, 7, 8, 9, A, B, C, D, E, and F.

Base 2 (binary) numbers are represented by a string of 1s and 0s, sometimes followed by the character B (for example, 1010B). The "B" designation is only used in situations where confusion as to the type of number might arise.

1.3.5.   Segmented Addressing

The processor uses byte addressing. This means memory is organized and accessed as a sequence of bytes. Whether one or more bytes are being accessed, a byte address is used to address memory. The memory that can be addressed with a byte address is called an *address space*.

The processor also supports segmented addressing. This is a form of addressing where a program may have many independent address spaces, called *segments*. For example, a program can keep its code (instructions) and stack in separate segments. Code addresses would always refer to the code space, and stack addresses would always refer to the stack space. The following notation is used to specify a byte address within a segment:

Segment-register:Byte-address

For example, the following segment address identifies the byte at address FF79H in the segment pointed by the DS register:

```
DS:FF79H
```

The following segment address identifies an instruction address in the code segment. The CS register points to the code segment and the EIP register contains the address of the instruction.

```
CS:EIP
```

1.3.6.   Exceptions

An exception is an event that typically occurs when an instruction causes an error. For example, an attempt to divide by zero generates an exception. However, some exceptions, such as breakpoints, occur under other conditions. Some types of exceptions may provide error codes. An error code reports additional information about the error. An example of the notation used to show an exception and error code is shown below.

```
#PF(fault code)
```

This example refers to a page-fault exception under conditions where an error code naming a type of fault is reported. Under some conditions, exceptions which produce error codes may not be able to report an accurate code. In this case, the error code is zero, as shown below for a general-protection exception.

```
#GP(0)
```

See Chapter 5, *Interrupt and Exception Handling*, in the *Pentium® Pro Family Developer's Manual, Volume 3* for a list of exception mnemonics and their descriptions.

1.4.   RELATED LITERATURE

The following books contain additional material related to Intel processors:

- *Intel Pentium® Pro Processor Specification Update*, Order Number 242689.

- AP-485, *Intel Processor Identification with the CPUID Instruction*, Order Number 241618.

- *Pentium® Processor Data Book*, Order Number 241428.

- *82496 Cache Controller and 82491 Cache SRAM Data Book For Use With the Pentium® Processor*, Order Number 241429.

- *Intel486™ Microprocessor Data Book*, Order Number 240440.

- *Intel486™ Processor Hardware Reference Manual*, Order Number 240552.

- *Intel486™ DX Processor Programmer's Reference Manual*, Order Number 240486.

- *Intel486™ SX CPU/Intel487™ SX Math CoProcessor Data Book*, Order Number 240950.

- *Intel486™ DX2 Microprocessor Data Book*, Order Number 241245.

- *Intel486™ Microprocessor Product Brief Book*, Order Number 240459.

- *Intel386™ Processor Hardware Reference Manual*, Order Number 231732.

- *Intel386™ DX Processor Programmer's Reference Manual*, Order Number 230985.

- *Intel386™ SX Processor Programmer's Reference Manual*, Order Number 240331.

- *Intel386™ Processor System Software Writer's Guide*, Order Number 231499.

- *Intel386™ High-Performance 32-Bit CHMOS Microprocessor with Integrated Memory Management*, Order Number 231630.

- *376 Embedded Processor Programmer's Reference Manual*, Order Number 240314.

- *80387 DX User's Manual Programmer's Reference*, Order Number 231917.

- *376 High-Performance 32-Bit Embedded Processor*, Order Number 240182.

- *Intel386™ SX Microprocessor*, Order Number 240187.

- *Microprocessor and Peripheral Handbook* (vol. 1), Order Number 230843.

- AP-485, *Intel Processor Identification with the CPUID Instruction*, Order Number 241618.

- AP-500, *Optimizations for Intel's 32-Bit Processors*, Order number 241799.

intel®

2

Introduction to the Intel Pentium® Pro Processor

CHAPTER 2

INTRODUCTION TO THE INTEL PENTIUM® PRO PROCESSOR

The Intel Pentium Pro processor is the first of a new family of Intel Architecture processors. While fully software compatible with earlier Intel Architecture processors, it offers several important new architectural and model-specific features. It also provides significant advances in processing speed. The Pentium Pro processor running at a 150 MHz clock rate executes industry standard benchmark programs more than twice as fast as the Intel Pentium processor running at 100 MHz. Table 2-1 provides an overview of the Pentium Pro processor's features.

Table 2-1. Overview of the Pentium® Pro Processor Features

Feature	Description
Number of Transistors	5.5 Million in CPU core.
Clock Rate	First processors, 150 MHz and 166 MHz; up to 200 MHz in the future.
Compatibility with Earlier Intel Architecture Processors	Fully compatible.
Microarchitecture	Three-way superscalar; five parallel execution units (two integer, two FPU, and one memory interface); dynamic execution.
Caches	Level 1 (L1) cache: 8-KByte, four-way set-associative, primary instruction cache; 8-KByte, dual-ported, two-way set-associative, primary data cache; both located on the CPU die. Level 2 (L2) cache: 256-KByte (static RAM) secondary cache; located on a separate die and closely coupled to the CPU die by means of a dedicated full clock-speed bus.
Process Technology	Four-layer metal BiCMOS; 0.6 microns; 2.9 Volts.
Package Design and Die Size	Package: Dual cavity PGA ceramic package; 387 pins. CPU die size: 306 millimeter square L2 Cache SRAM die size: 202 millimeter square
Power consumption	23 watts typical at 150 MHz clock rate.

The new features found in the Pentium Pro processor can be divided into three categories: new architectural features, new model-specific features, and advances in the microarchitecture. These features are described in the following sections.

2.1. NEW ARCHITECTURAL FEATURES

The new features that the Pentium Pro processor adds to the Intel Architecture include several new and extended instructions and new memory management capabilities. Several model-specific features have also been added to the Pentium Pro processor. The following sections describe these new features.

2.1.1. New and Extended Instructions

The following instructions are new in the Pentium Pro processor:

- CMOV*cc* (conditional move) instructions—Checks the state of the status flags in the EFLAGS registers and performs a move operation if the specified condition (state of the flags) is true. These instructions can be used to move a value from a memory location or general-purpose register to another register. They are provided to improve branch prediction performance. (See Chapter 11, "CMOVcc—Conditional Move").

- FCMOV*cc* (floating-point conditional move) instructions—Check the state of the status flags in the EFLAGS registers and perform a floating-point move operation if the specified condition is true. These instructions move the contents of a specified floating-point register [ST(i)] to the top of the register stack [ST(0)]. (see Chapter 11, "FCMOVcc—Floating-Point Conditional Move").

- FCOMI (floating-point compare and set EFLAGS) instructions—Compare the values in two floating-point registers and set the status flags in the EFLAGS register according to the results. (See Chapter 11, "FCOMI/FCOMIP/ FUCOMI/FUCOMIP—Compare Real and Set EFLAGS").

- RDPMC (read performance monitoring counters) instruction—Reads the contents of the specified performance monitoring counter. This instruction is associated with a new flag in control register CR4, bit 8. This flag, called the PCE (performance counter enable) flag, permits programs or procedures running at protection levels 1, 2, or 3 to execute the RDPMC instruction, which can normally only be executed only at privilege level 0. (See Chapter 11, "RDPMC—Read Performance-Monitoring Counters").

- UD2 (undefined) instruction—Generates an invalid opcode exception. This instruction is a no-op instruction provided for testing invalid-opcode exception handlers. (See Chapter 11, "UD2—Undefined Instruction").

In addition to these new instructions, the functions of the CPUID, RDMSR, and WRMSR instructions have been extended. The CPUID (CPU identification) instruction now indicates the existence of additional model-specific features and displays cache information (see Chapter 11, "CPUID—CPU Identification").

The RDMSR (read model-specific register) and WRMSR (write model-specific register) instructions now recognize a much larger number of model-specific registers. (See Chapter 11, "RDMSR—Read from Model Specific Register" and Chapter 11, "WRMSR—Write to Model Specific Register" for more information about these instructions.

2.1.2. New Memory Management Features

The Pentium Pro processor provides three new memory management features: physical memory addressing extension, the global bit in page table entries, and general support for larger page sizes. These features are only available when operating in protected mode.

The new PAE (physical address extension) flag in control register CR4, bit 5, enables four additional address lines on the processor, allowing 36-bit physical addresses. This option can only be used when paging is enabled, using an advance page-table mechanism provided to support the larger physical address range.

The new PGE (page global enable) flag in control register CR4, bit 7, provides a mechanism for preventing frequently used pages from being flushed from the translation lookaside buffer (TLB). When this flag is set, frequently used pages (such as pages containing kernel procedures or common data tables) can be marked global by setting the global flag in a page-table-directory or page-table entry. On a task switch or a write to control register CR3 (which normally causes the TLBs to be flushed), the entries in the TLB marked global will normally not be flushed. Marking pages global in this manner provides software with a mechanism for controlling unnecessary reloading of the TLB due to TLB misses on frequently used pages.

One of the new features available in the Pentium Pro processor is support for large page sizes. This support is enabled with the PSE (page size extension) flag in control register CR4, bit 4. When this flag is set, the processor supports 4-KByte and 4-MByte page sizes when normal paging is used and 4-KByte and 2-MByte page sizes when the physical address extension is used.

See Chapter 3, *Protected-Mode Memory Management*, in the *Pentium® Pro Family Developer's Manual, Volume 3* for more information about the physical memory addressing extension, global pages, and large page sizes.

2.2. NEW AND EXTENDED MODEL-SPECIFIC FEATURES

The Pentium Pro processor provides several model-specific features that are either new to Intel Architecture processors or extensions of existing features. Model-specific features appear in some Intel Architecture processors, but are not part of the Intel Architecture; that is, they are not guaranteed to be implemented in the same manner in future Intel Architecture processors. The new and extended model-specific features found in the Pentium Pro processor include more model specific registers, new *memory type range registers* (MTRRs), extensions to the *machine check architecture*, and new performance monitoring counters.

2.2.1. Model-Specific Registers

The concept of model-specific registers (MSRs) to control hardware functions in the processor or to monitor processor activity was introduced in the Pentium processor. The number of MSRs is greatly increased in the Pentium Pro processor. The new registers control the debug extensions, the performance counters, the machine-check exception capability, the machine check architecture, and the MTRRs. The MSRs can be read and written to using the RDMSR and WRMSR instructions, respectively.

See Chapter 8, *Processor Management and Initialization*, and Appendix C, *Model-Specific Registers (MSRs)*, in the *Pentium® Pro Family Developer's Manual, Volume 3* for more information on the MSRs.

2.2.2. Memory Type Range Registers

Memory type range registers (MTRRs) are a new feature introduced in the Pentium Pro processor that allow the processor to optimize memory operations for different types of memory, such as RAM, ROM, frame buffer memory, and memory-mapped I/O.

MTRRs are MSRs that configure an internal map of how physical address ranges are mapped to various types of memory. The processor uses this internal memory map to determine the cacheability of various physical memory locations and the optimal method of accessing memory locations. For example, if a memory location is specified in an MTRR as write-through memory, the processor handles accesses to this location as follows. It reads data from that location in lines and caches the read data or maps all writes to that location to the bus and updates the cache to maintain cache coherency. In mapping the physical address space with MTRRs, the processor recognizes five types of memory: uncacheable (UC), write-combining (WC), write-through (WT), write-protected (WP), and writeback (WB).

Earlier Intel Architecture processors (such as the Intel486 and the Pentium processor) used the #KEN (cache enable) pin and external logic to maintain an external memory map and signal cacheable accesses to the processor. The MTRR mechanism simplifies hardware designs by eliminating the #KEN pin and the external logic required to drive it.

See Chapter 8, *Processor Management and Initialization*, and Appendix C, *Model-Specific Registers (MSRs)*, in the *Pentium® Pro Family Developer's Manual, Volume 3* for more information on the MTRRs.

2.2.3. Machine-Check Exception and Architecture

The Pentium processor introduced a new exception called the machine-check exception (interrupt 18). This exception is used to signal hardware-related errors, such as a parity error on a read cycle. The Pentium Pro processor extends the types of errors that can be detected and that generate a machine-check exception. It also provides a new machine-check architecture that records information about a machine-check error and provides the basis for an extended error logging capability.

The machine-check architecture provides several banks of reporting registers for recording machine-check errors. Each bank of registers is associated with a specific hardware unit in the processor. The primary focus of the machine checks is on bus and interconnect operations; however, checks are also made of translation lookaside buffer (TLB) and cache integrity.

The machine-check architecture can correct some errors automatically and allow for reliable restart of instruction execution. It also collects sufficient information for software to use in logging other machine errors not corrected by hardware.

See Chapter 5, *Interrupt and Exception Handling*, and Chapter 16, *Machine Check Architecture*, in the *Pentium® Pro Family Developer's Manual, Volume 3* for more information on the machine-check exception and the machine-check architecture.

2.2.4. Performance Monitoring Counters

The Pentium Pro processor has two performance-monitoring counters for use in monitoring internal hardware operations. These counters are duration or event counters that can be programmed to count any of approximately 100 different types of events, such as the number of instructions decoded, number of interrupts received, or number of cache loads. Appendix C, *Model-Specific Registers (MSRs)*, in the *Pentium® Pro Family Developer's Manual, Volume 3* lists all the events that can be counted. The counters are set up, started, and stopped using two MSRs and the RDMSR and WRMSR instructions. The current count for a particular counter can be read using the new RDPMC instruction.

The performance-monitoring counters are useful for debugging programs, optimizing code, diagnosing system failures, or refining hardware designs. See Chapter 10, *Debugging and Performance Monitoring*, in the *Pentium® Pro Family Developer's Manual, Volume 3* for more information on these counters.

2.3. INTRODUCTION TO THE PENTIUM® PRO PROCESSOR'S ADVANCED MICROARCHITECTURE

The Pentium processor (introduced by Intel in 1993) set an impressive performance standard with its superscalar microarchitecture. In designing the Pentium Pro processor, one of the primary goals of the Intel chip architects was to exceed the performance of the 100-MHz Pentium processor significantly while still using the same 0.6-micrometer, four-layer, metal BICMOS manufacturing process. Using the same manufacturing process as the Pentium processor meant that performance gains could only be achieved through substantial advances in the microarchitecture.

The resulting Pentium Pro processor microarchitecture is a three-way superscalar, pipelined architecture. The term "three-way superscalar" means that using parallel processing techniques, the processor is able on average to decode, dispatch, and complete execution of (retire) three instructions per clock cycle. To handle this level of instruction throughput, the Pentium Pro processor uses a decoupled, 12-stage superpipeline that supports out-of-order instruction execution. Figure 2-1 shows a conceptual view of this pipeline, with the pipeline divided into four processing units (the fetch/decode unit, the dispatch/execute unit, the retire unit, and the instruction pool). Instructions and data are supplied to these units through the bus interface unit.

To insure a steady supply of instructions and data to the instruction execution pipeline, the Pentium Pro processor microarchitecture incorporates two cache levels. The L1 cache provides an 8-KByte instruction cache and an 8-KByte data cache, both closely coupled to the pipeline. The L2 cache is a 256-KByte static RAM that is coupled to the core processor through a full clock-speed, 64-bit, cache bus.

The centerpiece of the Pentium Pro processor microarchitecture is an innovative out-of-order execution mechanism called "dynamic execution." Dynamic execution incorporates three data-processing concepts:

- Deep branch prediction.
- Dynamic data flow analysis.
- Speculative execution.

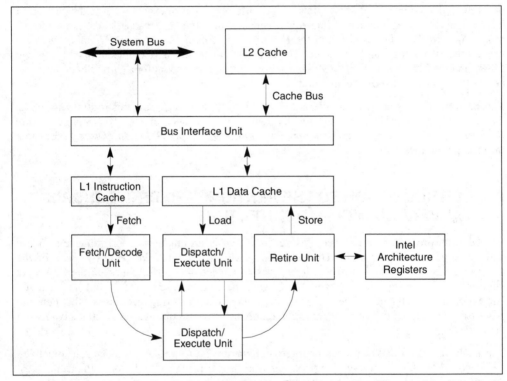

Figure 2-1. The Processing Units in the Pentium® Pro Processor Microarchitecture and Their Interface with the Memory Subsystem

Branch prediction is a concept found in most mainframe and high-speed microprocessor architectures. It allows the processor to decode instructions beyond branches to keep the instruction pipeline full. In the Pentium Pro processor, the instruction fetch/decode unit uses a highly optimized branch prediction algorithm to predict the direction of the instruction stream through multiple levels of branches, procedure calls, and returns.

Dynamic data flow analysis involves real-time analysis of the flow of data through the processor to determine data and register dependencies and to detect opportunities for out-of-order instruction execution. The Pentium Pro processor dispatch/execute unit can simultaneously monitor many instructions and execute these instructions in the order that optimizes the use of the processor's multiple execution units, while maintaining the integrity of the data being operated on. This out-of-order execution keeps the execution units even when cache misses and data dependencies among instructions occur.

Speculative execution refers to the processor's ability to execute instructions ahead of the program counter but ultimately to commit the results in the order of the original instruction stream. To make speculative execution possible, the Pentium Pro processor microarchitecture decouples the dispatching and executing of instructions from the commitment of results. The processor's dispatch/execute unit uses data-flow analysis to execute all available instructions in the instruction pool and store the results in temporary registers. The retirement unit then linearly searches the instruction pool for completed instructions that no longer have data dependencies with other instructions or unresolved branch predictions. When completed instructions are found, the retirement unit commits the results of these instructions to memory and/or the Intel Architecture registers (the processor's eight general-purpose registers and eight floating-point unit data registers) in the order they were originally issued and retires the instructions from the instruction pool.

Through deep branch prediction, dynamic data-flow analysis, and speculative execution, dynamic execution removes the constraint of linear instruction sequencing between the traditional fetch and execute phases of instruction execution. It allows instructions to be decoded deep into multi-level branches to keep the instruction pipeline full. It promotes out-of-order instruction execution to keep the processor's six instruction execution units running at full capacity. And finally it commits the results of executed instructions in original program order to maintain data integrity and program coherency.

The following section describes the Pentium Pro processor microarchitecture in greater detail.

2.4. DETAILED DESCRIPTION OF THE PENTIUM® PRO PROCESSOR MICROARCHITECTURE

Figure 2-2 shows a functional block diagram of the Pentium Pro processor microarchitecture. In this diagram, the following blocks make up the four processing units and the memory subsystem shown in Figure 2-1:

- Memory subsystem—System bus, L2 cache, bus interface unit, instruction cache (L1), data cache unit (L1), memory interface unit, and memory reorder buffer.

- Fetch/decode unit—Instruction fetch unit, branch target buffer, instruction decoder, microcode sequencer, and register alias table.

- Instruction pool—Reorder buffer

- Dispatch/execute unit—Reservation station, two integer units, two floating-point units, and two address generation units.

- Retire unit—Retire unit and retirement register file.

2.4.1. Memory Subsystem

The memory subsystem for the Pentium Pro processor consists of main system memory, the primary cache (L1), and the secondary cache (L2). The bus interface unit accesses system memory through the external system bus. This 64-bit bus is a transaction-oriented bus, meaning that each bus access is handled as separate request and response operations. While the bus interface unit is waiting for a response to one bus request, it can issue numerous additional requests.

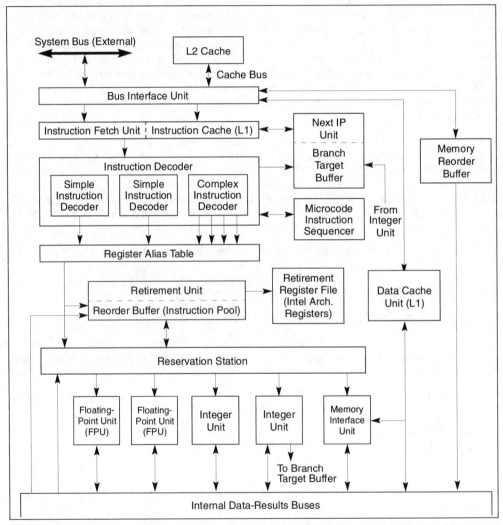

Figure 2-2. Functional Block Diagram of the Pentium® Pro Processor Microarchitecture

The bus interface unit accesses the close-coupled L2 cache through a 64-bit cache bus. This bus is also transactional oriented, supporting up to four concurrent cache accesses, and operates at the full clock speed of the processor.

Access to the L1 caches is through internal buses, also at full clock speed. The 8-KByte L1 instruction cache is four-way set associative; the 8-KByte L1 data cache is dual-ported and two-way set associative, supporting one load and one store operation per cycle.

Coherency between the caches and system memory are maintained using the MESI (modified, exclusive, shared, invalid) cache protocol. This protocol fosters cache coherency in single- and multiple-processor systems. It is also able to detect coherency problems created by self-modifying code.

Memory requests from the processor's execution units go through the memory interface unit and the memory order buffer. These units have been designed to support a smooth flow of memory access requests through the cache and system memory hierarchy to prevent memory access blocking. The L1 data cache automatically forwards a cache miss on to the L2 cache, and then, if necessary, the bus interface unit forwards an L2 cache miss to system memory.

Memory requests to the L2 cache or system memory go through the memory order buffer, which functions as a scheduling and dispatch station. This unit keeps track of all memory requests and is able to reorder some requests to prevent blocks and improve throughput. For example, the memory reorder buffer allows loads to pass stores. It also issues speculative loads. (Stores are always dispatched in order, and speculative stores are never issued.)

2.4.2.   The Fetch/Decode Unit

The fetch/decode unit reads a stream of Intel Architecture instructions from the L1 instruction cache and decodes them into a series of micro-operations called "micro-ops." This micro-op stream (still in the order of the original instruction stream) is then sent to the instruction pool.

The instruction fetch unit fetches one 32-byte cache line per clock from the instruction cache. It marks the beginning and end of the Intel Architecture instructions in the cache lines and transmits 16 aligned bytes to the decoder.

The instruction fetch unit computes the instruction pointer, based on inputs from the branch target buffer, the exception/interrupt status, and branch-misprediction indications from the integer execution units. The most important part of this process is the branch prediction performed by the branch target buffer. Using an extension of Yeh's algorithm, the 512 entry branch target buffer looks many instructions ahead of the retirement program counter. Within this instruction window there may be numerous branches, procedure calls, and returns that must be correctly predicted if the dispatch/execute unit is to do useful work.

The instruction decoder contains three parallel decoders: two simple-instruction decoders and one complex instruction decoder. Each decoder converts an Intel Architecture instruction into one or more triadic micro-ops (two logical sources and one logical destination per micro-op). Micro-ops are primitive instructions that are executed by the processor's six parallel execution units.

Many Intel Architecture instructions are converted directly into single micro-ops by the simple instruction decoders, and some instructions are decoded into from one to four micro-ops. The more complex Intel Architecture instructions are decoded into sequences of preprogrammed micro-ops obtained from the microcode instruction sequencer. The instruction decoders also handle the decoding of instruction prefixes and looping operations. The instruction decoder can generate up to six micro-ops per clock cycle (one each for the simple instruction decoders and four for the complex instruction decoder).

The Intel Architecture's register set can cause resource stalls due to register dependencies. To solve this problem, the processor provides 40 internal, general-purpose registers, which are used for the actual computations. These registers can handle both integer and floating-point values. To allocate the internal registers, the enqueued micro-ops from the instruction decoder are sent to the register alias table unit, where references to the logical Intel Architecture registers are converted into internal physical register references.

In the final step of the decoding process, the allocator in the resister alias table unit adds status bits and flags to the micro-ops to prepare them for out-of-order execution and sends the resulting micro-ops to the instruction pool.

2.4.3. Instruction Pool (Reorder Buffer)

Prior to entering the instruction pool (known formally as the reorder buffer), the micro-op instruction stream is in the same order as the Intel Architecture instruction stream that was sent to the instruction decoder. No reordering of instructions has taken place.

The reorder buffer is an array of content-addressable memory, arranged into 40 micro-op registers. It contains micro-ops that are waiting to be executed, as well as those that have already been executed but not yet committed to machine state. The dispatch/execute unit can execute instructions from the reorder buffer in any order.

2.4.4. Dispatch/Execute Unit

The dispatch/execute unit is an out-of-order unit that schedules and executes the micro-ops stored in the reorder buffer according to data dependencies and resource availability and temporarily stores the results of these speculative executions.

The scheduling and dispatching of micro-ops from the reorder buffer is handled by the reservation station. It continuously scans the reorder buffer for micro-ops that are ready to be executed (that is, all the source operands are available) and dispatches them to the available execution units. The results of a micro-op execution are returned to the reorder buffer and stored along with the micro-op until it is retired. This scheduling and dispatching process supports classic out-of-order execution, where micro-ops are dispatched to the execution units strictly according to data-flow constraints and execution resource availability, without regard to the original ordering of the instructions. When two or more micro-ops of the same type (for example, integer operations) are available at the same time, they are executed in a pseudo FIFO order in the reorder buffer.

Execution of micro-ops is handled by two integer units, two floating-point units, and one memory-interface unit, allowing up to five micro-ops can be scheduled per clock.

The two integer units can handle two integer micro-ops in parallel. One of the integer units is designed to handle branch micro-ops. This unit has the ability to detect branch mispredictions and signal the branch target buffer to restart the pipeline. This operation is handled as follows. The instruction decoder tags each branch micro-op with both branch destination addresses (the predicted destination and the fall-through destination). When the integer unit executes the branch micro-op, it is able to determine whether the predicted or the fall-through destination was taken. If the predicted branch is taken, then speculatively executed micro-ops are marked usable and execution continues along the predicted instruction path. If the predicted branch was not taken, a jump execution unit in the integer unit changes the status of all of the micro-ops following the branch to remove them from the instruction pool. It then provides the proper branch destination to the branch target buffer, which in turn restarts the pipeline from the new target address.

The memory interface unit handles load and store micro-ops. A load access only needs to specify the memory address, so it can be encoded in one micro-op. A store access needs to specify both an address and the data to be written, so it is encoded in two micro-ops. The part of the memory interface unit that handles stores has two ports allowing it to process the address and the data micro-op in parallel. The memory interface unit can thus execute both a load and a store in parallel in one clock cycle.

The floating-point execution units are similar to those found in the Pentium processor. Several new floating-point instructions have been added to the Pentium Pro processor to streamline conditional branches and moves.

2.4.5.   Retirement Unit

The retirement unit commits the results of speculatively executed micro-ops to permanent machine state and removes the micro-ops from the reorder buffer. Like the reservation station, the retirement unit continuously checks the status of micro-ops in the reorder buffer, looking for ones that have been executed and no longer have any dependencies with other micro-ops in the instruction pool. It then retires completed micro-ops in their original program order, taking into accounts interrupts, exceptions, breakpoints, and branch mispredictions.

The retirement unit can retire three micro-ops per clock. In retiring a micro-op, it writes the results to the retirement register file and/or memory. The retirement register file contains the Intel Architecture registers (eight general-purpose registers and eight floating-point data registers). After the results have been committed to machine state, the micro-op is removed from the reorder buffer.

intel®

3

Basic Execution
Environment

CHAPTER 3
BASIC EXECUTION ENVIRONMENT

This chapter describes the basic execution environment of the Pentium Pro processor as seen by assembly-language programmers. It describes how the processor executes instructions and how it stores and manipulates data. The parts of the execution environment described here include memory (the address space), the general-purpose data registers, the segment registers, the EFLAGS register, and the instruction pointer register.

The execution environment for the floating-point unit (FPU) is described in Chapter 7, *Floating-Point Unit.*

3.1. MODES OF OPERATION

The Pentium Pro processor has three operating modes: protected mode, real-address mode, and system management mode. The operating mode determines which instructions and architectural features are accessible:

- **Protected mode.** This is the native state of the processor. In this mode all instructions and architectural features are available, providing the highest performance and capability. This is the recommended mode for all new applications and operating systems.

    Among the capabilities of protected mode is the ability to directly execute "real-address mode" 8086 software in a protected, multi-tasking environment. This feature is called *virtual-8086 mode*, although it is not actually a processor mode. Virtual-8086 mode is actually a protected mode attribute that can be enabled for any task.

- **Real-address mode.** This operating mode provides the programming environment of the Intel 8086 processor, with a few extensions (such as the ability to switch to protected or system management mode). The processor is placed in real-address mode following power-up or a reset. From real-address mode, only a single instruction is required to switch to protected mode.

- **System management mode.** The system management mode (SMM) is a standard architectural feature unique to all Intel processors, beginning with the Intel386 SL processor. This mode provides an operating system or executive with a transparent mechanism for implementing platform-specific functions such as power management. The processor enters SMM the external SMM interrupt pin (SMI#) is activated or an SMI is received from the advanced programmable interrupt controller (APIC). In SMM, the processor switches to a separate address space while saving the entire context of the currently running program or task. SMM-specific code may then be executed transparently. Upon returning from SMM, the processor is placed back into its state prior to the system management interrupt.

The basic execution environment is the same for each of these operating modes, as is described in the remaining sections of this chapter.

3.2. OVERVIEW OF THE BASIC EXECUTION ENVIRONMENT

Any program or task running on a Pentium Pro processor is given a set of resources for executing instructions and for storing code, data, and state information. These resources (shown in Figure 3-1) include an address space of up to 2^{32} bytes, a set of general data registers, a set of segment registers, and a set of status and control registers. When a program calls a procedure, a procedure stack is added to the execution environment. (Procedure calls and the procedure stack implementation are described in Chapter 4, *Procedure Calls, Interrupts, and Exceptions.*)

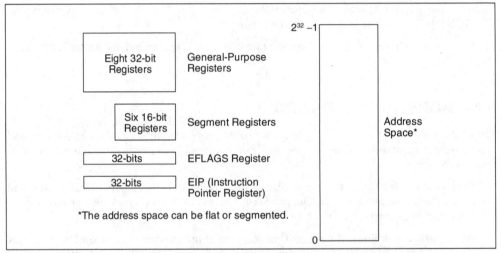

Figure 3-1. Pentium® Pro Processor Basic Execution Environment

3.3. MEMORY ORGANIZATION

The memory that the processor addresses on its bus is called *physical memory*. Physical memory is organized as a sequence of 8-bit bytes. Each byte is assigned a unique address, called a *physical address*. The *physical address space* ranges from zero to a maximum of $2^{32}-1$ (4 gigabytes).

Virtually any operating system or executive designed to work with the Pentium Pro processor will use the processor's memory management facilities to access memory. These facilities provide features such as segmentation and paging, which allow memory to be managed efficiently and reliably. Memory management is described in detail in Chapter 3, *Protected-Mode Memory Management*, of the *Pentium® Pro Family Developer's Manual, Volume 3*. The following paragraphs describe the basic methods of addressing memory when memory management is used.

When employing the processor's memory management facilities, programs do not directly address physical memory. Instead, they access memory using any of three memory models: flat, segmented, or real-address mode.

With the *flat* memory model (see Figure 3-2), memory appears to a program as a single, continuous address space, called a *linear address space*. Code (a program's instructions), data, and the procedure stack are all contained in this address space. The linear address space is byte addressable, with addresses running contiguously from 0 to $2^{32} - 1$. An address for any byte in the linear address space is called a *linear address*.

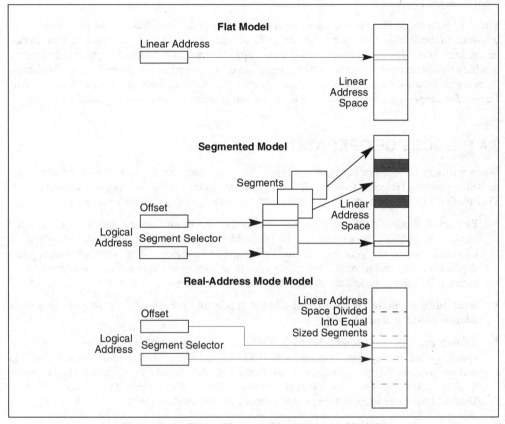

Figure 3-2. Three Memory Management Models

With the *segmented* memory mode, memory appears to a program as a group of independent address spaces called *segments*. When using this model, code, data, and stacks are typically contained in separate segments. To address a byte in a segment, a program must issue a *logical address*, which consists of a segment selector and an offset. (A logical address is often referred to as a *far pointer*.) The *segment selector* identifies the segment to be accessed and the offset identifies a byte in the address space of the segment. The programs running on a Pentium Pro processor can address up to 16,383 segments of different sizes and types.

Internally, all the segments that are defined for a system are mapped into the processor's linear address space. So, the processor translates each logical address into a linear address to access a memory location. This translation is transparent to the application program.

The primary reason for using segmented memory is to increase the reliability of programs and systems. For example, placing a program's stack in a separate segment prevents the stack from growing into the code or data space and overwriting instructions or data, respectively. And placing the operating system's or executive's code, data, and stack in separate segments protects them from the application program and vice versa.

The *real-address mode* model, uses the memory model for the Intel 8086 processor. It is provided in the Pentium Pro processor for compatibility with existing programs written to run on the Intel 8086. The real-address mode uses a specific implementation of segmented memory in which the linear address space for the program and the operating system/executive consists of an array of equally sized segments. (See Chapter 12, *8086 Emulation*, in the *Pentium® Pro Family Developer's Manual, Volume 3* for more information on this memory model.)

3.4. MODES OF OPERATION

When writing code for the Pentium Pro processor, a programmer needs to know the operating mode the processor is going to be in when executing the code and the memory model being used. The relationship between operating modes and memory models is as follows:

- **Protected mode.** When in protected mode, the processor can use any of the memory models described in this section. (The real-addressing mode memory model is ordinarily used only when the processor is in the virtual-8086 mode.) The memory model used depends on the design of the operating system or executive. When multitasking is implemented, individual tasks can use different memory models.

- **Real-address mode.** When in real-address mode, the processor only supports the real-address mode memory model.

- **System management mode.** When in SMM, the processor switches to a separate address space, called the system management RAM (SMRAM). The memory model used to address bytes in this address space is similar to the real-address mode model. (See Chapter 9, *System Management Mode (SMM)*, in the *Pentium® Pro Family Developer's Manual, Volume 3* for more information on the memory model used in SMM.)

3.5. 32-BIT VS. 16-BIT ADDRESS AND OPERAND SIZES

The processor can be configured for 32-bit or 16-bit address and operand sizes. With 32-bit address and operand sizes, the maximum linear address or segment offset is FFFFFFFFH (2^{32}), and operand sizes are typically 8 bits or 32 bits. With 16-bit address and operand sizes, the maximum linear address or segment offset is FFFFH (2^{16}), and operand sizes are typically 8 bits or 16 bits.

When using 32-bit addressing, a logical address (or far pointer) consists of a 16-bit segment selector and a 32-bit offset; when using 16-bit addressing, it consists of a 16-bit segment selector and a 16-bit offset.

Instruction prefixes allow temporary overrides of the default address and/or operand sizes from within a program.

When operating in protected mode, the segment descriptor for the currently executing code segment defines the default address and operand size. A segment descriptor is a system data structure not normally visible to application code. Assembler directives allow the default addressing and operand size to be chosen for a program. The assembler then sets up the segment descriptor for the code segment appropriately.

When operating in real-address mode, the default addressing and operand size is 16 bits. An address-size override can be used in real-address mode to enable 32 bit addressing; however, the maximum allowable 32-bit address is still 0000FFFFH (2^{16}).

3.6. REGISTERS

The processor provides 16 registers for use in general system and application programing. As shown in Figure 3-3, these registers can be grouped as follows:

- **General-purpose data registers**. These eight registers are available for storing operands and pointers.

- **Segment registers**. These registers hold up to six segment selectors.

- **Status and control registers**. These registers report and allow modification of the state of the processor and of the program being executed.

3.6.1.   General-Purpose Data Registers

The 32-bit general-purpose data registers EAX, EBX, ECX, EDX, ESI, EDI, EBP, and ESP are provided for holding the following items:

- Operands for logical and arithmetic operations

- Operands for address calculations

- Memory pointers.

Although all of these registers are available for general storage of operands, results, and pointers, caution should be used when referencing the ESP register. The ESP register holds the stack pointer and as a general rule should not be used for any other purpose.

Many instructions assign specific registers to hold operands. For example, string instructions use the contents of the ECX, ESI, and EDI registers as operands. When using a segmented memory model, some instructions assume that pointers in certain registers are relative to specific segments. For instance, some instructions assume that a pointer in the EBX register points to a memory location in the DS segment.

The special uses of general-purpose registers by instructions are described in Chapter 6, *Instruction Set Summary* and Chapter 11, *Instruction Set Reference*. The following is a summary of these special uses:

- EAX—Accumulator for operands and results data.

- EBX—Pointer to data in the DS segment.

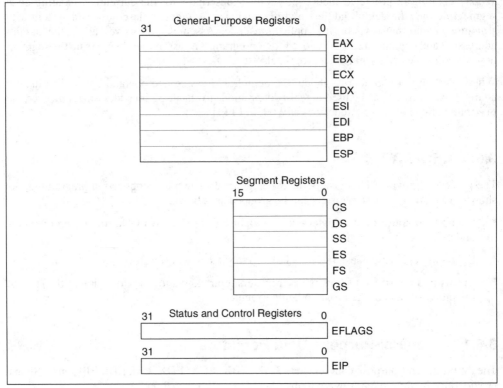

Figure 3-3. Application Programming Registers

- ECX—Counter for string and loop operations.

- EDX—I/O pointer.

- ESI—Pointer to data in the segment pointed to by the DS register; source pointer for string operations.

- EDI—Pointer to data (or destination) in the segment pointed to by the ES register; destination pointer for string operations.

- ESP—Stack pointer (in the SS segment).

- EBP—Pointer to data on the stack (in the SS segment).

As shown in Figure 3-4, the lower 16 bits of the general-purpose registers map directly to the register set found in the 8086 and Intel 286 processors and can be referenced with the names AX, BX, CX, DX, BP, SP, SI, and DI. Each of the lower two bytes of the EAX, EBX, ECX, and EDX registers can be referenced by the names AH, BH, CH, and DH (high bytes) and AL, BL, CL, and DL (low bytes).

General-Purpose Registers

31	16	15	8	7	0	**16-bit**	**32-bit**
		AH		AL		AX	EAX
		BH		BL		BX	EBX
		CH		CL		CX	ECX
		DH		DL		DX	EDX
			BP				EBP
			SI				ESI
			DI				EDI
			SP				ESP

Figure 3-4. Alternate General-Purpose Register Names

3.6.2. Segment Registers

The segment registers (CS, DS, SS, ES, FS, and GS) hold 16-bit segment selectors. A segment selector is a special pointer that identifies a segment in memory. To access a particular segment in memory, the segment selector for that segment must be present in the appropriate segment registers.

When writing application code, you generally create segment selectors with assembler directives and symbols. The assembler and/or linker then creates the actual segment selectors associated with these directives and symbols. If you are writing system code, you may need to create segment selectors directly. (A detailed description of the segment-selector data structure is given in Chapter 3, *Protected-Mode Memory Management*, of the *Pentium® Pro Family Developer's Manual, Volume 3*.)

How segment registers are used depends on the type of memory management model that the operating system or executive is using. When using the flat (unsegmented) memory model, all the segment registers are loaded with the same segment selector (as shown in Figure 3-5). Thus all memory accesses that a program makes are to a single linear-address space.

When using the segmented memory model, each segment register is ordinarily loaded with a different segment selector so that each segment register points to a different segment (as shown in Figure 3-6). At any time, a program can thus access up to six segments of memory. To access a segment not pointed to by one of the segment registers, a program must first load the segment selector for the segment to be accessed into a segment register.

Each of the segment registers is associated with one of three types of storage: code, data, or stack). For example, the CS register contains the segment selector for the *code segment*, where the instructions being executed are stored. The processor fetches instructions from the code segment, using a logical address made up of the segment selector in the CS register and the contents of the EIP register. The EIP register contains the linear address within the code segment of the next instruction to be executed. The CS register cannot be loaded explicitly by an application program. Instead it is loaded implicitly by instructions or internal processor operations that change program control (such as, procedure calls, interrupt handling, or task switching).

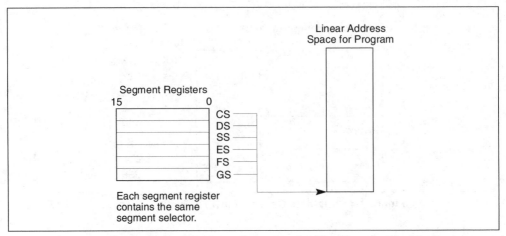

Figure 3-5. Use of Segment Selectors for Flat Memory Model

The DS, ES, FS, and GS registers point to four *data segments*. The availability of four data segments permits efficient and secure access to different types of data structures. For example, separate data segments can be created for the data structures of the current module, data exported from a higher-level module, a dynamically-created data structure, and data shared with another program. To access additional data segments, the application program must load segment selectors for these segments into the DS, ES, FS, and GS registers, as needed.

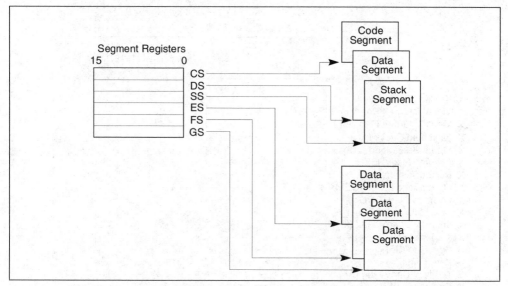

Figure 3-6. Use of Segment Selectors in Segmented Memory Model

The SS register contains the segment selector for a *stack segment*, where the procedure stack is stored for the program, task, or handler currently being executed. All stack operations use the SS register to find the stack segment. Unlike the CS register, the SS register can be loaded explicitly, which permits application programs to set up multiple stacks and switch among them.

See Section 3.1., "Modes of Operation" for an overview of how the segment registers are used in the virtual 8086 mode.

The four segment registers CS, DS, SS, and ES are the same as the segment registers found in the Intel 8086 and Intel 286 processors and the FS and GS registers were introduced into the Intel Architecture with the Intel386 family of processors.

3.6.3. EFLAGS Register

The 32-bit EFLAGS register contains a group of status flags, a control flag, and a group of system flags. Figure 3-7 defines the flags within this register. Following initialization of the processor (either by asserting the RESET pin or the INIT pin), the state of the EFLAGS register is 00000002H. Bits 1, 3, 5, 15, and 22 through 31 of this register are reserved. Software should not use or depend on the states of any of these bits.

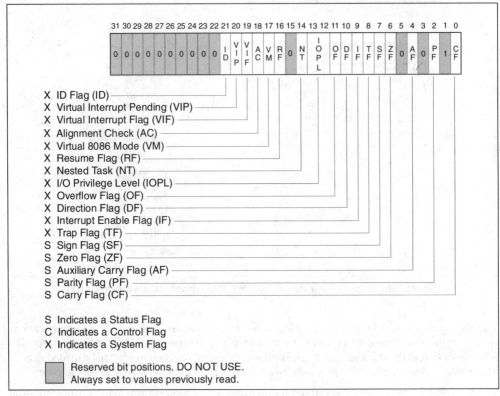

Figure 3-7. EFLAGS Register

Some of the flags in the EFLAGS register can be modified directly, using special-purpose instructions (described in the following sections). There are no instructions that allow the whole register to be examined or modified directly. However, the following instructions can be used to move groups of flags to and from the procedure stack or the EAX register: LAHF, SAHF, PUSHF, PUSHFD, POPF, and POPFD. After the contents of the EFLAGS register have been transferred to the procedure stack or EAX register, the flags can be examined and modified using the processor's bit manipulation instructions (BT, BTS, BTR, and BTC).

When suspending a task (using the processor's multitasking facilities), the processor automatically saves the state of the EFLAGS register in the task state segment (TSS) for the task being suspended. When binding itself to a new task, the processor loads the EFLAGS register with data from the new task's TSS.

When a call is made to an interrupt or exception handler procedure, the processor automatically saves the state of the EFLAGS registers on the procedure stack. When an interrupt or exception is handled with a task switch, the state of the EFLAGS register is saved in the TSS for the task being suspended.

As the Intel Architecture has evolved, various flags have been added to the EFLAGS register, but the arrangement of flags in the register has remained the same. As a result, all actions regarding these flags in software written for the Intel Architecture should work as expected.

3.6.3.1.   STATUS FLAGS

The status flags (bits 0, 2, 4, 6, 7, and 11) of the EFLAGS register indicate the results of arithmetic instructions, such as the ADD, SUB, MUL, and DIV instructions. The functions of the status flags are as follows:

CF (bit 0)   **Carry flag.** Set if an arithmetic operation generates a carry or a borrow out of the most-significant bit of the result; cleared otherwise. This flag indicates an overflow condition for unsigned-integer arithmetic. It is also used in multiple-precision arithmetic.

PF (bit 2)   **Parity flag.** Set if the least-significant byte of the result contains an even number of 1 bits; cleared otherwise.

AF (bit 4)   **Adjust flag.** Set if an arithmetic operation generates a carry or a borrow out of bit 3 of the result; cleared otherwise. This flag is used in binary-coded decimal (BCD) arithmetic.

ZF (bit 6)   **Zero flag.** Set if the result is zero; cleared otherwise.

SF (bit 7)   **Sign flag.** Set equal to the most-significant bit of the result, which is the sign bit of a signed integer. (0 indicates a positive value and 1 indicates a negative value.)

OF (bit 11)   **Overflow flag.** Set if the integer result is too large a positive number or too small a negative number (excluding the sign-bit) to fit in the destination operand; cleared otherwise. This flag indicates an overflow condition for signed-integer (two's complement) arithmetic.

Of these status flags, only the CF flag can be modified directly, using the STC, CLC, and CMC instructions.

The status flags allow a single arithmetic operation to produce results for three different data types: unsigned integers, signed integers, and BCD integers. If the result of an arithmetic operation is treated as an unsigned integer, the CF flag indicates an out-of-range condition (carry or a borrow); if treated as a signed integer (two's complement number), the OF flag indicates a carry or borrow; and if treated as a BCD digit, the AF flag indicates a carry or borrow. The SF flag indicates the sign of a signed integer. The ZF flag indicates either a signed- or an unsigned-integer zero.

When performing multiple-precision arithmetic on unsigned integers, the CF flag is used in conjunction with the add with carry (ADC) and subtract with borrow (SBB) instructions to propagate a carry or borrow from one computation to the next.

The condition instructions J*cc* (jump on condition code *cc*), SET*cc* (byte set on condition code *cc*), LOOP*cc*, and CMOV*cc* (conditional move) use one or more of the status flags as condition codes and test them for branch, set-byte, or end-loop conditions.

3.6.3.2.   DF FLAG

The direction flag (DF) is the only control flag in the EFLAGS register. This flag (bit 10 of the register) controls the string instructions (MOVS, CMPS, SCAS, LODS, and STOS). Setting the DF flag causes the string instructions to auto-decrement (that is, to process strings from high addresses to low addresses). Clearing the DF flag causes the string instructions to auto-increment (process strings from low addresses to high addresses).

The STD and CLD instructions set and clear the DF flag, respectively.

3.6.4.   System Flags and IOPL Field

The system flags and IOPL field in the EFLAGS register control operating-system or executive operations. **They should not be modified by application programs.** The functions of the status flags are as follows:

IF (bit 9)   **Interrupt enable flag.** Controls the response of the processor to maskable interrupt requests. Set to respond to maskable interrupts; cleared to inhibit maskable interrupts.

TF (bit 8)   **Trap flag.** Set to enable single-step mode for debugging; clear to disable single-step mode.

IOPL (bits 12 and 13) **I/O privilege level field.** Indicates the I/O privilege level of the currently running program or task. The current privilege level (CPL) of the currently running program or task must be less than or equal to the I/O privilege level to access the I/O address space. This field can only be modified by the POPF and IRET instructions when operating at a CPL of 0.

NT (bit 14)   **Nested task flag.** Controls the chaining of interrupted and called tasks. Set when the current task is linked to the previously executed task; cleared when the current task is not linked to another task.

RF (bit 16)   **Resume flag.** Controls the processor's response to debug exceptions.

VM (bit 17)   **Virtual 8086 mode flag.** Set to enable virtual-8086 mode; clear to return to protected mode.

AC (bit 18)   **Alignment check flag.** Set this flag and the AM bit in the CR0 register to enable alignment checking of memory references; clear the AC flag and/or the AM bit to disable alignment checking.

VIF (bit 19)   **Virtual interrupt flag.** Virtual image of the IF flag. Used in conjunction with the VIP flag. (To use this flag and the VIP flag the virtual mode extensions are enabled by setting the VME flag in control register CR4.)

VIP (bit 20)   **Virtual interrupt pending flag.** Set to indicate to that an interrupt is pending; clear when no interrupts are pending. (Software sets and clears this flag. The processor only reads it.) Used in conjunction with the VIF flag.

ID (bit 21)   **Identification flag.** The ability of a program to set or clear this flag indicates support for the CPUID instruction.

See Chapter 3, *Protected-Mode Memory Management*, in the *Pentium® Pro Family Developer's Manual, Volume 3* for a detail description of these flags.

3.7. INSTRUCTION POINTER

The instruction pointer (EIP) register contains the offset in the current code segment for the next instruction to be executed. It is advanced from one instruction boundary to the next in straight-line code or it is moved ahead or backwards by a number of instructions when executing JMP, Jcc, CALL, RET, and IRET instructions. The EIP cannot be accessed directly by software; it is controlled implicitly by control-transfer instructions (such as JMP, Jcc, CALL, and RET), interrupts, and exceptions. The EIP register can be loaded indirectly by modifying the value of a return instruction pointer on the procedure stack and executing a return instruction (RET or IRET). See Section 4.2.3.2., "Return Instruction Pointer".

Because of instruction prefetching, an instruction address read from the bus during an instruction load does not match the value of the EIP. The only way to read the EIP is to execute a CALL instruction and then read the value of the return instruction pointer from the procedure stack.

The EIP register is fully compatible with all software written to run on Intel Architecture processors.

3.8. OPERAND-SIZE AND ADDRESS-SIZE ATTRIBUTES

When processor is executing in protected mode, every code segment has a default operand-size attribute and address-size attribute. These attributes are selected with the D (default size) flag in the segment descriptor for the code segment (see Chapter 3, *Protected-Mode Memory Management*, in the *Pentium® Pro Family Developer's Manual, Volume 3*. When the B flag is set, the 32Hbit operand-size and address-size attributes are selected; when the flag is clear, the 16-bit size attributes are selected. When the processor is executing in real-address mode, virtual-8086 mode, or SMM, the default operand-size and address-size attributes are always 16 bits.

The operand-size attribute selects the sizes of operands that instructions operate on. When the 16-bit operand-size attribute is in force, operands can generally be either 8 bits or 16 bits, and when the 32-bit operand-size attribute is in force, operands can generally be 8 bits or 32 bits.

The address-size attribute selects the sizes of addresses used to address memory: 16 bits or 32 bits. When the 16-bit address-size attribute is in force, segment offsets and displacements are 16-bits. This restriction limits the size of a segment that can be addressed 64 KBytes. When the 32-bit address-size attribute is in force, segment offsets and displacements are 32-bits, allowing segments of up to 4 GBytes to be addressed.

The default operand-size attribute and/or address-size attribute can be overridden for a particular instruction by adding an operand-size and/or address-sized prefix to an instruction (see Section 11.1.1., "Instruction Prefixes"). The effect of this prefix applies only to the instruction it is attached to.

Table 3-1 shows effective operand size and address size (when executing in protected mode), depending on the settings of the B flag and the operand-size and address-size prefixes.

Table 3-1. Effective Operand- and Address-Size Attributes

B Flag in Code Segment Descriptor	0	0	0	0	1	1	1	1
Operand-Size Prefix 66H	N	N	Y	Y	N	N	Y	Y
Address-Size Prefix 67H	N	Y	N	Y	N	Y	N	Y
Effective Operand Size	16	16	32	32	32	32	16	16
Effective Address Size	16	32	16	32	32	16	32	16

NOTES:

Y Yes, this instruction prefix is present

N No, this instruction prefix is not present

intel®

4

Procedure Calls, Interrupts, and Exceptions

CHAPTER 4

PROCEDURE CALLS, INTERRUPTS, AND EXCEPTIONS

This chapter describes the facilities in the Pentium Pro processor for executing calls to procedures or subroutines. It also describes how interrupts and exceptions are handled from the perspective of an application programmer.

4.1. PROCEDURE CALL TYPES

The processor supports procedure calls in two different ways:

- CALL and RET instructions.

- ENTER and LEAVE instructions, in conjunction with the CALL and RET instructions.

Both of these procedure call mechanisms use the procedure stack, commonly referred to simply as "the stack," to save the state of the calling procedure, pass parameters to the called procedure, and store local variables for the currently executing procedure.

The processor's facilities for handling interrupts and exceptions is similar to those used by the CALL and RET instructions.

4.2. PROCEDURE STACK

The procedure stack (shown in Figure 4-1) is a contiguous array of memory locations. It is contained in a segment and identified by the segment selector in the SS register. (When using the flat memory model, the stack can be located anywhere in the linear address space for the program.) A stack can be up to 4 gigabytes long, the maximum size of a segment.

The next available memory location on the stack is called the top of stack. At any given time, the stack pointer (contained in the ESP register) gives the address (that is the offset from the base of the SS segment) of the top of the stack.

Items are placed on the stack using the PUSH instruction and removed from the stack using the POP instruction. When an item is pushed onto the stack, the processor decrements the ESP register, then writes the item at the new top of stack. When an item is popped off the stack, the processor reads the item from the top of stack, then increments the ESP register. In this manner, the stack grows *down* in memory (towards lesser addresses) when items are pushed on the stack and grows *up* (towards greater addresses) when the items are popped from the stack.

A program, operating system, or executive can set up many stacks. For example, in multitasking systems, each task can be given its own stack. The number of stacks in a system is limited by the maximum number of segments and the available physical memory. When a system sets up many stacks, only one stack, the *current stack*, is available at a time. The current stack is the one contained in the segment referenced by the SS register.

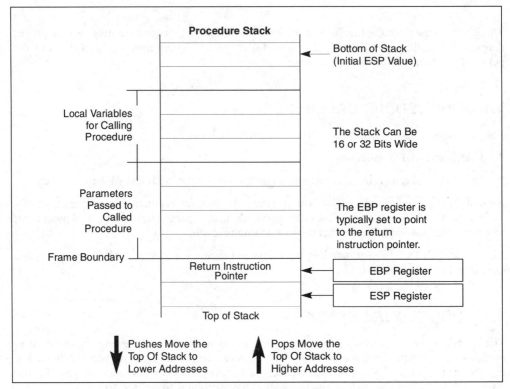

Figure 4-1. Procedure Stack Structure

The processor references the SS register automatically for all stack operations. For example, when the ESP register is used as a memory address, it automatically points to an address in the current stack. Also, the CALL, RET, PUSH, POP, ENTER, and LEAVE instructions all perform operations on the current stack.

4.2.1. Stack Alignment

The stack pointer for a stack segment should be aligned on 16-bit (word) or 32-bit (double-word) boundaries, depending on the width of the stack segment. The Bflag in the segment descriptor for the current code segment sets the stack-segment width (see the discussion of segment descriptors in Chapter 3, *Protected-Mode Memory Management*, in the *Pentium® Pro Family*

Developer's Manual, Volume 3). The PUSH and POP instructions use the Bflag to determine how much to decrement or increment the stack pointer on a push or pop operation, respectively. When the stack width is 16 bits, the stack pointer is incremented or decremented in 16-bit increments; when the width is 32 bits, the stack pointer is incremented or decremented in 32-bit increments. If a 16-bit value is pushed onto a 32-bit wide stack, the value is automatically padded with zeros out to 32 bits.

The processor does not check stack pointer alignment. It is the responsibility of the programs, tasks, and system procedures running on the processor to maintain proper alignment of stack pointers. Misaligning a stack pointer can cause serious performance degradation and in some instances program failures.

4.2.2.   Address-Size Attribute for Stack

Instructions that use the stack implicitly (such as the PUSH and POP instructions) have an address-size attribute of either 16 or 32 bits. Instructions with a address-size attribute of 16 use the 16-bit SP stack pointer register and can use a maximum stack address of FFFFH; instructions with a address-size attribute of 32 bits use the 32-bit ESP register and can use a maximum address of FFFFFFFFH.

The default address-size attribute for data segments used as stacks is controlled by the Bflag of the segment's segment descriptor. When this flag is clear, the default address-size attribute is 16; when the flag is set, the address-size attribute is 32.

4.2.3.   Procedure Linking Information

The processor provides two pointers for linking of procedures: the stack-frame base pointer and the return instruction pointer. When used in conjunction with a standard software procedure-call technique, these pointers permit reliable and coherent linking of procedures

4.2.3.1.   STACK-FRAME BASE POINTER

The stack is typically divided into frames. Each stack frame can then contain local variables, parameters to be passed to another procedure, and procedure linking information. The stack-frame base pointer (contained in the EBP register) identifies a fixed reference point within the stack frame for the called procedure. To use the stack-frame base pointer, the called procedure typically copies the contents of the ESP register into the EBP register prior to pushing any local variables on the stack. The stack-frame base pointer then permits easy access to data structures passed on the stack, to the return instruction pointer, and to local variables added to the stack by the called procedure.

Like the ESP register, the EBP register automatically points to an address in the current stack.

4.2.3.2. RETURN INSTRUCTION POINTER

Prior to branching to the first instruction of the called procedure, the CALL instruction pushes the address in the EIP register into onto the current stack. This address is then called the return-instruction pointer and it points to the instruction where execution of the calling procedure should resume following a return from the called procedure. Upon returning from a called procedure, the RET instruction pops the return-instruction pointer from the stack back into the EIP register. Execution of the calling procedure then resumes.

The processor does not keep track of the location of the return-instruction pointer. It is thus up to the programmer to insure that stack pointer is pointing to the return-instruction pointer on the stack, prior to issuing a RET instruction. A common way to reset the stack pointer to the point to the return-instruction pointer is to move the contents of the EBP register into the ESP register. If the EBP register is loaded with the stack pointer following a procedure call, it should point to the return instruction pointer on the stack.

The processor does not require that the return instruction pointer point back to the calling procedure. Prior to executing the RET instruction, the return instruction pointer can be manipulated in software to point to any address in the code segment. Performing such an operation, however, should be undertaken very cautiously, using only well defined code entry points.

4.3. CALLING PROCEDURES USING CALL AND RET

The CALL instructions allows jumps to procedures within the current code segment (*near call*) and in a different code segment (*far call*). (When using the flat memory model, a near call references a procedure within the current linear address space and a far call references a procedure in another linear address space.) Near calls provide access to procedures within the currently running program or task. Far calls are used to access operating system procedures or procedures in a different task. See Chapter 11, "CALL—Call Procedure" for a detailed description of the CALL instruction.

The RET instruction also allows near and far returns to match the near and far versions of the CALL instruction. In addition, the RET instruction allows a program to increment the stack pointer on a return to release parameters from the stack. The number of bytes released from the stack is determined by an optional argument to the RET instruction. See Chapter 11, "RET—Return from Procedure" for a detailed description of the RET instruction.

4.3.1. Near CALL and RET Operation

When executing a near call, the processor does the following:

1. Pushes the current value of the EIP register on the stack.

2. Loads the address of the called procedure in the EIP register.

3. Begins execution of the called procedure.

When executing a near return, the processor performs these actions:

1. Pops the top-of-stack value (the return instruction pointer) into the EIP register.

2. (Optional) Increments the stack pointer by the amount specified in an optional RET instruction parameter.

3. Resumes execution of the calling procedure.

4.3.2.   Far CALL and RET Operation

When executing a far call, the processor performs these actions:

1. Pushes current value of the CS register on the stack.

2. Pushes the current value of the EIP register on the stack.

3. Loads the segment selector of the segment that contains the called procedure in the CS register.

4. Loads the address of the called procedure in the EIP register.

5. Begins execution of the called procedure.

When executing a far return, the processor does the following:

1. Pops the top-of-stack value (the return instruction pointer) into the EIP register.

2. Pops the top-of-stack value (the segment selector for the code segment being returned to) into the CS register.

3. (Optional) Increments the stack pointer by the amount specified in an optional RET instruction parameter.

4. Resumes execution of the calling procedure.

4.3.3.   Parameter Passing

Parameters can be passed between procedures in any of three ways: through general-purpose registers, in an argument list, or on the stack.

4.3.3.1.   PASSING PARAMETERS THROUGH THE GENERAL-PURPOSE REGISTERS

The processor does not save the state of the general-purpose registers on procedure calls. A calling procedure can thus pass up to six parameter to the called procedure by copying the parameters into any of these registers (except the ESP and EBP registers) prior to executing the CALL instruction. The called procedure can likewise pass parameters back to the calling procedure through general-purpose registers.

4.3.3.2. PASSING PARAMETERS ON THE STACK

To pass a large number of parameters to the called procedure, the parameters can be placed on the stack, in the stack frame for the calling procedure. Here, it is useful to use the stack-frame base pointer (in the EBP register) to make a frame boundary for easy access to the parameters.

The stack can also be used to pass parameters back from the called procedure to the calling procedure.

4.3.3.3. PASSING PARAMETERS IN AN ARGUMENT LIST

An alternate method of passing a larger number of parameters (or a data structure) to the called procedure is to place the parameters in an argument list in memory (in one of the data segments). A pointer to the argument list can then be passed to the called procedure through a general-purpose register or the stack. Parameters can also be passed back to the calling procedure in this same manner.

4.3.4. Saving Procedure State Information

The processor does not save the contents of the general-purpose registers, segment registers, or the EFLAGS register on a procedure call. A calling procedure should explicitly save the values in any of the general-purpose registers that it will need when it resumes execution after a return. These values can be saved on the stack or in memory in one of the data segments.

The PUSHA and POPA instruction facilitates saving and restoring the contents of the general-purpose registers. PUSHA pushes the values in all the general-purpose registers on the stack in the following order: EAX, ECX, EDX, EBX, ESP (the value prior to executing the PUSHA instruction), EBP, ESI, and EDI. The POPA instruction pops all the register values saved with a PUSHA instruction (except the ESI value) from the stack to their respective registers.

If a called procedure changes the state of any of the segment registers explicitly, it should restore them to their former value before executing a return to the calling procedure.

If a calling procedure needs to maintain the state of the EFLAGS register it can save and restore all or part of the register using the PUSHF, PUSHFH, POPF, and POPFH instructions. The PUSHF instruction pushes the lower word of the EFLAGS register on the stack and the PUSHFH instruction pushes the entire register. The POPF instruction pops a word from the stack into the lower word of the EFLAGS register and the POPFH instruction pops a double word from the stack into the register.

4.3.5. Calls to Other Privilege Levels

The Pentium Pro processor's protection mechanism recognizes four privilege levels, numbered from 0 to 3, where greater numbers mean lesser privileges. The primary reason to use these privilege levels is to improve the reliability of operating systems. For example, Figure 4-2 shows how privilege levels can be interpreted as rings of protection.

In this example, the highest privilege level 0 (at the center of the diagram) is used for segments that contain the most critical code modules in the system, usually the kernel of an operating system. The outer rings (with progressively lower privileges) are used for segments that contain code modules for less critical software.

Code modules in lower privilege segments can only access modules operating at higher privilege segments by means of a tightly controlled and protected interface called a *gate*. Attempts to access higher privilege segments without going through a protection gate and without having sufficient access rights causes a general-protection exception (#GP) to be generated.

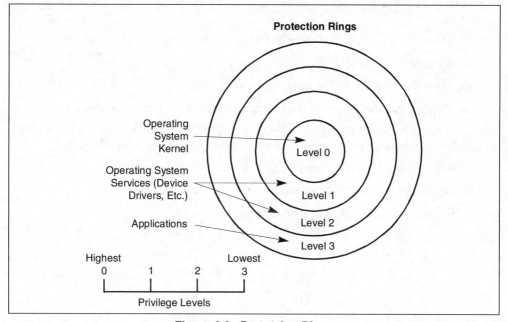

Figure 4-2. Protection Rings

If an operating system or executive uses this multilevel protection mechanism, a call to a procedure that is in a more privileged protection level than the calling procedure is handled in a similar manner as a far call (see Section 4.3.2., "Far CALL and RET Operation"). The differences are as follows:

- The segment selector provided in the CALL instruction references a special data structure called a *call gate descriptor*. Among other things, the call gate descriptor provides the following:

  — Access rights information.

  — The segment selector for the code segment of the called procedure.

  — An offset into the code segment (that is, the instruction pointer for the called procedure).

- The processor switches to a new stack to execute the called procedure. The segment selector for the new stack is also contained in the call gate descriptor. On a return from the called procedure, the processor restores the stack of the calling procedure.

The use of a call gate and the stack switch are transparent to the calling procedure, except when a general-protection exception is raised.

4.3.6. CALL and RET Operation Between Privilege Levels

When making a call to a more privileged protection level, the processor does the following (see Figure 4-3):

1. Pushes current values of the CS and EIP register on the stack.

2. Performs an access rights check (privilege check).

3. Switches to the stack for the privilege level being called.

4. Copies the SS and ESP values for the calling procedure's stack to the new stack.

5. Copies the parameters from the calling procedure's stack to the new stack. (A value in the call gate descriptor determines how many parameters to copy to the new stack.)

6. Copies the CS and EIP values from the calling procedure's stack to the new stack.

7. Loads the address of the called procedure in the EIP register.

8. Begins execution of the called procedure.

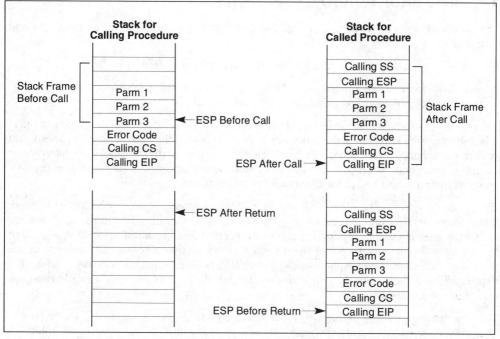

Figure 4-3. Stack Switch on a Call to a Different Privilege Level

When executing a return from the privileged procedure, the processor performs these actions:

1. Performs a privilege check.

2. Restores the CS, EIP, SS, and ESP registers to their values prior to the call.

3. Switches back to the stack of the calling procedure

4. (Optional) Increments the stack pointer by the amount specified in an optional RET instruction parameter.

5. Resumes execution of the calling procedure.

See Chapter 4, *Protection*, in the *Pentium® Pro Family Developer's Manual, Volume 3* for detailed information on calls to privileged levels and the call gate descriptor.

4.4. INTERRUPTS AND EXCEPTIONS

The processor provides two mechanisms for interrupting program execution: interrupts and exceptions:

- An *interrupt* is an asynchronous events that is typically triggered by an I/O device.

- An *exception* is a synchronous event that is generated when the processor detects one or more predefined conditions while executing an instruction.

The processor responds to interrupts and exceptions in essentially the same way. When an interrupt and exception is signaled, the processor halts execution of the current program or task and switches to a handler procedure that has been written specifically to handle the interrupt or exception condition. When the handler has completed handling the interrupt or exception, program control is returned to the interrupted program or task.

The operating system, executive, and/or device drivers normally handle interrupts and exceptions independently from application programs or tasks. Application programs can, however, access the interrupt and exception handlers incorporated in an operating system or executive through assembly-language calls. The remainder of this section gives a brief overview of the processor's interrupt and exception handling mechanism. See Chapter 5, *Interrupt and Exception Handling*, in the *Pentium® Pro Family Developer's Manual, Volume 3* for a detailed description of this mechanism.

The Pentium Pro processor defines 16 predefined interrupts and exceptions and 224 user defined interrupts. Each interrupt and exception is identified with a number, called a *vector*. Table 4-1 lists the interrupts and exceptions that the processor recognizes and their respective vector numbers. Vectors 0 through 8, 10 through 14, and 16 through 18 are the predefined interrupts and exceptions, and vectors 32 through 255 are the user-defined interrupts, called *maskable interrupts*.

When the processor detects an interrupt or exception, it does one of the following things:

- Executes an implicit call to a handler procedure.

- Executes an implicit call to a handler task.

Table 4-1. Exceptions and Interrupts

Vector No.	Description	Source
0	Divide Error (#DE)	DIV and IDIV instructions.
1	Debug (#DB)	Any code or data reference.
2	NMI Interrupt	External interrupt.
3	Breakpoint (#BP)	INT 3 instruction.
4	Overflow (#OF)	INTO instruction.
5	BOUND Range Exceeded (#BR)	BOUND instruction.
6	Invalid Opcode (#UD)	UD2 instruction or reserved opcode.
7	Device Not Available (#NM)	Floating-point or WAIT/FWAIT instruction.
8	Double Fault (#DF)	Any instruction.
9	CoProcessor Segment Overrun (reserved)	Floating-point instruction. Pentium® Pro processor does not generate this exception.
10	Invalid TSS (#TS)	Task switch.
11	Segment Not Present (#NP)	Loading segment registers or accessing system segments.
12	Stack Fault (#SS)	Stack operations.
13	General Protection (#GP)	Any memory reference.
14	Page Fault (#PF)	Any memory reference.
15	(Intel reserved. Do not use.)	
16	Floating-Point Error (#MF)	Floating-point or WAIT/FWAIT instruction.
17	Alignment Check (#AC)	Any data reference in memory.
18	Machine Check (#MC)	Model dependent.
19-31	(Intel reserved. Do not use.)	
32-255	Maskable Interrupts	External interrupt or INT n instruction.

4.4.1. Call and Return Operation for Interrupt or Exception Handling Procedures

A call to an interrupt or exception handler procedure is similar to a procedure call to another protection level (as described in Section 4.3.6., "CALL and RET Operation Between Privilege Levels"). Here, the interrupt vector references one of two kinds of gates: an *interrupt gate* or a *trap gate*. Interrupt and trap gates are similar to call gates in that they provide the following information:

* Access rights information.

* The segment selector for the code segment that contains the handler procedure.

* An offset into the code segment to the first instruction of the handler procedure.

The difference between an interrupt gate and a trap gate are as follows. If an interrupt or exception handler is called through an interrupt gate, the processor clears the interrupt enable (IF) flag in the EFLAGS register to prevent subsequent interrupts from interfering with the execution of the handler. When a handler is called through a trap gate, the state of the IF flag is not changed.

If the code segment for the handler procedure has the same privilege level as the currently executing program or task, the handler procedure uses the current stack; if the handler executes at a more privileged level, the processor switches to the stack for the handler's privilege level.

If no stack switch occurs, the processor does the following when calling an interrupt or exception handler (see Figure 4-4):

1. Pushes the current contents of the EFLAGS, CS, and EIP registers (in that order) on the stack.

2. Pushes an error code (if appropriate) on the stack.

3. If the call is through an interrupt gate, clears the IF flag in the EFLAGS register.

4. Transfers program control to the handler procedure.

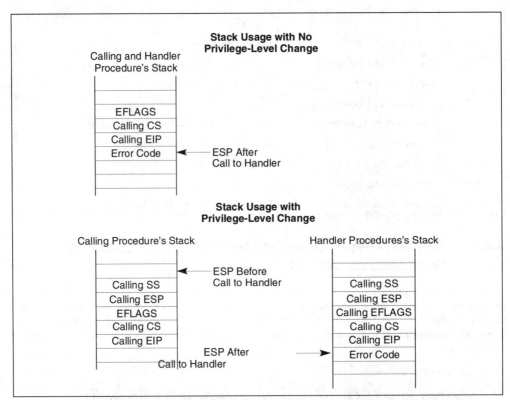

Figure 4-4. Stack Usage on Calls to Interrupt and Exception Handling Routines

If a stack switch does occur, the processor does the following:

1. Pushes the current contents of the SS, ESP, EFLAGS, CS, and EIP registers (in that order) on the stack.

2. Switches to the handler's stack.

3. Copies the SS, ESP, EFLAGS, CS, and EIP values from the interrupted procedure's stack to the new stack.

4. Pushes an error code on the new stack (if appropriate).

5. If the call is through an interrupt gate, clears the IF flag in the EFLAGS register.

6. Transfers program control to the handler procedure.

A return from an interrupt or exception handler is initiated with the IRET instruction. The IRET instruction is similar to the RET instruction, except that it also restores the contents of the EFLAGS register for the interrupted procedure:

When executing a return from an interrupt or exception handler from the same privilege level as the interrupted procedure, the processor performs these actions:

1. Restores the CS and EIP registers to their values prior to the interrupt or exception.

2. Restores the EFLAGS register.

3. Increments the stack pointer appropriately

4. Resumes execution of the interrupted procedure.

When executing a return from an interrupt or exception handler from a different privilege level than the interrupted procedure, the processor performs these actions:

1. Performs a privilege check.

2. Restores the CS and EIP registers to their values prior to the interrupt or exception.

3. Restores the EFLAGS register.

4. Restores the SS and ESP registers to their values prior to the interrupt or exception.

5. Switches back to the stack of the calling procedure

6. Resumes execution of the calling procedure.

4.4.2. Calls to an Interrupt or Exception Handler Tasks

Interrupt and exception handler routines can also be executed in a separate task. Here, an interrupt or exception causes a task switch to a handler task. The handler task is given its own address space and (optionally) can execute at a higher protection level than application programs or tasks.

The switch to the handler task is accomplished with an implicit task call that references a *task gate descriptor*. The task gate provides access to the address space for the handler task. As part of the task switch, the processor saves complete state information for the interrupted program or task. Upon returning from the handler task, the state of the interrupted program or task is restored and execution continues. See Chapter 5, *Interrupt and Exception Handling*, in the *Pentium® Pro Family Developer's Manual, Volume 3* for a detailed description of the processor's mechanism for handling interrupts and exceptions through handler tasks.

4.4.3. Interrupt and Exception Handling in Real-Address Mode

When operating in real-address mode, the processor responds to an interrupt or exception with a far call to an interrupt or exception handler. The processor uses the interrupt or exception vector number as an index into an interrupt table. The interrupt table contains instruction pointers to the interrupt and exception handler procedures.

The processor saves the state of the EFLAGS register, the EIP register, the CS register, and an optional error code on the stack before switching to the handler procedure.

A return from the interrupt or exception handler is carried out with the IRET instruction.

See Chapter 12, *8086 Emulation*, in the *Pentium® Pro Family Developer's Manual, Volume 3* for more information on handling interrupts and exceptions in real-address mode.

4.4.4. INT*n*, INTO, INT3, and BOUND Instructions

The INT*n*, INTO, INT3, and BOUND instructions allow a program or task to explicitly call an interrupt or exception handler. The INT*n* instruction uses an interrupt vector as an argument, which allows a program to call any interrupt handler.

The INTO instruction explicitly calls the overflow exception (#OF) handler if the overflow flag (OF) in the EFLAGS register is set. The OF flag indicates overflow on arithmetic instructions, but it does not automatically raise an overflow exception. An overflow exception can only be raised explicitly in either of the following ways:

- Execute the INTO instruction.

- Test the OF flag and execute the INT*n* instruction with an argument of 4 (the vector number of the overflow exception) if the flag is set.

Both the methods of dealing with overflow conditions allow a program to test for overflow at specific places in the instruction stream.

The INT3 instruction explicitly calls the breakpoint exception (#BP) handler. The action of this instruction is slightly different than that of the INT 3 instruction (see Chapter 11, "INTn/INTO/INT3—Call to Interrupt Procedure").

The BOUND instruction explicitly calls the BOUND-range exceeded exception (#BR) handler if an operand is found to be not within predefined boundaries in memory. This instruction is provided for checking references to arrays and other data structures. Like the overflow exception, the BOUND-range exceeded exception can only be raised explicitly with the BOUND instruction or the INT*n* instruction with an argument of 5 (the vector number of the bounds-check exception). The processor does not implicitly perform bounds checks and raise the BOUND-range exceeded exception.

4.5. PROCEDURE CALLS FOR BLOCK-STRUCTURED LANGUAGES

The Pentium Pro processor supports an alternate method of performing procedure calls with the ENTER (enter procedure) and LEAVE (leave procedure) instructions. These instructions automatically create and release, respectively, stack frames for called procedures. The stack frames have predefined spaces for local variables and the necessary pointers to allow coherent returns from called procedures. They also allow scope rules to be implemented, so that procedures can access their own local variables and some number of other variables located in other stack frames.

The ENTER and LEAVE instructions offer two benefits:

- They provide machine-language support for implementing block-structured languages, such as C and Pascal.

- They simplify procedure entry and exit in compiler-generated code.

4.5.1. ENTER Instruction

The enter procedure instruction (ENTER) creates a stack frame compatible with the scope rules typically used in block-structured languages. In block-structured languages, the scope of a procedure is the set of variables to which it has access. The rules for scope vary among languages. They may be based on the nesting of procedures, the division of the program into separately-compiled files, or some other modularization scheme.

The ENTER instruction has two operands. The first specifies the number of bytes to be reserved on the stack for dynamic storage for the procedure being called. Dynamic storage is the memory allocated for variables created when the procedure is called, also known as automatic variables. The second parameter is the lexical nesting level (from 0 to 31) of the procedure. The nesting level is the depth of a procedure in a hierarchy of procedure calls. The lexical level is unrelated to either the protection privilege level or to the I/O privilege level of the currently running program or task.

The ENTER instruction in the following example, allocates 2K bytes of dynamic storage on the stack and sets up pointers to two previous stack frames in the stack frame for this procedure.

```
ENTER 2048,3
```

The lexical nesting level determines the number of stack frame pointers to copy into the new stack frame from the preceding frame. A stack frame pointer is a doubleword used to access the variables of a procedure. The set of stack frame pointers used by a procedure to access the variables of other procedures is called the display. The first doubleword in the display is a pointer to the previous stack frame. This pointer is used by a LEAVE instruction to undo the effect of an ENTER instruction by discarding the current stack frame.

After the ENTER instruction creates the display for a procedure, it allocates the dynamic (automatic) local variables for the procedure by decrementing the contents of the ESP register by the number of bytes specified in the first parameter. This new value in the ESP register serves as the initial top-of-stack for all PUSH and POP operations within the procedure.

To allow a procedure to address its display, the ENTER instruction leaves the EBP register pointing to the first doubleword in the display. Because stacks grow down, this is actually the doubleword with the highest address in the display. Data manipulation instructions that specify the EBP register as a base register automatically address locations within the stack segment instead of the data segment.

The ENTER instruction can be used in two ways: nested and non-nested. If the lexical level is 0, the non-nested form is used. The non-nested form pushes the contents of the EBP register on the stack, copies the contents of the ESP register into the EBP register, and subtracts the first operand from the contents of the ESP register to allocate dynamic storage. The non-nested form differs from the nested form in that no stack frame pointers are copied. The nested form of the ENTER instruction occurs when the second parameter (lexical level) is not zero.

The following pseudo code shows the formal definition of the ENTER instruction. STORAGE is the number of bytes of dynamic storage to allocate for local variables, and LEVEL is the lexical nesting level.

```
PUSH EBP;
FRAME_PTR ← ESP;
IF LEVEL > 0
    THEN
        REPEAT (LEVEL − 1) times
            EBP ← EBP − 4;
            PUSH Pointer(EBP); (* doubleword pointed to by EBP *)
        TAEPER
    PUSH FRAME_PTR;
FI;
EBP ← FRAME_PTR;
ESP ← ESP − STORAGE;
```

The main procedure (in which all other procedures are nested) operates at the highest lexical level, level 1. The first procedure it calls operates at the next deeper lexical level, level 2. A level 2 procedure can access the variables of the main program, which are at fixed locations specified by the compiler. In the case of level 1, the ENTER instruction allocates only the requested dynamic storage on the stack because there is no previous display to copy.

A procedure which calls another procedure at a lower lexical level gives the called procedure access to the variables of the caller. The ENTER instruction provides this access by placing a pointer to the calling procedure's stack frame in the display.

A procedure which calls another procedure at the same lexical level should not give access to its variables. In this case, the ENTER instruction copies only that part of the display from the calling procedure which refers to previously nested procedures operating at higher lexical levels.

The new stack frame does not include the pointer for addressing the calling procedure's stack frame.

The ENTER instruction treats a re-entrant procedure as a call to a procedure at the same lexical level. In this case, each succeeding iteration of the re-entrant procedure can address only its own variables and the variables of the procedures within which it is nested. A re-entrant procedure always can address its own variables; it does not require pointers to the stack frames of previous iterations.

By copying only the stack frame pointers of procedures at higher lexical levels, the ENTER instruction makes certain that procedures access only those variables of higher lexical levels, not those at parallel lexical levels (see Figure 4-5).

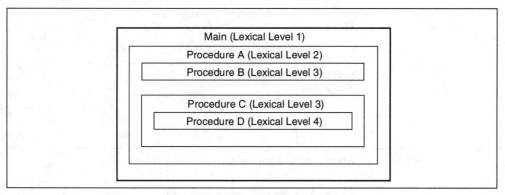

Figure 4-5. Nested Procedures

Block-structured languages can use the lexical levels defined by ENTER to control access to the variables of nested procedures. In Figure 4-5, for example, if procedure A calls procedure B which, in turn, calls procedure C, then procedure C will have access to the variables of the MAIN procedure and procedure A, but not those of procedure B because they are at the same lexical level. The following definition describes the access to variables for the nested procedures in Figure 4-5.

1. MAIN has variables at fixed locations.

2. Procedure A can access only the variables of MAIN.

3. Procedure B can access only the variables of procedure A and MAIN. Procedure B cannot access the variables of procedure C or procedure D.

4. Procedure C can access only the variables of procedure A and MAIN. procedure C cannot access the variables of procedure B or procedure D.

5. Procedure D can access the variables of procedure C, procedure A, and MAIN. Procedure D cannot access the variables of procedure B.

In Figure 4-6, an ENTER instruction at the beginning of the MAIN procedure creates three doublewords of dynamic storage for MAIN, but copies no pointers from other stack frames. The first doubleword in the display holds a copy of the last value in the EBP register before the ENTER instruction was executed. The second doubleword holds a copy of the contents of the EBP register following the ENTER instruction. After the instruction is executed, the EBP register points to the first doubleword pushed on the stack, and the ESP register points to the last doubleword in the stack frame.

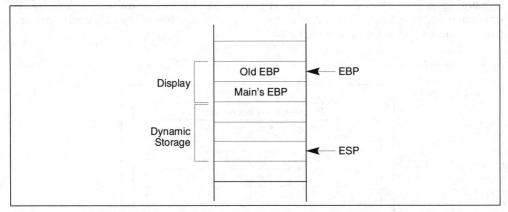

Figure 4-6. Stack Frame after Entering the MAIN Procedure

When MAIN calls procedure A, the ENTER instruction creates a new display (see Figure 4-7). The first doubleword is the last value held in MAIN's EBP register. The second doubleword is a pointer to MAIN's stack frame which is copied from the second doubleword in MAIN's display. This happens to be another copy of the last value held in MAIN's EBP register. Procedure A can access variables in MAIN because MAIN is at level 1. Therefore the base address for the dynamic storage used in MAIN is the current address in the EBP register, plus four bytes to account for the saved contents of MAIN's EBP register. All dynamic variables for MAIN are at fixed, positive offsets from this value.

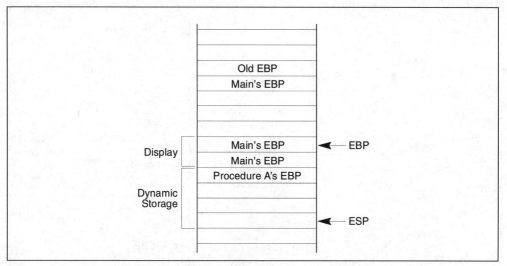

Figure 4-7. Stack Frame after Entering Procedure A

When procedure A calls procedure B, the ENTER instruction creates a new display (see Figure 4-8). The first doubleword holds a copy of the last value in procedure A's EBP register. The second and third doublewords are copies of the two stack frame pointers in procedure A's display. Procedure B can access variables in procedure A and MAIN by using the stack frame pointers in its display.

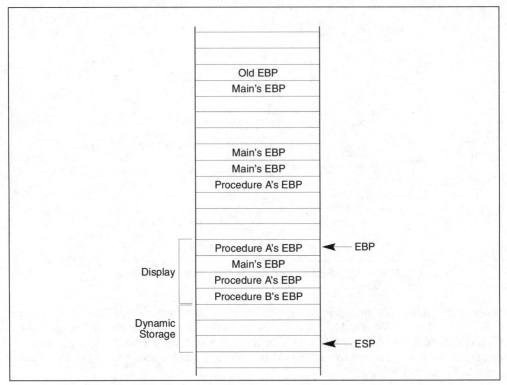

Figure 4-8. Stack Frame after Entering Procedure B

When procedure B calls procedure C, the ENTER instruction creates a new display for procedure C (see Figure 4-9). The first doubleword holds a copy of the last value in procedure B's EBP register. This is used by the LEAVE instruction to restore procedure B's stack frame. The second and third doublewords are copies of the two stack frame pointers in procedure A's display. If procedure C were at the next deeper lexical level from procedure B, a fourth doubleword would be copied, which would be the stack frame pointer to procedure B's local variables.

Note that procedure B and procedure C are at the same level, so procedure C is not intended to access procedure B's variables. This does not mean that procedure C is completely isolated from procedure B; procedure C is called by procedure B, so the pointer to the returning stack frame is a pointer to procedure B's stack frame. In addition, procedure B can pass parameters to procedure C either on the stack or through variables global to both procedures (that is, variables in the scope of both procedures).

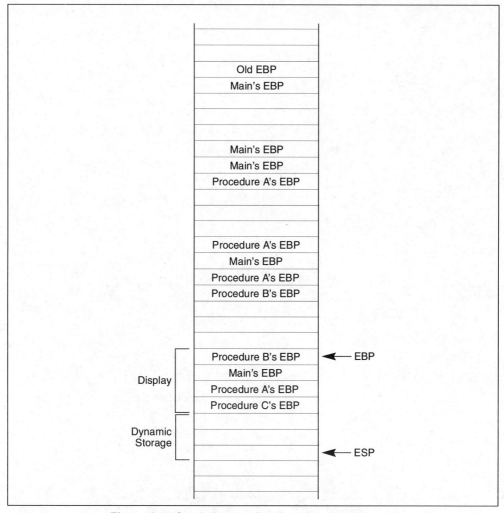

Figure 4-9. Stack Frame after Entering Procedure C

4.5.2. LEAVE Instruction

The LEAVE instruction reverses the action of the previous ENTER instruction. The LEAVE instruction does not have any operands. The LEAVE instruction copies the contents of the EBP register into the ESP register to release all stack space allocated to the procedure. Then the LEAVE instruction restores the old value of the EBP register from the stack. This simultaneously restores the ESP register to its original value. A subsequent RET instruction then can remove any arguments and the return address pushed on the stack by the calling program for use by the procedure.

intel®

5

Data Types and
Addressing Modes

CHAPTER 5
DATA TYPES AND ADDRESSING MODES

This chapter describes data types and addressing modes available to programmers of the Pentium Pro processor.

5.1. FUNDAMENTAL DATA TYPES

The fundamental data types of the Pentium Pro processor are bytes, words, doublewords, and quadwords (see Figure 5-1). A byte is eight bits, a word is 2 bytes (16 bits), a doubleword is 4 bytes (32 bits), and a quadword is 8 bytes (64 bits).

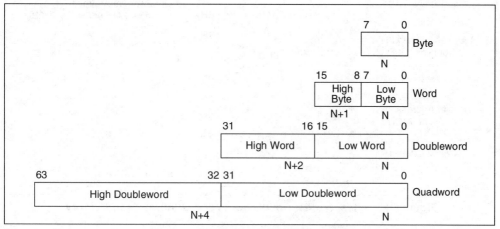

Figure 5-1. Fundamental Data Types

Figure 5-2 shows the byte order of each of the fundamental data types when referenced as operands in memory. The low byte (bits 0 through 7) of each data type occupies the lowest address in memory and that address is also the address of the operand.

5.1.1. Alignment of Words, Doublewords, and Quadwords

Words, doublewords, and quadwords do not need to be aligned in memory on natural boundaries. (The natural boundaries for words, double words, and quadwords are even-numbered addresses, addresses evenly divisible by four, and addresses evenly divisible by eight, respectively.) To improve the performance of programs, however, data structures (especially stacks) should be aligned on natural boundaries whenever possible. The reason for this is that the processor requires two clock cycles to make an unaligned memory access; whereas, aligned accesses require only one clock cycle. For the Pentium Pro processor, a word or doubleword operand that crosses a 4-byte boundary and a quadword operand that crosses an 8-byte boundary is considered an unaligned and requires two clock cycles to access; a word that starts on an odd address but does not cross a word boundary is considered aligned and can still be accessed in one clock cycle.

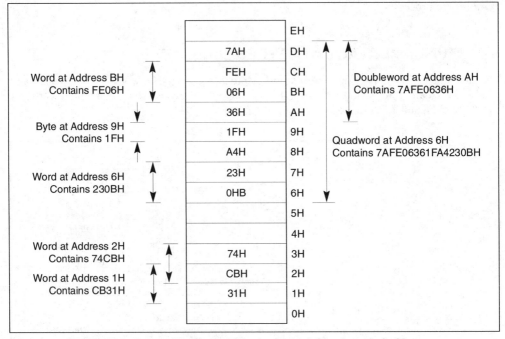

Figure 5-2. Bytes, Words, Doublewords and Quadwords in Memory

5.2. NUMERIC, POINTER, BIT FIELD, AND STRING DATA TYPES

Although bytes, words, and doublewords are the fundamental data types for the Pentium Pro processor, some instructions recognize and operate on additional numeric, pointer, bit field, and string data types (see in Figure 5-3). These additional data types are described in the following sections.

5.2.1. Integers

Integers are signed binary numbers held in a byte, word, or doubleword. All operations assume a two's complement representation. The sign bit is located in bit 7 in a byte integer, bit 15 in a word integer, and bit 31 in a doubleword integer. The sign bit is set for negative integers and cleared for positive integers and zero. Integer values range from −128 to +127 for a byte integer, from −32,768 to +32,767 for a word integer, and from -2^{31} to $+2^{31} - 1$ for a doubleword integer.

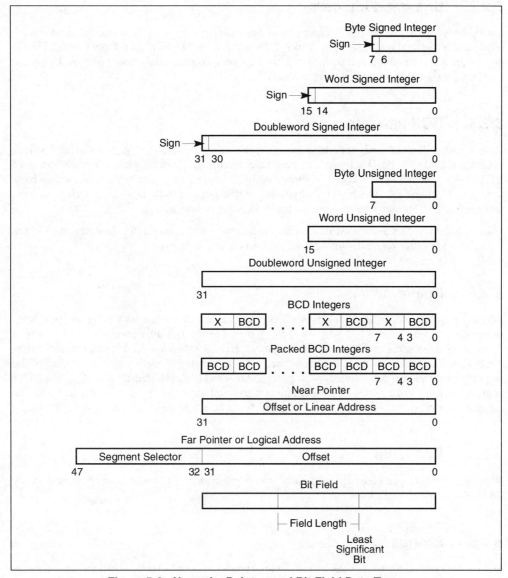

Figure 5-3. Numeric, Pointer, and Bit Field Data Types

5.2.2. Unsigned Integers

Unsigned integers are unsigned binary numbers contained in a byte, word, or doubleword. Unsigned integer values range from 0 to 255 for an unsigned byte integer, from 0 to 65,535 for an unsigned word integer, and from 0 to $2^{32} - 1$ for an unsigned doubleword integer. Unsigned integers are sometimes referred to as *ordinals*.

5.2.3. BCD Integers

Binary-coded decimal integers (BCD integers) are unsigned 4-bit integers with valid values ranging from 0 to 9. BCD integers can be unpacked (one BCD digit per byte) or packed (two BCD digits per byte). The value of an unpacked BCD integer is the binary value of the low half-byte (bits 0 through 3). The high half-byte (bits 4 through 7) can be any value during addition and subtraction, but must be zero during multiplication and division.

Packed BCD integers allow two BCD digits to be contained in one byte. Here, the digit in the high half-byte is more significant than the digit in the low half-byte.

5.2.4. Pointers

Pointers are addresses of locations in memory. The Pentium Pro processor recognizes two types of pointers: a *near pointer* (32 bits) and a *far pointer* (48 bits). A near pointer is a 32-bit offset (also called an *effective address*) within a segment. Near pointers are used for all memory references in a flat memory model or for references in a segmented model where the identity of the segment being accessed is implied. A far pointer is a 48-bit logical address, consisting of a 16-bit segment selector and a 32-bit offset. Far pointers are used for memory references in a segmented memory model where the identity of a segment being accessed must be specified explicitly.

5.2.5. Bit Fields

A *bit field* is a contiguous sequence of bits. It can begin at any bit position of any byte in memory and can contain up to 32 bits.

5.2.6. Strings

Strings are continuous sequences of bits, bytes, words, or doublewords. A *bit string* can begin at any bit position of any byte and can contain up to $2^{32} - 1$ bits. A *byte string* can contain bytes, words, or doublewords and can range from zero to $2^{32} - 1$ bytes (4 gigabytes).

5.2.7. Floating-Point Data Types

The processor's floating-point instructions also recognize a set of real, integer, and BCD integer data types (see Chapter 7, *Floating-Point Unit*).

5.3. OPERAND ADDRESSING

A Pentium Pro processor machine-instruction acts on zero or more operands. Some operands are specified explicitly in an instruction and others are implicit to an instruction. Whether specified explicitly or implicitly, an operand can be located in any of the following places:

- The instruction itself (an immediate operand).
- A register.
- A memory location.
- An I/O port.

5.3.1. Immediate Operands

Some instructions use data encoded in the instruction itself as a source operand. These operands are called *immediate* operands (or simply immediates). For example, the following ADD instruction adds an immediate value of 14 to the contents of the EAX register:
```
ADD EAX, 14
```

All the arithmetic instructions (except the DIV and IDIV instructions) allow the source operand to be an immediate value. The maximum value allowed for an immediate value varies among instructions, but can never be greater than the maximum value of an unsigned doubleword integer (2^{32}).

5.3.2. Register Operands

Source and destination operands can be located in any of the following registers, depending on the instruction being executed:

- The 32-bit general-purpose registers (EAX, EBX, ECX, EDX, ESI, EDI, ESP, or EBP).
- The 16-bit general-purpose registers (AX, BX, CX, DX, SI, DI, SP, or BP).
- The 8-bit general-purpose registers (AH, BH, CH, DH, AL, BL, CL, or DL).
- The segment registers (CS, DS, SS, ES, FS, and GS).
- The EFLAGS register.
- System registers, such as the global descriptor table (GDTR) or the interrupt descriptor table register (IDTR).

Some instructions (such as the DIV and MUL instructions) use quadword operands contained in a pair of 32-bit registers. Register pairs are represented with a colon separating them. For example, in the register pair EDX:EAX, EDX contains the high order bits and EAX contains the low order bits of a quadword operand.

Several instructions (such as the PUSHFD and POPFD instructions) are provided to load and store the contents of the EFLAGS register or to set or clear individual flags in this register. Other instructions (such as the Jcc instructions) use the state of the status flags in the EFLAGS register as condition codes for branching or other decision making operations.

The processor contains a selection of system registers that are used to control memory management, interrupt and exception handling, task management, processor management, and debugging activities. Some of these system registers are accessible by an application program, the operating system, or the executive through a set of system instructions. When accessing a system register with a system instruction, the register is generally an implied operand of the instruction.

5.3.3. Memory Operands

Source and destination operands in memory are referenced by means of a segment selector and an offset (see Figure 5-4). The segment selector specifies the segment containing the operand and the offset (the number of bytes from the beginning of the segment to the first byte of the operand) specifies the linear or effective address of the operand.

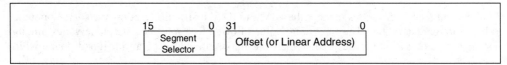

Figure 5-4. Memory Operand Address

5.3.3.1. SPECIFYING A SEGMENT SELECTOR

The segment selector can be specified either implicitly or explicitly. The most common method of specifying a segment selector is to load it in a segment register and then allow the processor to select the register implicitly, depending on the type of operation being performed. The processor automatically chooses a segment according to the rules given in Table 5-1.

Table 5-1. Default Segment Selection Rules

Type of Reference	Register Used	Segment Used	Default Selection Rule
Instructions	CS	Code Segment	All instruction fetches.
Stack	SS	Stack Segment	All stack pushes and pops. Any memory reference which uses the ESP or EBP register as a base register.
Local Data	DS	Data Segment	All data references, except when relative to stack or string destination.
Destination Strings	ES	Data Segment pointed to with the ES register	Destination of string instructions.

When storing data in or loading data from memory, the DS segment default can be overridden to allow other segments to be accessed. Within an assembler, the segment override is generally handled with a colon ":" operator. For example, the following MOV instruction moves a value from register EAX into the segment pointed to by the ES register. The offset into the segment is contained in the EBX register:

```
MOV ES:[EBX], EAX;
```

(At the machine level, a segment override is specified with a segment-override prefix, which is a byte placed at the beginning of an instruction.) The following default segment selections cannot be overridden:

- Instruction fetches must be made from the code segment.

- Destination strings in string instructions must be stored in the data segment pointed to by the ES register.

- Push and pop operations must always reference the SS segment.

Some instructions require a segment selector to be specified explicitly. In these cases, the 16-bit segment selector can be located in a memory location or in a 16-bit register. For example, the following MOV instruction moves a segment selector located in register BX into segment register DS:

```
MOV DS, BX
```

Segment selectors can also be specified explicitly as part of a 48-bit far pointer in memory. Here, the first doubleword in memory contains the offset and the next word contains the segment selector.

5.3.3.2.   SPECIFYING AN OFFSET

The offset part of a memory address can be specified either directly as an static value (called a *displacement*) or through an address computation made up of one or more of the following components:

- Displacement—An 8-, 16-, or 32-bit value.

- Base—The value in a general-purpose register.

- Index—The value in a general-purpose register.

- Scale factor—A value of 2, 4, or 8 that is multiplied by the index value.

The offset which results from adding these components is called an *effective address*. Each of these components can have either a positive or negative (2s complement) value, with the exception of the scaling factor. Figure 5-5 shows all the possible ways that these components can be combined to create an effective address in the selected segment.

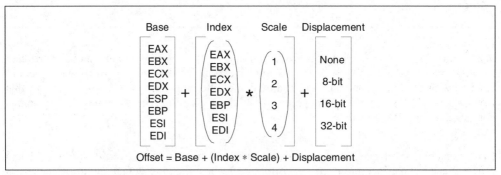

Figure 5-5. Offset (or Effective Address) Computation

The uses of general-purpose registers as base or index components are restricted in the following manner:

- The ESP register cannot be used as an index register.

- When the ESP or EBP register is used as the base, the SS segment is the default selection. In all other cases, the DS segment is the default selection.

The base, index, and displacement components can be used in any combination, and any of these components can be null. A scale factor can be used only when an index also is used. Each possible combination is useful for data structures commonly used by programmers in high-level languages and assembly language. The following addressing modes suggest uses for common combinations of address components.

Displacement

A displacement alone represents a direct (uncomputed) offset to the operand. Because the displacement is encoded in the instruction, this form of an address is sometimes called an absolute or static address. It is commonly used to access a statically allocated scalar operand.

Base

A base alone represents an indirect offset to the operand. Since the value in the base register can change, it can be used for dynamic storage of variables and data structures.

Base + Displacement

A base register and a displacement can be used together for two distinct purposes:

- As an index into an array when the element size is not 2, 4, or 8 bytes. The displacement component encodes the static offset to the beginning of the array. The base register holds the results of a calculation to determine the offset to a specific element within the array.

- To access a field of a record. The base register holds the address of the beginning of the record, while the displacement is an static offset to the field.

An important special case of this combination is access to parameters in a procedure activation record. A procedure activation record is the stack frame created when a procedure is entered. Here, the EBP register is the best choice for the base register, because it automatically selects the stack segment. This is a compact encoding for this common function.

(Index * Scale) + Displacement

This address mode offers an efficient way to index into a static array when the element size is 2, 4, or 8 bytes. The displacement locates the beginning of the array, the index register holds the subscript of the desired array element, and the processor automatically converts the subscript into an index by applying the scaling factor.

Base + Index + Displacement

Using two registers together supports either a two-dimensional array (the displacement holds the address of the beginning of the array) or one of several instances of an array of records (the displacement is an offset to a field within the record).

Base + (Index * Scale) + Displacement

Using all the addressing components together allows efficient indexing of a two-dimensional array when the elements of the array are 2, 4, or 8 bytes in size.

5.3.3.3.   ASSEMBLER ADDRESSING MODES

At the machine level, the selected combination of displacement, base register, index register, and scale factor is encoded in an instruction. All assemblers provide addressing modes based on combinations of these addressing components.

5.3.4.   I/O Port Addressing

The processor supports an I/O address space that contains up to 65,536 8-bit I/O ports. An I/O port can be addressed with either an immediate operand or a value in the DX register. See Chapter 8, *Input/Output*, for more information about I/O port addressing.

intel®

6

Instruction Set Summary

CHAPTER 6
INSTRUCTION SET SUMMARY

This chapter lists all the instructions in the Pentium Pro processor's instruction set, divided into three functional groups: integer, floating-point, and system. It also briefly describes each of the integer instructions.

Brief descriptions of the floating-point instructions are given in Chapter 7, *Floating-Point Unit*; brief descriptions of the system instructions are given in the *Pentium® Pro Family Developer's Manual, Volume 3.*

Detailed descriptions of all the Pentium Pro processor instructions are given in Chapter 11, *Instruction Set Reference*. Included in this chapter are a description of each instruction's encoding and operation, the effect of an instruction on the EFLAGS flags, and the exceptions an instruction may generate.

6.1. NEW INSTRUCTIONS IN THE PENTIUM® PRO PROCESSOR

The following instructions are new in the Pentium Pro processor:

- CMOV*cc*—Conditional move (see Section 6.3.1.2., "Conditional Move Instructions").

- FCMOV*cc*—Floating-point conditional move on condition-code flags in EFLAGS register (see Section 7.5.3., "Data Transfer Instructions").

- FCOMI/FCOMIP/FUCOMI/FUCOMIP—Floating-point compare and set condition-code flags in EFLAGS register (see Section 7.5.6., "Comparison and Classification Instructions").

- RDPMC—Read performance monitoring counters (see Chapter 11, "RDPMC—Read Performance-Monitoring Counters").

- UD2—Undefined instruction (see Section 6.15.4., "No-Operation and Undefined Instructions").

6.2. INSTRUCTION SET LIST

This section lists all the Pentium Pro processor instructions divided into three major groups: inter, floating-point, and system instructions. For each instruction, the mnemonic and descriptive names are given. When two or more mnemonics are given (for example, CMOVA/CMOVNBE), they represent different mnemonics for the same instruction opcode. Assemblers support redundant mnemonics for some instructions to make it easier to read code listings. For instance, CMOVA (Conditional move if above) and CMOVNBE (Conditional move is not below or equal) represent the same condition.

6.2.1.   Integer Instructions

Integer instructions perform the integer arithmetic, logic, and program flow control operations that programmers commonly use to write application and system software to run on the Pentium Pro processor. In the following sections, the integer instructions are divided into several instruction subgroups.

6.2.1.1.   DATA TRANSFER INSTRUCTIONS

MOV	Move
CMOVE/CMOVZ	Conditional move if equal/Conditional move if zero
CMOVNE/CMOVNZ	Conditional move if not equal/Conditional move if not zero
CMOVA/CMOVNBE	Conditional move if above/Conditional move if not below or equal
CMOVAE/CMOVNB	Conditional move if above or equal/Conditional move if not below
CMOVB/CMOVNAE	Conditional move if below/Conditional move if not above or equal
CMOVBE/CMOVNA	Conditional move if below or equal/Conditional move if not above
CMOVG/CMOVNLE	Conditional move if greater/Conditional move if not less or equal
CMOVGE/CMOVNL	Conditional move if greater or equal/Conditional move if not less
CMOVL/CMOVNGE	Conditional move if less/Conditional move if not greater or equal
CMOVLE/CMOVNG	Conditional move if less or equal/Conditional move if not greater
CMOVC	Conditional move if carry
CMOVNC	Conditional move if not carry
CMOVO	Conditional move if overflow
CMOVNO	Conditional move if not overflow
CMOVS	Conditional move if sign (negative)
CMOVNS	Conditional move if not sign (non-negative)
CMOVP/CMOVPE	Conditional move if parity/Conditional move if parity even
CMOVNP/CMOVPO	Conditional move if not parity/Conditional move if parity odd
XCHG	Exchange

BSWAP	Byte swap
XADD	Exchange and add
CMPXCHG	Compare and exchange
CMPXCHG8B	Compare and exchange 8 bytes
PUSH	Push onto stack
POP	Pop off of stack
PUSHA/PUSHAD	Push general-purpose registers onto stack
POPA/POPAD	Pop general-purpose registers from stack
IN	Read from a port
OUT	Write to a port
CWD/CDQ	Convert word to doubleword/Convert doubleword to quadword
CBW/CWDE	Convert byte to word/Convert word to doubleword
MOVSX	Move and sign extend
MOVZX	Move and zero extend

6.2.1.2. BINARY ARITHMETIC

ADD	Integer add
ADC	Add with carry
SUB	Subtract
SBB	Subtract with borrow
IMUL	Signed multiply
MUL	Unsigned multiply
IDIV	Signed divide
DIV	Unsigned divide
INC	Increment
DEC	Decrement
NEG	Negate
CMP	Compare

6.2.1.3. DECIMAL ARITHMETIC

| DAA | Decimal adjust after addition |
| DAS | Decimal adjust after subtraction |

AAA	ASCII adjust after addition
AAS	ASCII adjust after subtraction
AAM	ASCII adjust after multiplication
AAD	ASCII adjust before division

6.2.1.4.   LOGIC INSTRUCTIONS

AND	And
OR	Or
XOR	Exclusive or
NOT	Not
SAR	Shift arithmetic right
SHR	Shift logical right
SAL/SHL	Shift arithmetic left/Shift logical left
SHRD	Shift right double
SHLD	Shift left double
ROR	Rotate right
ROL	Rotate left
RCR	Rotate through carry right
RCL	Rotate through carry left

6.2.1.5.   BIT AND BYTE INSTRUCTIONS

BT	Bit test
BTS	Bit test and set
BTR	Bit test and reset
BTC	Bit test and complement
BSF	Bit scan forward
BSR	Bit scan reverse
SETE/SETZ	Set byte if equal/Set byte if zero
SETNE/SETNZ	Set byte if not equal/Set byte if not zero
SETA/SETNBE	Set byte if above/Set byte if not below or equal
SETAE/SETNB/SETNC	Set byte if above or equal/Set byte if not below/Set byte if not carry

SETB/SETNAE/SETC	Set byte if below/Set byte if not above or equal/Set byte if carry
SETBE/SETNA	Set byte if below or equal/Set byte if not above
SETG/SETNLE	Set byte if greater/Set byte if not less or equal
SETGE/SETNL	Set byte if greater or equal/Set byte if not less
SETL/SETNGE	Set byte if less/Set byte if not greater or equal
SETLE/SETNG	Set byte if less or equal/Set byte if not greater
SETS	Set byte if sign (negative)
SETNS	Set byte if not sign (non-negative)
SETO	Set byte if overflow
SETNO	Set byte if not overflow
SETPE/SETP	Set byte if parity even/Set byte if parity
SETPO/SETNP	Set byte if parity odd/Set byte if not parity
TEST	Logical compare

6.2.1.6. CONTROL TRANSFER INSTRUCTIONS

JMP	Jump
JE/JZ	Jump if equal/Jump if zero
JNE/JNZ	Jump if not equal/Jump if not zero
JA/JNBE	Jump if above/Jump if not below or equal
JAE/JNB	Jump if above or equal/Jump if not below
JB/JNAE	Jump if below/Jump if not above or equal
JBE/JNA	Jump if below or equal/Jump if not above
JG/JNLE	Jump if greater/Jump if not less or equal
JGE/JNL	Jump if greater or equal/Jump if not less
JL/JNGE	Jump if less/Jump if not greater or equal
JLE/JNG	Jump if less or equal/Jump if not greater
JC	Jump if carry
JNC	Jump if not carry
JO	Jump if overflow
JNO	Jump if not overflow

JS	Jump if sign (negative)
JNS	Jump if not sign (non-negative)
JPO/JNP	Jump if parity odd/Jump if not parity
JPE/JP	Jump if parity even/Jump if parity
JCXZ/JECXZ	Jump register CX zero/Jump register ECX zero
LOOP	Loop with ECX counter
LOOPZ/LOOPE	Loop with ECX and zero/Loop with ECX and equal
LOOPNZ/LOOPNE	Loop with ECX and not zero/Loop with ECX and not equal
CALL	Call procedure
RET	Return
IRET	Return from interrupt
INT	Software interrupt
INTO	Interrupt on overflow
BOUND	Detect value out of range
ENTER	High-level procedure entry
LEAVE	High-level procedure exit

6.2.1.7. STRING INSTRUCTIONS

MOVS/MOVSB	Move string/Move byte string
MOVS/MOVSW	Move string/Move word string
MOVS/MOVSD	Move string/Move doubleword string
CMPS/CMPSB	Compare string/Compare byte string
CMPS/CMPSW	Compare string/Compare word string
CMPS/CMPSD	Compare string/Compare doubleword string
SCAS/SCASB	Scan string/Scan byte string
SCAS/SCASW	Scan string/Scan word string
SCAS/SCASD	Scan string/Scan doubleword string
LODS/LODSB	Load string/Load byte string
LODS/LODSW	Load string/Load word string
LODS/LODSD	Load string/Load doubleword string
STOS/STOSB	Store string/Store byte string

STOS/STOSW   Store string/Store word string

STOS/STOSD   Store string/Store doubleword string

REP   Repeat while ECX not zero

REPE/REPZ   Repeat while equal/Repeat while zero

REPNE/REPNZ   Repeat while not equal/Repeat while not zero

INS/INSB   Input string from port/Input byte string from port

INS/INSW   Input string from port/Input word string from port

INS/INSD   Input string from port/Input doubleword string from port

OUTS/OUTSB   Output string to port/Output byte string to port

OUTS/OUTSW   Output string to port/Output word string to port

OUTS/OUTSD   Output string to port/Output doubleword string to port

6.2.1.8.   FLAG CONTROL INSTRUCTIONS

STC   Set carry flag

CLC   Clear the carry flag

CMC   Complement the carry flag

CLD   Clear the direction flag

STD   Set direction flag

LAHF   Load flags into AH register

SAHF   Store AH register into flags

PUSHF/PUSHFD   Push EFLAGS onto stack

POPF/POPFD   Pop EFLAGS from stack

STI   Set interrupt flag

CLI   Clear the interrupt flag

6.2.1.9.   SEGMENT REGISTER INSTRUCTIONS

LDS   Load far pointer using DS

LES   Load far pointer using ES

LFS   Load far pointer using FS

LGS   Load far pointer using GS

LSS   Load far pointer using SS

6.2.1.10. MISCELLANEOUS INSTRUCTIONS

LEA	Load effective address
NOP	No operation
UB2	Undefined instruction
XLAT/XLATB	Table lookup translation
CPUID	Processor Identification

6.2.2. Floating-Point Instructions

The floating-point instructions are those that are executed by the processor's floating-point unit (FPU). These instructions are used to operate on floating-point (real), extended integer, and binary-coded decimal (BCD) operands. As with the integer instructions, the following list of floating-point instructions is divided into subgroups.

6.2.2.1. DATA TRANSFER

FLD	Load real
FST	Store real
FSTP	Store real and pop
FILD	Load integer
FIST	Store integer
FISTP	Store integer and pop
FBLD	Load BCD
FBSTP	Store BCD and pop
FXCH	Exchange registers
FCMOVE	Floating-point conditional move if equal
FCMOVNE	Floating-point conditional move if not equal
FCMOVB	Floating-point conditional move if below
FCMOVBE	Floating-point conditional move if below or equal
FCMOVNB	Floating-point conditional move if not below
FCMOVNBE	Floating-point conditional move if not below or equal
FCMOVU	Floating-point conditional move if unordered
FCMOVNU	Floating-point conditional move if not unordered

6.2.2.2. BASIC ARITHMETIC

FADD	Add real
FADDP	Add real and pop
FIADD	Add integer
FSUB	Subtract real
FSUBP	Subtract real and pop
FISUB	Subtract integer
FSUBR	Subtract real reverse
FSUBRP	Subtract real reverse and pop
FISUBR	Subtract integer reverse
FMUL	Multiply real
FMULP	Multiply real and pop
FIMUL	Multiply integer
FDIV	Divide real
FDIVP	Divide real and pop
FIDIV	Divide integer
FDIVR	Divide real reverse
FDIVRP	Divide real reverse and pop
FIDIVR	Divide integer reverse
FPREM	Partial remainder
FPREMI	IEEE Partial remainder
FABS	Absolute value
FCHS	Change sign
FRNDINT	Round to integer
FSCALE	Scale by power of two
FSQRT	Square root
FXTRACT	Extract exponent and significand

6.2.2.3. COMPARISON

FCOM	Compare real
FCOMP	Compare real and pop

FCOMPP	Compare real and pop twice
FUCOM	Unordered compare real
FUCOMP	Unordered compare real and pop
FUCOMPP	Unordered compare real and pop twice
FICOM	Compare integer
FICOMP	Compare integer and pop
FCOMI	Compare real and set EFLAGS
FUCOMI	Unordered compare real and set EFLAGS
FCOMIP	Compare real, set EFLAGS, and pop
FUCOMIP	Unordered compare real, set EFLAGS, and pop
FTST	Test real
FXAM	Examine real

6.2.2.4.   TRANSCENDENTAL

FSIN	Sine
FCOS	Cosine
FSINCOS	Sine and cosine
FPTAN	Partial tangent
FPATAN	Partial arctangent
F2XM1	$2^x - 1$
FYL2X	$y*\log_2 x$
FYL2XP1	$y*\log_2(x+1)$

6.2.2.5.   LOAD CONSTANTS

FLD1	Load $+1.0$
FLDZ	Load $+0.0$
FLDPI	Load π
FLDL2E	Load $\log_2 e$
FLDLN2	Load $\log_e 2$
FLDL2T	Load $\log_2 10$
FLDLG2	Load $\log_{10} 2$

6.2.2.6. FPU CONTROL

FINCSTP	Increment FPU register stack pointer
FDECSTP	Decrement FPU register stack pointer
FFREE	Free floating-point register
FINIT	Initialize FPU after checking error conditions
FNINIT	Initialize FPU without checking error conditions
FCLEX	Clear floating-point exception flags after checking for error conditions
FNCLEX	Clear floating-point exception flags without checking for error conditions
FSTCW	Store FPU control word after checking error conditions
FNSTCW	Store FPU control word without checking error conditions
FLDCW	Load FPU control word
FSTENV	Store FPU environment after checking error conditions
FNSTENV	Store FPU environment without checking error conditions
FLDENV	Load FPU environment
FSAVE	Save FPU state after checking error conditions
FNSAVE	Save FPU state without checking error conditions
FRSTOR	Restore FPU state
FSTSW	Store FPU status word after checking error conditions
FNSTSW	Store FPU status word without checking error conditions
WAIT/FWAIT	Wait for FPU
FNOP	FPU no operation

6.2.3. System Instructions

The following system instructions are used to control those functions of the processor that are provided to support for operating systems and executives.

LGDT	Load global descriptor table (GDT) register
SGDT	Store global descriptor table (GDT) register
LLDT	Load local descriptor table (LDT) register
SLDT	Store local descriptor table (LDT) register
LTR	Load task register

STR	Store task register
LIDT	Load interrupt descriptor table (IDT) register
SIDT	Store interrupt descriptor table (IDT) register
MOV	Load and store control registers
LMSW	Load machine status word
SMSW	Store machine status word
CLTS	Clear the task-switched flag
ARPL	Adjust requested privilege level
LAR	Load access rights
LSL	Load segment limit
VERR	Verify segment for reading
VERW	Verify segment for writing
MOV	Load and store debug registers
INVD	Invalidate cache, with writeback
WBINVD	Invalidate cache, no writeback
INVLPG	Invalidate TLB Entry
LOCK (prefix)	Lock Bus
HLT	Halt processor
RSM	Return from system management mode (SSM)
RDMSR	Read model-specific register
WRMSR	Write model-specific register
RDPMC	Read performance monitoring counters
RDTSC	Read time stamp counter

6.3. DATA MOVEMENT INSTRUCTIONS

The data movement instructions move bytes, words, doublewords, or quadwords both between memory and the processor's registers and between registers. These instructions are divided into three groups:

- General-purpose data movement.
- Exchange.
- Stack manipulation.
- Type-conversion.

6.3.1. General-Purpose Data Movement Instructions

The MOV (move) and CMOVcc (conditional move) instructions transfer data between memory and registers or between registers.

6.3.1.1. MOVE INSTRUCTION

The MOV instruction performs basic load data and store data operations between memory and the processor's registers and data movement operations between registers. It handles data transfers along the paths listed in Table 6-1. (See Chapter 11, "MOV—Move to/from Control Registers" and Chapter 11, "MOV—Move to/from Debug Registers" for information on moving data to and from the control and debug registers.)

Table 6-1. Move Instruction Operations

Type of Data Movement	Source → Destination
From memory to a register	Memory location → General-purpose register Memory location → Segment register
From a register to memory	General-purpose register → Memory location Segment register → Memory location
Between registers	General-purpose register → General-purpose register General-purpose register → Segment register Segment register → General-purpose register General-purpose register → Control register Control register → General-purpose register General-purpose register → Debug register Debug register → General-purpose register
Immediate data to a register	Immediate → General-purpose register
Immediate data to memory	Immediate → Memory location

The MOV instruction cannot move data from one memory location to another or from one segment register to another segment register. Memory-to-memory moves can be performed with the MOVS (string move) instruction (see Section 6.10., "String Operations").

6.3.1.2. CONDITIONAL MOVE INSTRUCTIONS

The CMOVcc instructions are a group of instructions that check the state of the status flags in the EFLAGS register and perform a move operation if the flags are in a specified state (or condition). These instructions can be used to move a 16- or 32-bit value from memory to a general-purpose register or from one general-purpose register to another. The flag state being tested for each instruction is specified with a condition code (cc) that is associated with the instruction. If the condition is not satisfied, a move is not performed and execution continues with the instruction following the CMOVcc instruction.

Table 6-4 shows the mnemonics for the CMOVcc instructions and the conditions being tested for each instruction. The condition code mnemonics are appended to the letters "CMOV" to form the mnemonics for the CMOVcc instructions. The instructions listed in Table 6-4 as pairs (for example, CMOVA/CMOVNBE) are alternate names for the same instruction. The assembler provides these alternate names to make it easier to read program listings.

Table 6-2. Conditional Move Instructions

Instruction Mnemonic	Status Flag States	Condition Description
Unsigned Conditional Moves		
CMOVA/CMOVNBE	(CF or ZF)=0	Above/not below or equal
CMOVAE/CMOVNB	CF=0	Above or equal/not below
CMOVNC	CF=0	Not carry
CMOVB/CMOVNAE	CF=1	Below/not above or equal
CMOVC	CF=1	Carry
CMOVBE/CMOVNA	(CF or ZF)=1	Below or equal/not above
CMOVE/CMOVZ	ZF=1	Equal/zero
CMOVNE/CMOVNZ	ZF=0	Not equal/not zero
CMOVP/CMOVPE	PF=1	Parity/parity even
CMOVNP/CMOVPO	PF=0	Not parity/parity odd
Signed Conditional Moves		
CMOVGE/CMOVNL	(SF xor OF)=0	Greater or equal/not less
CMOVL/CMOVNGE	(SF xor OF)=1	Less/not greater or equal
CMOVLE/CMOVNG	((SF xor OF) or ZF)=1	Less or equal/not greater
CMOVO	OF=1	Overflow
CMOVNO	OF=0	Not overflow
CMOVS	SF=1	Sign (negative)
CMOVNS	SF=0	Not sign (non-negative)

The CMOVcc instructions are useful for optimizing small IF constructions. They also help eliminate branching overhead for IF statements and the possibility of branch mispredictions by the processor.

These instructions may not be supported on some processors in the Pentium Pro processor family. Software can check if the CMOVcc instructions are supported by checking the processor's feature information with the CPUID instruction (see Chapter 11, "CPUID—CPU Identification").

intel

6.3.1.3. EXCHANGE INSTRUCTIONS

The exchange instructions swap the contents of one or more operands and, in some cases, performs additional operations such as asserting the LOCK signal or modifying flags in the EFLAGS register.

The XCHG (exchange) instruction swaps the contents of two operands. This instruction takes the place of three MOV instructions and does not require a temporary location to save the contents of one operand location while the other is being loaded. When a memory operand is used with the XCHG instruction, the processor's LOCK signal is automatically asserted. This instruction is thus useful for implementing semaphores or similar data structures for process synchronization. (See Chapter 7, *Multiple Processor Management*, in the *Pentium® Pro Family Developer's Manual, Volume 3* for more information on bus locking.)

The BSWAP (byte swap) instruction reverses the byte order in a 32-bit register operand. Bit positions 0 through 7 are exchanged with 24 through 31, and bit positions 8 through 15 are exchanged with 16 through 23. Executing this instruction twice in a row leaves the register in the same value as before. The BSWAP instruction is useful for converting between "big-endian" and "little-endian" data formats. This instruction also speeds execution of decimal arithmetic. (The XCHG instruction can be used two swap the bytes in a word.)

The XADD (exchange and add) instruction swaps two operands and then stores the sum of the two operands in the destination operand. The status flags in the EFLAGS register indicate the result of the addition. This instruction can be combined with the LOCK prefix (see Chapter 11, "LOCK—Assert LOCK# Signal Prefix") in a multiprocessing system to allow multiple processors to execute one DO loop.

The CMPXCHG (compare and exchange) and CMPXCHG8B (compare and exchange 8 bytes) instructions are used to synchronize operations in systems that use multiple processors. The CMPXCHG instruction requires three operands: a source operand in a register, another source operand in the EAX register, and a destination operand. If the values contained in the destination operand and the EAX register are equal, the destination operand is replaced with the value of the other source operand (the value not in the EAX register). Otherwise, the original value of the destination operand is loaded in the EAX register. The status flags in the EFLAGS register reflect the result that would have been obtained by subtracting the destination operand from the value in the EAX register.

The CMPXCHG instruction is commonly used for testing and modifying semaphores. It checks to see if a semaphore is free. If the semaphore is free it is marked allocated, otherwise it gets the ID of the current owner. This is all done in one uninterruptible operation. In a single-processor system, the CMPXCHG instruction eliminates the need to switch to protection level 0 (to disable interrupts) before executing multiple instructions to test and modify a semaphore. For multiple processor systems, CMPXCHG can be combined with the LOCK prefix to perform the compare and exchange operation atomically.

The CMPXCHG8B instruction also requires three operands: a 64-bit value in EDX:EAX, a 64-bit value in ECX:EBX, and a destination operand in memory. The instruction compares the 64-bit value in the EDX:EAX registers with the destination operand. If they are equal, the 64-bit value in the ECX:EBX register is stored in the destination operand. If the EDX:EAX register and the destination are not equal, the destination is loaded in the EDX:EAX register. The CMPXCHG8B instruction can be combined with the LOCK prefix to perform the operation atomically.

6.3.2. Stack Manipulation Instructions

The PUSH, POP, PUSHA (push all registers), and POPA (pop all registers) instructions let you move data to and from the procedure stack. The PUSH instruction decrements the stack pointer (contained in the ESP register), then copies the source operand to the top of stack (see Figure 6-1). It operates on memory operands, immediate operands, and register operands (including segment registers). The PUSH instruction is commonly used to place parameters on the stack before calling a procedure. It can also be used to reserve space on the stack for temporary variables.

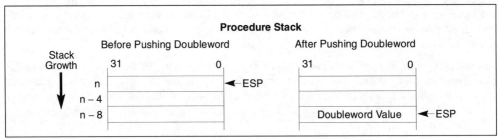

Figure 6-1. Operation of the PUSH Instruction

The PUSHA instruction saves the contents of the eight general-purpose registers on the stack (see Figure 6-2). This instruction simplifies procedure calls by reducing the number of instructions required to save the contents of the general-purpose registers. The registers are pushed on the stack in the following order: EAX, ECX, EDX, EBX, the initial value of ESP before EAX was pushed, EBP, ESI, and EDI.

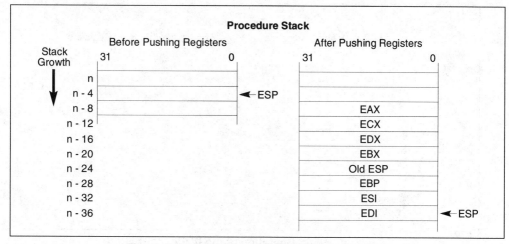

Figure 6-2. Operation of the PUSHA Instruction

The POP instruction copies the word or doubleword at the current top of stack (indicated by the ESP register) to the location specified with the destination operand, and then increments the ESP register to point to the new top of stack (see Figure 6-3). The destination operand may specify a general-purpose register, a segment register, or a memory location.

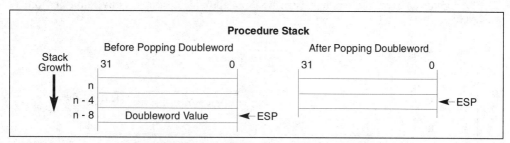

Figure 6-3. Operation of the POP Instruction

The POPA instruction reverses the effect of the PUSHA instruction. It pops the top eight words or doublewords from the top of the stack into the general-purpose registers, except for the ESP register (see Figure 6-4). If the address-size attribute is 32, the doublewords on the stack are transferred to the registers in the following order: EDI, ESI, EBP, ignore doubleword, EBX, EDX, ECX, and EAX. The ESP register is restored by the action of popping the stack. If the address-size attribute is 16, the words on the stack are transferred to the registers in the following order: DI, SI, BP, ignore word, BX, DX, CX, and AX.

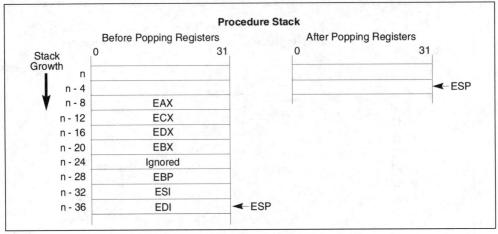

Figure 6-4. Operation of the POPA Instruction

6.3.2.1. TYPE CONVERSION INSTRUCTIONS

The type conversion instructions convert bytes into words, words into doublewords, and double-words into quadwords. These instructions are especially useful for converting integers to larger integer formats, because they perform sign extension (see Figure 6-5).

Two kinds of type conversion instructions are provided: simple conversion and move and convert.

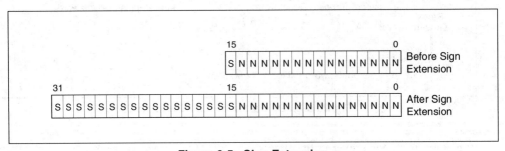

Figure 6-5. Sign Extension

6.3.2.2. SIMPLE CONVERSION

The CBW (convert byte to word), CWDE (convert word to doubleword extended), CWD (convert word to doubleword), and CDQ (convert doubleword to quadword) instructions perform sign extension to double the size of the source operand.

The CBW instruction copies the sign (bit 7) of the byte in the AL register into every bit position of the upper byte of the AX register. The CWDE instruction copies the sign (bit 15) of the word in the AX register into every bit position of the high word of the EAX register.

The CWD instruction copies the sign (bit 15) of the word in the AX register into every bit position in the DX register. The CDQ instruction copies the sign (bit 31) of the doubleword in the EAX register into every bit position in the EDX register. The CWD instruction can be used to produce a doubleword dividend from a word before a word division, and the CDQ instruction can be used to produce a quadword dividend from a doubleword before doubleword division.

6.3.2.3.   MOVE AND CONVERT

The MOVSX (move with sign extension) and MOVZX (move with zero extension) instructions move the source operand into a register then perform the sign extension.

The MOVSX instruction extends an 8-bit value to a 16-bit value or an 8- or 16-bit value to 32-bit value by sign extending the source operand, as shown in Figure 6-5. The MOVZX instruction extends an 8-bit value to a 16-bit value or an 8- or 16-bit value to 32-bit value by zero extending the source operand.

6.4.   BINARY ARITHMETIC INSTRUCTIONS

The binary arithmetic instructions operate on 8-, 16-, and 32-bit numeric data encoded as signed or unsigned binary integers. Operations include the add, subtract, multiply, and divide as well as increment, decrement, compare, and change sign (negate). The binary arithmetic instructions may also be used in algorithms that operate on decimal (BCD) values.

6.4.1.   Addition and Subtraction Instructions

The ADD (add integers), ADC (add integers with carry), SUB (subtract integers), and SBB (subtract integers with borrow) instructions perform addition and subtraction operations on signed or unsigned integer operands.

The ADD instruction computes the sum of two integer operands.

The ADC instruction computes the sum of two integer operands, plus 1 if the CF flag is set. This instruction is used to propagate a carry when adding numbers in stages.

The SUB instruction computes the difference of two integer operands.

The SBB instruction computes the difference of two integer operands, minus 1 if the CF flag is set. This instruction is used to propagate a borrow when subtracting numbers in stages.

6.4.2.   Increment and Decrement Instructions

The INC (increment) and DEC (decrement) instructions add 1 to or subtract 1 from an unsigned integer operand, respectively. A primary use of these instructions is for implementing counters.

6.4.3. Comparison and Sign Change Instruction

The CMP (compare) instruction computes the difference between two integer operands and updates the OF, SF, ZF, AF, PF, and CF flags according to the result. The source operands are not modified, nor is the result saved. The CMP instruction is commonly used in conjunction with a J*cc* (jump) or SET*cc* (byte set on condition) instruction, with the latter instructions performing an action based on the result of a CMP instruction.

The NEG (negate) instruction subtracts a signed integer operand from zero. The effect of the NEG instruction is to change the sign of a two's complement operand while keeping its magnitude.

6.4.4. Multiplication and Divide Instructions

The processor provides two multiply instructions, MUL (unsigned multiply) and IMUL signed multiply), and two divide instructions, DIV (unsigned divide) and IDIV (signed divide).

The MUL instruction multiplies two unsigned integer operands. The result is computed to twice the size of the source operands (for example, if word operands are being multiplied, the result is a doubleword).

The IMUL instruction multiplies two signed integer operands. The result is computed to twice the size of the source operands; however, in some cases the result is truncated to the size of the source operands (see Chapter 11, "IMUL—Signed Multiply").

The DIV instruction divides one unsigned operand by another unsigned operand and returns a quotient and a remainder.

The IDIV instruction is identical to the DIV instruction, except that IDIV performs a signed division.

6.5. DECIMAL ARITHMETIC INSTRUCTIONS

Decimal arithmetic can be performed with the Pentium Pro processor by combining the binary arithmetic instructions ADD, SUB, MUL, and DIV (discussed in Section 6.4., "Binary Arithmetic Instructions") with the decimal arithmetic instructions. The decimal arithmetic instructions are provided to carry out the following operations:

* To adjust the results of a previous binary arithmetic operation to produce a valid BCD result.

* To adjust the operands of a subsequent binary arithmetic operation so that the operation will produce a valid BCD result.

These instructions operate only on both packed and unpacked BCD values.

6.5.1. Packed BCD Adjustment Instructions

The DAA (decimal adjust after addition) and DAS (decimal adjust after subtraction) instructions adjust the results of operations performed on packed BCD integers (see Section 5.2.3., "BCD Integers"). Adding two packed BCD values requires two instructions: an ADD instruction followed by a DAA instruction. The ADD instruction adds (binary addition) the two values and stores the result in the AL register. The DAA instruction then adjusts the value in the AL register to obtain a valid, 2-digit, packed BCD value and sets the CF flag if a decimal carry occurred as the result of the addition.

Likewise, subtracting one packed BCD value from another requires a SUB instruction followed by a DAS instruction. The SUB instruction subtracts (binary subtraction) one BCD value from another and stores the result in the AL register. The DAS instruction then adjusts the value in the AL register to obtain a valid, 2-digit, packed BCD value and sets the CF flag if a decimal borrow occurred as the result of the subtraction.

6.5.2. Unpacked BCD Adjustment Instructions

The AAA (ASCII adjust after addition), AAS (ASCII adjust after subtraction), AAM (ASCII adjust after multiplication), and AAD (ASCII adjust before division) instructions adjust the results of arithmetic operations performed in unpacked BCD values (see Section 5.2.3., "BCD Integers"). All these instructions assume that the value to be adjusted in stored in the AL register or, in one instance, the AL and AH registers.

The AAA instruction adjusts the contents of the AL register following the addition of two unpacked BCD values. It converts the binary value in the AL register into a decimal value and stores the result in the AL register in unpacked BCD format (the decimal number is stored in the lower 4 bits of the register and the upper 4 bits are cleared). If a decimal carry occurred as a result of the addition, the CF flag is set and the contents of the AH register are incremented by 1.

The AAS instruction adjusts the contents of the AL register following the subtraction of two unpacked BCD values. Here again, a binary value is converted into an unpacked BCD value. If a borrow was required to complete the decimal subtract, the CF flag is set and the contents of the AH register are decremented by 1.

The AAM instruction adjusts the contents of the AL register following a multiplication of two unpacked BCD values. It converts the binary value in the AL register into a decimal value and stores the least significant digit of the result in the AL register (in unpacked BCD format) and the most significant digit, if there is one, in the AH register (also in unpacked BCD format).

The AAD instruction adjusts a two-digit BCD value so that when the value is divided with the DIV instruction, a valid unpacked BCD result is obtained. The instruction converts the BCD value in registers AH (most significant digit) and AL (least significant digit) into a binary value and stores the result in register AL. When the value in AL is divided by an unpacked BCD value, the quotient and remainder will be automatically encoded in unpacked BCD format.

6.6. LOGICAL INSTRUCTIONS

The logical instructions AND, OR, XOR (exclusive or), and NOT perform the standard Boolean operations for which they are named. The AND, OR, and XOR instructions require two operands; the NOT instruction operates on a single operand.

6.7. SHIFT AND ROTATE INSTRUCTIONS

The shift and rotate instructions rearrange the bits within an operand. These instructions fall into the following classes:

- Shift.
- Double shift.
- Rotate.

6.7.1. Shift Instructions

The SAL (shift arithmetic left), SHL (shift logical left), SAR (shift arithmetic right), SHR (shift logical right) instructions perform an arithmetic or logical shift of the bits in a byte, word, or doubleword.

The SAL and SHL instructions perform the same operation (see Figure 6-6). They shift the source operand left by from 1 to 31 bit positions. Empty bit positions are cleared. The CF flag is loaded with the last bit shifted out of the operand.

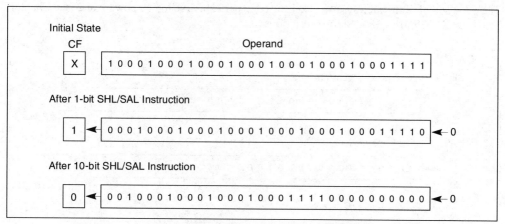

Figure 6-6. SHL/SAL Instruction Operation

The SHR instruction shifts the source operand right by from 1 to 31 bit positions (see Figure 6-7). As with the SHL/SAL instruction, the empty bit positions are cleared and the CF flag is loaded with the last bit shifted out of the operand.

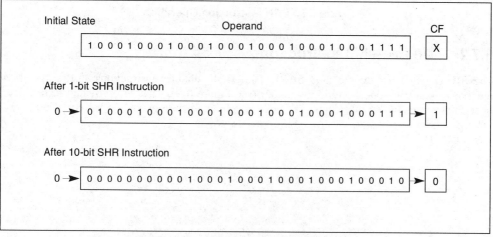

Figure 6-7. SHR Instruction Operation

The SAR instruction shifts the source operand right by from 1 to 31 bit positions (see Figure 6-8). This instruction differs from the SHR instruction in that it preserves the sign of the source operand by clearing empty bit positions if the operand is positive or setting the empty bits if the operand is negative. Again, the CF flag is loaded with the last bit shifted out of the operand.

The SAR and SHR instructions can also be used to perform division by powers of 2 (see Chapter 11, "SAL/SAR/SHL/SHR—Shift Instructions").

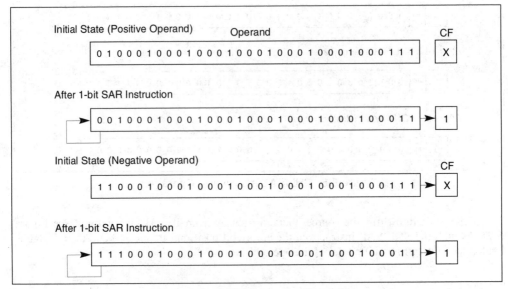

Figure 6-8. SAR Instruction Operation

6.7.2. Double-shift Instructions

The SHLD (shift left double) and SHRD (shift right double) instructions shift a specified number of bits from one operand to another (see Figure 6-9). They are provided to facilitate operations on unaligned bit strings. They can also be used to implement a variety of bit string move operations.

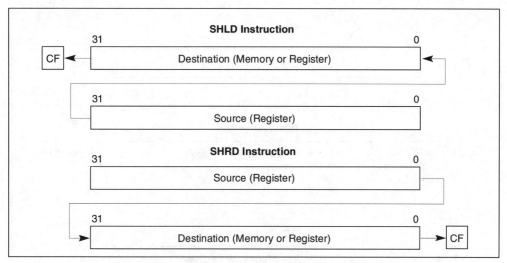

Figure 6-9. SHLD and SHRD Instruction Operations

The SHLD instruction shifts the bits in the destination operand to the left and fills the empty bit positions (in the destination operand) with bits shifted out of the source operand. The destination and source operands must be the same length (either words or doublewords). The shift count can range from 0 to 31 bits. The result of this shift operation is stored in the destination operand, and the source operand is not modified. The CF flag is loaded with the last bit shifted out of the destination operand.

The SHRD instruction operates the same as the SHLD instruction except bits are shifted to the left in the destination operand, with the empty bit positions filled with bits shifted out of the source operand.

6.7.3.   Rotate Instructions

The ROL (Rotate Left), ROR (rotate right), RCL (rotate through carry left) and RCR (rotate through carry right) instructions rotate the bits in the destination operand out of one end of an operand and back through the other end (see Figure 6-10). Unlike a shift, no bits are lost during a rotation. The rotate count can range from 0 to 31.

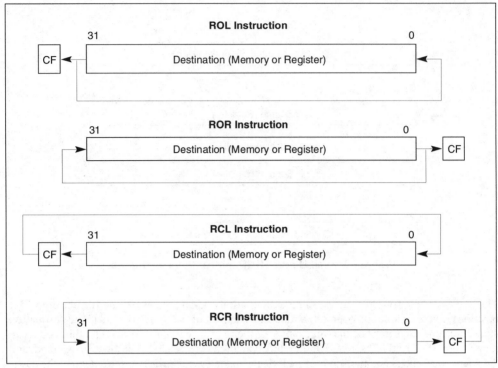

Figure 6-10. ROL, ROR, RCL, and RCR Instruction Operations

The ROL instruction rotates the bits in the operand to the left (toward more significant bit locations). The ROR instruction rotates the operand right (toward less significant bit locations).

The RCL instruction rotates the bits in the operand to the left, through the CF flag). This instruction treats the CF flag as a one-bit extension on the upper end of the operand. Each bit which exits from the most significant bit location of the operand moves into the CF flag. At the same time, the bit in the CF flag enters the least significant bit location of the operand.

The RCR instruction rotates the bits in the operand to the right through the CF flag.

For all the rotate instructions, the CF flag always contains the value of the last bit rotated out of the operand, even if the instruction does not use the CF flag as an extension of the operand. The value of this flag can then be tested by a conditional jump instruction (JC or JNC).

6.8. BIT AND BYTE INSTRUCTIONS

The bit and byte instructions operate on bit or byte strings. They are divided into three groups:

- Bit test and modify instructions.
- Bit scan instructions.
- Byte set on condition.
- Test

6.8.1. Bit Test and Modify Instructions

The bit test and modify instructions (see Table 6-3) operate on a single bit, which can be in an operand. The location of the bit is specified as an offset from the least significant bit of the operand. When the processor identifies the bit to be tested and modified, it first loads the CF flag with the current value of the bit. Then it assigns a new value to the selected bit, as determined by the modify operation for the instruction.

Table 6-3. Bit Test and Modify Instructions

Instruction	Effect on CF Flag	Effect on Selected Bit
BT (Bit Test)	CF flag ← Selected Bit	No effect
BTS (Bit Test and Set)	CF flag ← Selected Bit	Selected Bit ← 1
BTR (Bit Test and Reset)	CF flag ← Selected Bit	Selected Bit ← 0
BTC (Bit Test and Complement)	CF flag ← Selected Bit	Selected Bit ← NOT (Selected Bit)

6.8.2. Bit Scan Instructions

The BSF (bit scan forward) and BSR (bit scan reverse) instructions scan a bit string in a source operand for a set bit and store the bit index of the first set bit found in a destination register. The bit index is the offset from the least significant bit (bit 0) in the bit string to the first set bit. The BSF instruction scans the source operand low-to-high (from bit 0 of the source operand toward the most significant bit); the BSR instruction scans high-to-low (from the most significant bit toward the least significant bit).

6.8.3. Byte-Set-On-Condition Instructions

The SETcc (set byte on condition) instructions set a destination-operand byte to 0 or 1, depending on the state of selected status flags (CF, OF, SF, ZF, and PF) in the EFLAGS register. The suffix (*cc*) added to the SET mnemonic determines the condition being tested for. For example, the SETO instruction tests for overflow. If the OF flag is set, destination byte is set to 1; if OF is clear, the destination byte is cleared to 0. Appendix B, *EFLAGS Condition Codes* lists the conditions it is possible to test for with this instruction.

6.8.4. Test Instruction

The TEST instruction performs a logical AND of two operands and sets the SF, ZF, and PF flags according to the results. The flags can then be tested by the conditional jump or loop instructions or the SET*cc* instructions. The TEST instruction differs from the AND instruction in that it does not alter either of the operands.

6.9. CONTROL TRANSFER INSTRUCTIONS

The processor provides both conditional and unconditional control transfer instructions to direct the flow of program execution. Conditional transfers are taken only for specified states of the status flags in the EFLAGS register. Unconditional control transfers are always executed.

6.9.1. Unconditional Transfer Instructions

The JMP, CALL, RET, INT, and IRET instructions transfer program control to another location (destination address) in the instruction stream. The destination can be within the same code segment (near transfer) or in a different code segment (far transfer).

6.9.1.1. JUMP INSTRUCTION

The JMP (jump) instruction unconditionally transfers program control to a destination instruction. The transfer is a one-way: a return address is not saved. A destination operand specifies the address (the instruction pointer) of the destination instruction. The address can be a *relative address* or an *absolute address*.

A relative address is a displacement (offset) with respect to the address in the EIP register. The destination address (a near pointer) is formed by adding the displacement to the address in the EIP register. The displacement is specified with a signed integer, allowing jumps either forward or backward in the instruction stream.

An absolute address is a offset from address 0 of a segment. It can be specified in either of the following ways:

- **An address in a general-purpose register.** This address is treated as a near pointer, which is copied into the EIP register. Program execution then continues at the new address within the current code segment.

- **An address specified using the standard addressing modes of the processor.** Here, the address can be a near pointer or a far pointer. If the address is for a near pointer, the address is translated into an offset and copied into the EIP register. If the address is for a far pointer, the address is translated into a segment selector (which is copied into the CS register) and an offset (which is copied into the EIP register).

In protected mode, the JMP instruction also allows jumps to a call gate, a task gate, and a task-state segment.

6.9.1.2. CALL AND RETURN INSTRUCTIONS

The CALL (call procedure) and RET (return from procedure) instructions allow a jump from one procedure (or subroutine) to another and a subsequent jump back (return) to the calling procedure.

The CALL instruction transfers program control from the current (or calling procedure) to another procedure (the called procedure). To allow a subsequent return to the calling procedure, the CALL instructions saves the current contents of the EIP register on the procedure stack before jumping to the called procedure. The EIP register (prior to transferring program control) contains address of the instruction following the CALL instruction. When this address is pushed on the stack is referred to as the *return instruction pointer.*

The address of the called procedure (the address of the first instruction in the procedure being jumped to) is specified in a CALL instruction the same way as it is in a JMP instruction (see Section 6.9.1.1., "Jump Instruction"). The address can be specified with as a relative address or an absolute address. If an absolute address is specified, it can be either a near or a far pointer.

The RET instruction transfers program control from the procedure currently being executed (the called procedure) back to the procedure that called it (the calling procedure). Transfer of control is accomplished by copying the return instruction pointer from the stack into the EIP register. Program execution then continues with the instruction pointed to by the EIP register.

The RET instruction has an optional operand, the value of which is added to the contents of the ESP register as part of the return operation. This operand allows to stack pointer to be incremented to remove parameters from the stack that were pushed on the stack by the calling procedure.

See Section 4.3., "Calling Procedures Using CALL and RET", for more information on the mechanics of making procedure calls with the CALL and RET instructions.

6.9.1.3. RETURN-FROM-INTERRUPT INSTRUCTION

When the processor services in interrupt, it performs an implicit call to an interrupt-handling procedure. The IRET (return from interrupt) instruction returns program control from an interrupt handler to the interrupted procedure (that is, the procedure that was executing when the interrupt occurred). The IRET instruction performs a similar operation to the RET instruction (see Section 6.9.1.2., "Call and Return Instructions") except that it also restores the EFLAGS register from the procedure stack. The contents of the EFLAGS register are automatically stored on the stack along with the return instruction pointer when the processor services an interrupt. (As with the RET instruction, the IRET instruction has an optional operand for adjusting the stack pointer.)

6.9.2. Conditional Transfer Instructions

The conditional transfer instructions execute jumps or loops that transfer program control to another instruction in the instruction stream if specified conditions are met. The conditions for control transfer are specified with a set of condition codes that define various states of the status flags (CF, ZF, OF, PF, and SF) in the EFLAGS register.

6.9.2.1. CONDITIONAL JUMP INSTRUCTIONS

The Jcc (conditional) jump instructions transfers program control to a destination instruction if the conditions specified with the condition code (cc) associated with the instruction are satisfied. If the condition is not satisfied, execution continues with the instruction following the Jcc instruction. As with the JMP instruction, the transfer is a one-way; that is, a return address is not saved.

The destination operand specifies a relative address (a signed offset with respect to the address in the EIP register) that points to a instruction in the current code segment. The Jcc instructions do not support far transfers; however, far transfers can be accomplished with a combination of a Jcc and a JMP instruction (see Chapter 11, "Jcc—Jump if Condition Is Met").

Table 6-4 shows the mnemonics for the Jcc instructions and the conditions being tested for each instruction. The condition code mnemonics are appended to the letter "J" to form the mnemonic for a Jcc instruction. The instructions are divided into two groups: unsigned and signed conditional jumps. These groups correspond to the results of operations performed on unsigned and signed integers, respectively. Those instructions listed as pairs (for example, JA/JNBE) are alternate names for the same instruction. The assembler provides these alternate names to make it easier to read program listings.

The JCXZ and JECXZ instructions test the CX and ECX registers, respectively, instead of one or more status flags. See Section 6.9.2.3., "Jump If Zero Instructions" for more information about these instructions.

Table 6-4. Conditional Jump Instructions

Instruction Mnemonic	Condition (Flag States)	Description
Unsigned Conditional Jumps		
JA/JNBE	(CF or ZF)=0	Above/not below nor equal
JAE/JNB	CF=0	Above or equal/not below
JB/JNAE	CF=1	Below/not above nor equal
JBE/JNA	(CF or ZF)=1	Below or equal/not above
JC	CF=1	Carry
JE/JZ	ZF=1	Equal/zero
JNC	CF=0	Not carry
JNE/JNZ	ZF=0	Not equal/not zero
JNP/JPO	PF=0	Not parity/parity odd
JP/JPE	PF=1	Parity/parity even
JCXZ	CX=0	Register CX is zero
JECXZ	ECX=0	Register ECX is zero
Signed Conditional Jumps		
JG/JNLE	((SF xor OF) or ZF) =0	Greater/not less nor equal
JGE/JNL	(SF xor OF)=0	Greater or equal/not less
JL/JNGE	(SF xor OF)=1	Less/not greater nor equal
JLE/JNG	((SF xor OF) or ZF)=1	Less or equal/not greater
JNO	OF=0	Not overflow
JNS	SF=0	Not sign (non-negative)
JO	OF=1	Overflow
JS	SF=1	Sign (negative)

6.9.2.2. LOOP INSTRUCTIONS

The LOOP (loop while ECX not zero), LOOPE (loop while equal), LOOPZ (loop while zero), LOOPNE (loop while not equal), and LOOPNZ (loop while not zero) instructions are conditional jump instructions that use the value of the ECX register as a count for the number of times to execute a loop. All the loop instructions decrement the count in the ECX register each time they are executed and terminate a loop when zero is reached. Some of the loop instructions also accept the ZF flag as a condition for terminating the loop before the count reaches zero.

The LOOP instruction decrements the contents of the ECX register (or the CX register, if the address-size attribute is 16), then tests the register for the loop-termination condition. If the count in the ECX register are non-zero, program control is transferred to the instruction address specified by the destination operand. The destination operand is a relative address (that is, a offset relative to the contents of the EIP register), and it generally points the first instruction in the block of code that is to be executed in the loop. When the count in the ECX register reaches zero, program control is transferred to the instruction immediately following the LOOP instruction, which terminates the loop. If the count in the ECX register is zero when the LOOP instruction is first executed, the register is pre-decremented to FFFFFFFFH, causing the loop to be executed 2^{32} times.

The LOOPE and LOOPZ instructions perform the same operation (they are mnemonics for the same instruction). These instructions operate the same as the LOOP instruction, except that they also test the ZF flag. If the count in the ECX register is not zero and the ZF flag is set, program control is transferred to destination operand. When the count reaches zero or the ZF flag is clear, the loop is terminated by transferring program control to the instruction immediately following the LOOPE/LOOPZ instruction.

The LOOPNE and LOOPNZ instructions (mnemonics for the same instruction) operate the same as the LOOPE/LOOPPZ instructions, except that they terminate the loop if the ZF flag is set.

6.9.2.3. JUMP IF ZERO INSTRUCTIONS

The JECXZ (jump if ECX zero) instruction jumps to the location specified in the destination operand if the ECX register contains the value zero. This instruction can be used in combination with a loop instruction (LOOP, LOOPE, LOOPZ, LOOPNE, or LOOPNZ) to test the ECX register prior to beginning a loop. As described in Section 6.9.2.2., "Loop Instructions", the loop instructions decrement the contents of the ECX register before testing for zero. If the value in the ECX register is zero initially, it will be decremented to FFFFFFFFH on the first loop instruction, causing the loop to be executed 2^{32} times. To prevent this problem, a JECXZ instruction can be inserted at the beginning of the code block for the loop, causing a jump out the loop if the EAX register count is initially zero. When used with repeated string scan and compare instructions, the JECXZ instruction can determine whether the loop terminated because the count reached zero or because the scan or compare conditions were satisfied.

The JCXZ (jump if CX is zero) instruction operates the same as the JECXZ instruction when the 16-bit address-size attribute is used. Here, the CX register is tested for zero.

6.9.3. Software Interrupts

The INTn (software interrupt), INTO (interrupt on overflow), and BOUND (detect value out of range) instructions allow a program to explicitly raise a specified interrupt or exception, which in turn causes the handler routine for the interrupt or exception to be called.

The INTn instruction can raise any of the processors interrupts or exceptions by encoding the vector number or the interrupt or exception in the instruction. This instruction can be used to support software generated interrupts or to test the operation of interrupt and exception handlers. The IRET instruction (see Section 6.9.1.3., "Return-From-Interrupt Instruction") allows returns from interrupt handling routines.

The INTO instruction raises the overflow exception, if the OF flag is set. If the flag is clear, execution continues without raising the exception. This instruction allows software to access the overflow exception handler explicitly to check for overflow conditions.

The BOUND instruction compares a signed value against upper and lower bounds, and raises the "BOUND range exceeded" exception if the value is less than the lower bound or greater than the upper bound. This instruction is useful for operations such as checking an array index to make sure it falls within the range defined for the array.

6.10. STRING OPERATIONS

The MOVS (Move String), CMPS (Compare string), SCAS (Scan string), LODS (Load string), and STOS (Store string) instructions permit large data structures, such as alphanumeric character strings, to be moved and examined in memory. These instructions operate on individual elements in a string, which can be a byte, word, or doubleword. The string elements to be operated on are identified with the ESI (source string element) and EDI (destination string element) registers. Both of these registers contain absolute addresses (offsets into a segment) that point to a string element.

By default, the ESI register addresses the segment identified with the DS segment register. A segment-override prefix allows the ESI register to be associated with the CS, SS, ES, FS, or GS segment register. The EDI register addresses the segment identified with the ES segment register; no segment override is allowed for the EDI register. The use of two different segment registers in the string instructions permits operations to be performed on strings located in different segments. Or by associating the ESI register with the ES segment register, both the source and destination strings can be located in the same segment.

The MOVS instruction moves the string element addressed by the ESI register to the location addressed by the EDI register. The assembler recognizes three versions of this instruction, which specify the size of the string to be moved: MOVSB (move byte string), MOVSW (move word string), and MOVSD (move doubleword string).

The CMPS instruction subtracts the destination string element from the source string element and updates the status flags (CF, ZF, OF, SF, PF, and AF) in the EFLAGS register according to the results. Neither string element is written back to memory. The assembler recognizes three versions of the CMPS instruction: CMPSB (compare byte strings), CMPSW (compare word strings), and CMPSD (compare doubleword strings).

The SCAS instruction subtracts the destination string element from the contents of the EAX, AX, or AL register (depending on operand length) and updates the status flags according to the results. The string element and register contents are not modified. The following variations of the SCAS instruction specifies the operand length: SCASB (scan byte string), SCASW (scan word string), and SCASD (scan doubleword string).

The LODS instruction loads the source string element identified by the ESI register into the EAX register (for a doubleword string), the AX register (for a word string), or the AL register (for a byte string). The mnemonics normally used for this instruction are LODSB (load byte string), LODSW (load word string), and LODSD (load doubleword string). This instruction is usually used in a loop, where other instructions process each element of the string after they are loaded into the target register.

The STOS instruction stores the source string element from the EAX (doubleword string), AX (word string), or AL (byte string) register into the memory location identified with the EDI register. The mnemonics normally used for this instruction are STOSB (store byte string), STOSW (store word string), and STOSD (store doubleword string). This instruction is also normally used in a loop. Here a string is commonly loaded into the register with a LODS instruction, operated on by other instructions, and then stored again in memory with a STOS instruction.

The I/O instructions (see Section 6.11., "I/O Instructions") also perform operations on strings in memory.

6.10.1. Repeating String Operations

The string instructions described in Section 6.10., "String Operations" perform one iteration of a string operation. To operate strings longer than a doubleword, the string instructions can combined with a repeat prefix (REP) to create a repeating instruction or be placed in a loop.

When used in string instructions, the ESI and EDI registers are automatically incremented or decremented after each iteration of an instruction to point to the next element (byte, word, or doubleword) in the string. String operations can thus begin at higher addresses and work toward lower ones, or they can begin at lower addresses and work toward higher ones. The DF flag in the EFLAGS register controls whether the registers are incremented (DF=0) or decremented (DF=1). The STD and CLD instructions set and clear this flag, respectively.

The following repeat prefixes can be used in conjunction with a count in the ECX register to cause a string instruction to repeat:

- REP—Repeat while the ECX register not zero.
- REPE/REPZ—Repeat while the ECX register not zero and the ZF flag is set.
- REPNE/REPNZ—Repeat while the ECX register not zero and the ZF flag is clear.

When a string instruction has a repeat prefix, the operation executes until one of the termination conditions specified by the prefix is satisfied. The REPE/REPZ and REPNE/REPNZ prefixes are used only with the CMPS and SCAS instructions. Also, note that a A REP STOS instruction is the fastest way to initialize a large block of memory.

6.11. I/O INSTRUCTIONS

The IN (input from port to register), INS (input from port to string), OUT (output from register to port), and OUTS (output string to port) instructions move data between the processor's I/O ports and either a register or memory.

The register I/O instructions (IN and OUT) move data between an I/O port and the EAX register (32-bit I/O), the AX register (16-bit I/O), or the AL (8-bit I/O) register. The I/O port being read or written to is specified with an immediate operand or an address in the DX register.

The block I/O instructions (INS and OUTS) instructions move blocks of data (strings) between an I/O port and memory. These instructions operate similar to the string instructions (see Section 6.10., "String Operations"). The ESI and EDI registers are used to specify string elements in memory and the repeat prefixes (REP) are used to repeat the instructions to implement block moves. The assembler recognizes the following alternate mnemonics for these instructions: INSB (input byte), INSW (input word), and INSD (input doubleword), and OUTB (output byte), OUTW (output word), and OUTD (output doubleword).

The INS and OUTS instructions use an address in the DX register to specify the I/O port to be read or written to.

6.12. ENTER AND LEAVE INSTRUCTIONS

The ENTER and LEAVE instructions provide machine-language support for procedures calls in block-structured languages, such as C and Pascal. These instructions and the call and return mechanism that they support are described in detail in Section 4.5., "Procedure Calls for Block-Structured Languages".

6.13. EFLAGS INSTRUCTIONS

The EFLAGS instructions allow the state of selected flags in the EFLAGS register to be read or modified.

6.13.1. Carry and Direction Flag Instructions

The STC (set carry flag), CLC (clear carry flag), and CMC (complement carry flag) instructions allow the CF flags in the EFLAGS register to be modified directly. They are typically used to initialize the CF flag to a known state before an instruction that uses the state the flag in an operation is executed. They are also used in conjunction with the rotate-with-carry instructions (RCL and RCR).

The STD (set direction flag) and CLD (clear direction flag) instructions allow the DF flag in the EFLAGS register to be modified directly. The DF flag determines the direction in which index registers ESI and EDI are stepped when executing string processing instructions. If the DF flag is clear, the index registers are incremented after each iteration of a string instruction; if the DF flag is set, the registers are decremented.

6.13.2. Interrupt Flag Instructions

The STI (set interrupt flag) and CTI (clear interrupt flag) instructions allow the interrupt IF flag in the EFLAGS register to be modified directly. The IF flag controls the servicing of hardware-generated interrupts (those received at the processor's INTR pin). If the IF flag is set, the processor services hardware interrupts; if the F flag is clear, hardware interrupts are masked.

6.13.3. EFLAGS Transfer Instructions

The EFLAGS transfer instructions allow groups of flags in the EFLAGS register to copied to a register or memory or be loaded from a register or memory.

The LAHF (load AH from flags) and SAHF (store AH into flags) instructions operate on five of the EFLAGS status flags (SF, ZF, AF, PF, and CF). The LAHF instruction copies the status flags to bits 7, 6, 4, 2, and 0 of the AH register, respectively. The contents of the remaining bits in the register 5, 3, and 1 are undefined, and the contents of the EFLAGS register remain unchanged. The SAHF instruction copies bits 7, 6, 4, 2, and 0 from the AH register into the SF, ZF, AF, PF, and CF flags, respectively in the EFLAGS register.

The PUSHF (push flags), PUSHFD (push flags double), POPF (pop flags), and POPFD (pop flags double) instructions copy the flags in the EFLAGS register to and from the procedure stack. The PUSHF instruction pushes the lower word of the EFLAGS register onto the stack (see Figure 6-11). The PUSHFD instruction pushes the entire EFLAGS register onto the stack (with the RF and VM flags read as clear).

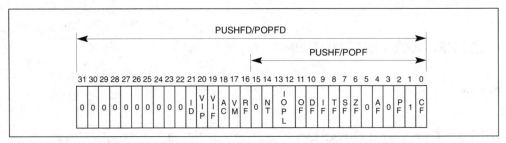

Figure 6-11. Flags Affected by the PUSHF, POPF, PUSHFD, and POPFD instructions

The POPF instruction pops a word from the stack into the EFLAGS register. Only bits 11, 10, 8, 7, 6, 4, 2, and 0 of the EFLAGS register are affected with all uses of this instruction. If the current privilege level (CPL) of the current code segment is 0 (most privileged), the IOPL bits (bits 13 and 12) also are affected. If the I/O privilege level (IOPL) is 0, the IF flag (bit 9) also is affected.

The POPFD instruction pops a doubleword into the EFLAGS register. This instruction can change the state of the AC bit (bit 18) and the ID bit (bit 21), as well as the bits affected by a POPF instruction.

6.13.4. Interrupt Flag Instructions

The CLI (clear interrupt flag) and STI (set interrupt flag) instructions clear and set the interrupt flag (IF) in the EFLAGS register, respectively. Clearing the IF flag causes external interrupts to be ignored. The ability to execute these instructions depends on the operating mode of the processor and the current privilege level (CPL) of the program or task attempting to execute these instructions.

6.14. SEGMENT REGISTER INSTRUCTIONS

The processor provides a variety of instructions that address the segment registers of the processor directly. These instructions are only used when an operating system or executive is using the segmented or the real-address mode memory model.

6.14.1. Segment-Register Load and Store Instructions

The MOV instruction (introduced in Section 6.3.1., "General-Purpose Data Movement Instructions") and the PUSH and POP instructions (introduced in Section 6.3.2., "Stack Manipulation Instructions") can transfer 16-bit segment selectors to and from segment registers (DS, ES, FS, GS, and SS). The transfers are always made to or from a segment register and a general-purpose register or memory. Transfers between segment registers are not supported.

The POP and MOV instructions cannot place a value in the CS register. Only the far control-transfer versions of the JMP, CALL, and RET instructions (see Section 6.14.2., "Far Control Transfer Instructions") affect the CS register directly.

6.14.2. Far Control Transfer Instructions

The JMP and CALL instructions (see Section 6.9., "Control Transfer Instructions") both accept a far pointer as a source operand to transfer program control to a segment other than the segment currently being pointed to by the CS register. When a far call is made with the CALL instruction, the current values of the EIP and CS registers are both pushed on the stack.

The RET instruction (see Section 6.9.1.2., "Call and Return Instructions") can be used to execute a far return. Here, program control is transferred from a code segment that contains a called procedure back to the code segment that contained the calling procedure. The RET instruction restores the values of the CS and EIP registers for the calling procedure from the stack.

6.14.3. Software Interrupt Instructions

The software interrupt instructions INT, INTO, BOUND, and IRET (see Section 6.9.3., "Software Interrupts") can also call and return from interrupt and exception handler procedures that are located in a code segment other than the current code segment. With these instructions, however, the switching of code segments is handled transparently from the application program.

6.14.4. Load Far Pointer Instructions

The load far pointer instructions LDS (load far pointer using DS), LES (load far pointer using ES), LFS (load far pointer using FS), LGS (load far pointer using GS), and LSS (load far pointer using SS) load a far pointer from memory into a segment register and a general-purpose general register. The segment selector part of the far pointer is loaded into the selected segment register and the offset is loaded into the selected general-purpose register.

6.15. MISCELLANEOUS INSTRUCTIONS

The following instructions perform miscellaneous operations that are of interest to applications programmers.

6.15.1. Address Computation Instruction

The LEA (load effective address) instruction computes the effective address in memory (offset within a segment) of a source operand and places it in a general-purpose register. This instruction can interpret any of the Pentium Pro processor's addressing modes and can perform any indexing or scaling that may be needed. It is especially useful for initializing the ESI or EDI registers before the execution of string instructions or for initializing the EBX register before an XLAT instruction.

6.15.2. Table Lookup Instructions

The XLAT and XLATB (table lookup) instructions replace the contents of the AL register with a byte read from a translation table in memory. The initial value in the AL register is interpreted as an unsigned index into the translation table. This index is added to the contents of the EBX register (which contains the base address of the table) to calculate the address of the table entry. These instructions are used for applications such as converting character codes from one alphabet into another (for example, an ASCII code could be used to look up its EBCDIC equivalent in a table).

6.15.3. Processor Identification Instruction

The CPUID (processor identification) instruction provides information about the processor on which the instruction is executed. To obtain processor information, a value of from 0 to 2 is loaded in the EAX register and then the CPUID instruction is executed. The resulting processor information is placed in the EAX, EBX, ECX, and EDX registers. Table 6-5 shows the information that is provided depending on the value initially entered in the EAX register. See Section 9.1., "Processor Identification" for detailed information on the output of the CPUID instruction.

Table 6-5. Information Provided by the CPUID Instruction

Initial EAX Value	Information Provided about the Processor
0	Maximum CPUID input value. Vendor identification string ("GenuineIntel").
1	Version information (family ID, model ID, and stepping ID). Feature information (identifies the feature set for the processor model).

Table 6-5. Information Provided by the CPUID Instruction (Contd.)

Initial EAX Value	Information Provided about the Processor
2	Cache information (about the processor's internal cache memory).

6.15.4. No-Operation and Undefined Instructions

The NOP (no operation) instruction increments the EIP register to point at the next instruction, but affects nothing else.

The UD2 (undefined) instruction generates an invalid opcode exception. Intel reserves the opcode for this instruction for this function. The instruction is provided to allow software to test an invalid opcode exception handler.

intel®

7

Floating-Point Unit

CHAPTER 7
FLOATING-POINT UNIT

The Pentium Pro processor's Floating-Point Unit (FPU) provides high-performance floating-point processing capabilities. It supports the real, integer, and BCD-integer data types and the floating-point processing algorithms and exception handling architecture defined in the IEEE 754 and 854 Standards for Floating-Point Arithmetic. The FPU executes instructions from the processor's normal instruction stream and greatly improves the efficiency of the processor in handling the types of high-precision floating-point processing operations commonly found in scientific, engineering, and business applications.

This chapter describes the data types that the FPU operates on, the FPU's execution environment, and the FPU-specific instruction set. Detailed descriptions of the FPU instructions are given in Chapter 11, *Instruction Set Reference*.

7.1. COMPATIBILITY WITH INTEL ARCHITECTURE MATH COPROCESSORS

The Pentium Pro processor's FPU extends the floating-point processing capability of earlier math coprocessors in the Intel Architecture family of processors. It is fully compatible with the Intel486 DX and Pentium processors.

The Pentium Pro processor's FPU offers several new instructions to improve processing throughput. The FCMOV*cc* (floating-point conditional move) instructions perform a floating-point move operation based on the state of the status flags in the EFLAGS register (see Chapter 11, "FCMOVcc—Floating-Point Conditional Move"). The FCOMI (floating-point compare and set EFLAGS) instructions set the status flags in the EFLAGS register according to the results of a comparison of two floating-point values (see Chapter 11, "FCOMI/FCOMIP/FUCOMI/FUCOMIP—Compare Real and Set EFLAGS").

7.2. REAL NUMBERS AND FLOATING-POINT FORMATS

This section describes how real numbers are represented in floating-point format in the Pentium Pro processor's FPU. It also introduces terms such as normalized numbers, denormalized numbers, biased exponents, signed zeros, and NaNs. Readers who are already familiar with floating-point processing techniques and the IEEE standards may wish to skip this section.

7.2.1. Real Number System

As shown in Figure 7-1, the real-number system comprises the continuum of real numbers from minus infinity ($-\infty$) to plus infinity ($+\infty$).

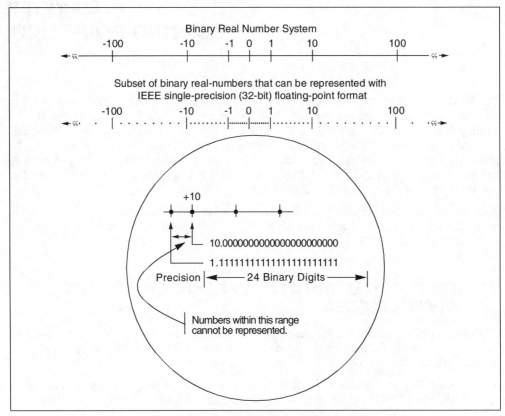

Figure 7-1. Binary Real Number System

Because the size and number of registers that any computer can have is limited, only a subset of the real-number continuum can be used in real-number calculations. As shown at the bottom of Figure 7-1, the subset of real numbers that a particular FPU supports represents an approximation of the real number system. The range and precision of this real-number subset is determined by the format that the FPU uses to represent real numbers.

7.2.2. Floating-Point Format

To increase the speed and efficiency of real-number computations, computers or FPUs typically represent real numbers in a binary floating-point format. In this format, a real number has three parts: a sign, a significand, and an exponent. Figure 7-2 shows the binary floating-point format that the Pentium Pro processor uses. This format conforms to the IEEE standard.

The sign is a binary value that indicates whether the number is positive (0) or negative (1). The significand has two parts: a 1-bit binary integer (also referred to as the J-bit) and a binary fraction. The J-bit is often not represented, but instead is an implied value. The exponent is a binary integer that represents the base-2 power that the significand is raised to.

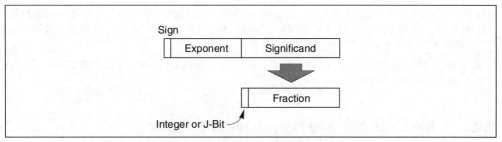

Figure 7-2. Binary Floating-Point Format

Table 7-1 shows how the real number 178.125 (in ordinary decimal format) is stored in floating-point format. The table lists a progression of real number notations that leads to the format that the FPU uses. In this format, the binary real number is normalized and the exponent is biased (see Section 7.2.2.1., "Normalized Numbers" and Section 7.2.2.2., "Biased Exponent").

Table 7-1. Real Number Notation

Notation	Value		
Ordinary Decimal	178.125		
Scientific Decimal	$1.78125E_{10}2$		
Scientific Binary	$1.0110010001E_2111$		
Scientific Binary (Biased Exponent)	$1.0110010001E_210000110$		
Single Format (Normalized)	Sign	Biased Exponent	Significand
	0	10000110	01100100010000000000000 1. (Implied)

7.2.2.1. NORMALIZED NUMBERS

In most cases, the FPU represents real numbers in normalized form. This means that except for zero, the significand is always made up of an integer of 1 and the following fraction:

1.fff...ff

For values less than 1, leading zeros are eliminated. (For each leading zero eliminated, the exponent is decremented by one.)

Representing numbers in normalized form maximizes the number of significant digits that can be accommodated in a significand of a given width. To summarize, a normalized real number consists of a normalized significand that represents a real number between 1 and 2 and an exponent that specifies the number's binary point.

7.2.2.2.　BIASED EXPONENT

The FPU represents exponents in a biased form. This means that a constant is added to the actual exponent so that the biased exponent is always a positive number. The value of the biasing constant depends on the number of bits available for representing exponents in the floating-point format being used. The biasing constant is chosen so that the smallest normalized number can be reciprocated without overflow.

(See Section 7.4.1., "Real Numbers" for a list of the biasing constants that the FPU uses for the various sizes of real data-types.)

7.2.3.　Real Number and Non-Number Encodings

A variety of real numbers and special values can be encoded in the FPU's floating-point format. These numbers and values are generally divided into the following classes:

- Signed zeros.
- Denormalized finite numbers.
- Normalized finite numbers.
- Signed infinities.
- NaNs.
- Indefinite numbers.

(The term NaN stands for "Not a Number.")

Figure 7-3 shows how the encodings for these numbers and non-numbers fit into the real number continuum. The encodings shown here are for the IEEE single-precision (32-bit) format, where the term "S" indicates the sign bit, "E" the biased exponent, and "F" the fraction. (The exponent values are given in decimal.)

The FPU can operate on and/or return any of these values, depending on the type of computation being performed. The following sections describe these number and non-number classes.

7.2.3.1.　SIGNED ZEROS

Zero can be represented as a +0 or a −0 depending on the sign bit. Both encodings are equal in value. The sign of a zero result depends on the operation being performed and the rounding mode being used. Signed zeros have been provided to aid in implementing interval arithmetic. The sign of a zero may indicate the direction from which underflow occurred, or it may indicate the sign of an ∞ that has been reciprocated.

7.2.3.2. NORMALIZED AND DENORMALIZED FINITE NUMBERS

Non-zero, finite numbers are divided into two classes: normalized and denormalized. The normalized finite numbers comprise all the non-zero finite values that can be encoded in a normalized real number format between zero and ∞. In the single-real format shown in Figure 7-3, this group of numbers includes all the numbers with biased exponents ranging from 1 to 254_{10} (unbiased, the exponent range is from -126_{10} to $+127_{10}$).

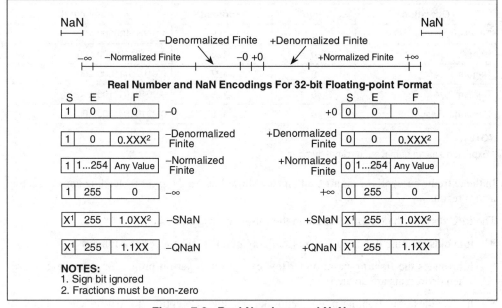

Figure 7-3. Real Numbers and NaNs

When real numbers become very close to zero, the normalized-number format can no longer be used to represent the numbers. This is because the range of the exponent is not large enough to compensate for shifting the binary point to the right to eliminate leading zeros.

When the biased exponent is zero, smaller numbers can only be represented by making the integer bit (and perhaps other leading bits) of the significand zero. The numbers in this range are called *denormalized* (or *tiny*) numbers. The use of leading zeros with denormalized numbers allows smaller numbers to be represented. However, this denormalization causes a loss of precision (the number of significant bits in the fraction is reduced by the leading zeros).

When performing normalized floating-point computations, an FPU normally operates on normalized numbers and produces normalized numbers as results. Denormalized numbers represent an *underflow* condition.

A denormalized number is computed through a technique called gradual underflow. Table 7-2 gives an example of gradual underflow in the denormalization process. Here the single-real format is being used, so the minimum exponent (unbiased) is -126_{10}. The true result in this example requires an exponent of -129_{10} in order to have a normalized number. Since -129_{10} is beyond the allowable exponent range, the result is denormalized by inserting leading zeros until the minimum exponent of -126_{10} is reached.

Table 7-2. Denormalization Process

Operation	Sign	Exponent*	Significand
True Result	0	−129	1.01011100000...00
Denormalize	0	−128	0.10101110000...00
Denormalize	0	−127	0.01010111000...00
Denormalize	0	−126	0.00101011100...00
Denormal Result	0	−126	0.00101011100...00

NOTE:
* Expressed as an unbiased, decimal number.

In the extreme case, all the significant bits are shifted out to the right by leading zeros, creating a zero result.

The FPU deals with denormal values in the following ways:

- It avoids creating denormals by normalizing numbers whenever possible.

- It provides the floating-point underflow exception to permit programmers to detect cases when denormals are created.

- It provides the floating-point denormal-operand exception to permit procedures or programs to detect when denormals are being used as source operands for computations.

When a denormal number in single- or double-real format is used as a source operand and the denormal exception is masked, the FPU automatically *normalizes* the number when it is converted to extended-real format.

7.2.3.3. SIGNED INFINITIES

The two infinities, $+\infty$ and $-\infty$, represent the maximum positive and negative real numbers, respectively, that can be represented in the floating-point format. Infinity is always represented by a zero significand (fraction and integer bit) and the maximum biased exponent allowed in the specified format (for example, 255_{10} for the single-real format).

The signs of infinities are observed, and comparisons are possible. Infinities are always interpreted in the affine sense; that is, $-\infty$ is less than any finite number and $+\infty$ is greater than any finite number. Arithmetic on infinities is always exact. Exceptions are generated only when the use of an infinity as a source operand constitutes an invalid operation.

Whereas denormalized numbers represent an underflow condition, the two infinity numbers represent the result of an overflow condition. Here, the normalized result of a computation has a biased exponent greater than the largest allowable exponent for the selected result format.

7.2.3.4. NANS

Since NaNs are non-numbers, they are not part of the real number line. In Figure 7-3, the encoding space for NaNs in the FPU floating-point formats is shown above the ends of the real number line. This space includes any value with the maximum allowable biased exponent and a non-zero fraction. (The sign bit is ignored for NaNs.)

The IEEE standard defines two classes of NaN: quiet NaNs (QNaNs) and signaling NaNs (SNaNs). A QNaN is a NaN with the most significant fraction bit set; an SNaN is a NaN with the most significant fraction bit clear. QNaNs are allowed to propagate through most arithmetic operations without signaling an exception. SNaNs generally signal an invalid-operation exception whenever they appear as operands in arithmetic operations. Exceptions are discussed in Section 7.7., "Floating-Point Exception Handling".

See Section 7.6., "Operating on NaNs" for detailed information on how the FPU handles NaNs.

7.2.4. Indefinite

For each FPU data type, one unique encoding is reserved for representing the special value *indefinite*. For example, when operating on real values, the real indefinite value is a QNaN (see Section 7.4.1., "Real Numbers"). The FPU produces indefinite values as responses to a masked floating-point exceptions.

7.3. FPU ARCHITECTURE

From an abstract, architectural view, the FPU is a coprocessor that operates in parallel with the processor's integer unit (see Figure 7-4). The FPU gets its instructions from the same instruction decoder and sequencer as the integer unit and shares the system bus with the integer unit. Other than these connections, the integer unit and FPU operate independently and in parallel. (The actual microarchitecture of the Pentium Pro processor has two integer units and two FPUs, see Section 2.4.4., "Dispatch/Execute Unit".)

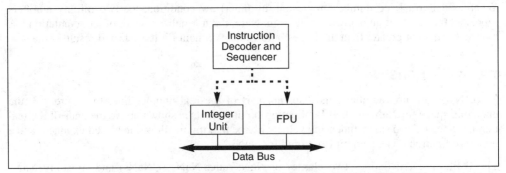

Figure 7-4. Relationship Between the Integer Unit and the FPU

The instruction execution environment of the FPU (see Figure 7-5) consists of 8 data registers (called the FPU data registers) and the following special-purpose registers:

- The status register.

- The control register.

- The tag word register.

- Instruction pointer register.

- Last operand (data pointer) register.

- Opcode register.

These registers are described in the following sections.

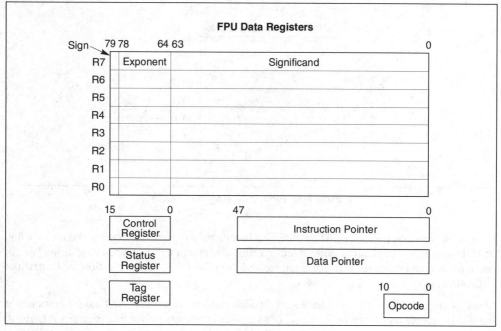

Figure 7-5. FPU Execution Environment

7.3.1. The FPU Data Registers

The FPU data registers (shown in Figure 7-5) consist of eight 80-bit registers. Values are stored in these registers in the extended-real format shown in Figure 7-17. When real, integer, or packed BCD integer values are loaded from memory into any of these registers, the values are automatically converted into extended-real format (see Section 7.4., "Floating-Point Data Types and Formats"). Computation results are subsequently converted back into one of the FPU data formats when they are transferred back into memory from any of the FPU registers.

The FPU instructions treat the eight FPU data registers as a register stack (see Figure 7-6). All addressing of the data registers is relative to the register on the top of the stack. The register number of the current top-of-stack register is stored in the TOP (stack TOP) field in the FPU status word. Load operations decrement TOP by one and load a value into the new top-of-stack register, and store operations store the value from the current TOP register in memory and then increment TOP by one. (For the FPU, a load operation is equivalent to a push and a store operation is equivalent to a pop.)

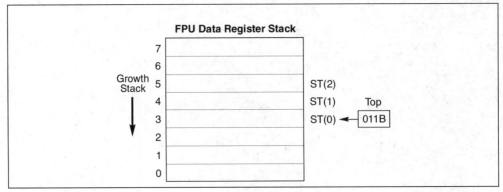

Figure 7-6. FPU Data Register Stack

If a load operation is performed when TOP is at 0, register wraparound occurs and the new value of TOP is set to 7. The floating-point stack-overflow exception indicate when wraparound might cause an unsaved value to be overwritten (see Section 7.8.1.1., "Stack Overflow or Underflow Exception (#IS)").

Many floating-point instructions have several addressing modes that permit the programmer to implicitly operate on the top of the stack, or to explicitly operate on specific registers relative to the TOP. Assemblers supports these register addressing modes, using the expression ST(0), or simply ST, to represent the current stack top and ST(i) to specify the ith register from TOP in the stack ($0 \le i \le 7$). For example, if TOP contains 011B (register 3 is the top of the stack), the following instruction would add the contents of two registers in the stack (registers 3 and 5):

```
FADD ST, ST(2);
```

Figure 7-7 shows an example of how the stack structure of the FPU registers and instructions are typically used to perform a series of computations. Here, a two-dimensional dot product is computed, as follows:

1. The first instruction (`FLD value1_ptr`) decrements the stack register pointer (TOP) and loads the value 5.6 from memory into ST(0). The result of this operation is shown in snap-shot (a).

2. The second instruction multiplies the value in ST(0) by the value 2.4 from memory and stores the result in ST(0), shown in snap-shot (b).

3. The third instruction decrements TOP and loads the value 3.8 in ST(0).

4. The fourth instruction multiplies the value in ST(0) by the value 10.3 from memory and stores the result in ST(0), shown in snap-shot (c).

5. The fifth instruction adds the value and the value in ST(1) and stores the result in ST(0), shown in snap-shot (d).

The style of programming demonstrated in this example, is supported by the floating-point instruction set. In cases where the stack structure causes computation bottlenecks, the FXCH (exchange FPU register contents) instruction can be used to streamline a computation.

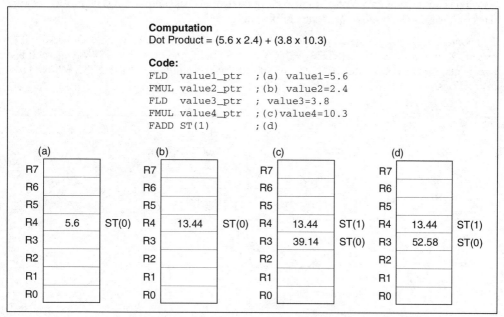

Figure 7-7. Example FPU Dot Product Computation

7.3.1.1. PARAMETER PASSING WITH THE FPU REGISTER STACK

Like the general-purpose registers in the processor's integer unit, the contents of the FPU data registers are unaffected by procedure calls, or in other words, the values are maintained across procedure boundaries. A calling procedure can thus use the FPU data registers (as well as the procedure stack) for passing parameter between procedures. The called procedure can reference parameters passed through the register stack using the current stack register pointer (TOP) and the ST(0) and ST(i) nomenclature.

7.3.2. FPU Status Register

The 16-bit FPU status register (see in Figure 7-8) indicates the current state of the FPU. The flags in the FPU status register include the FPU busy flag, top-of-stack (TOP) pointer, condition code flags, error summary status flag, stack fault flag, and exception flags. The FPU sets the flags in this register to show the results of operations.

The contents of the FPU status register (referred to as the FPU status word) can be stored in memory using the FSTSW/FNSTSW, FSTENV/FNSTENV, and FSAVE/FNSAVE instructions. It can also be stored in the AX register of the integer unit, using the FSTSW/FNSTSW instructions.

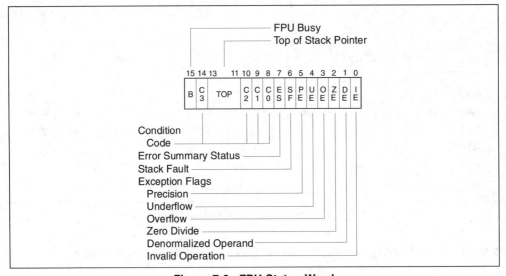

Figure 7-8. FPU Status Word

7.3.2.1. TOP OF STACK (TOP) POINTER

A pointer to the FPU data register that is currently at the top of the FPU register stack is contained in bits 11 through 13 of the FPU status word. This pointer, which is commonly referred to as TOP (for top-of-stack), is a binary value from 0 to 7. See Section 7.3.1., "The FPU Data Registers" for more information about the TOP pointer.

7.3.2.2. CONDITION CODE FLAGS

The four FPU condition code flags (C0 through C3) indicate the results of floating-point comparison and arithmetic operations. Table 7-3 summarizes the manner in which the floating-point instructions set the condition code flags. These condition code bits are used principally for conditional branching and for storage of information used in exception handling (see Section 7.3.3., "Branching and Conditional Moves on FPU Condition Codes").

As shown in Table 7-3, the C1 condition code flag is used for a variety of functions. When both the IE and SF flags in the FPU status word are set, indicating a stack overflow or underflow exception (#IS), the C1 flag distinguishes between overflow (C1=1) and underflow (C1=0). When the PE flag in the status word is set, indicating an inexact (rounded) result, the C1 flag is set to 1 if the last rounding by the instruction was upward. The FXAM instruction sets C1 to the sign of the value being examined.

Table 7-3. FPU Condition Code Interpretation

Instruction	C0	C3	C2	C1
FCOM, FCOMP, FCOMPP, FICOM, FICOMP, FTST, FUCOM, FUCOMP, FUCOMPP	Result of Comparison		Operands are not Comparable	0 or #IS
FCOMI, FCOMIP, FUCOMI, FUCOMIP	Undefined. (These instructions set the status flags in the EFLAGS register.)			#IS
FXAM	Operand class			Sign
FPREM, FPREM1	Q2	Q1	0=reduction complete 1=reduction incomplete	Q0 or #IS
F2XM1, FADD, FADDP, FBSTP, FCMOVcc, FIADD, FDIV, FDIVP, FDIVR, FDIVRP, FIDIV, FIDIVR, FIMUL, FIST, FISTP, FISUB, FISUBR, FMUL, FMULP, FPATAN, FRNDINT, FSCALE, FST, FSTP, FSUB, FSUBP, FSUBR, FSUBRP, FSQRT, FYL2X, FYL2XP1	Undefined			Roundup or #IS
FCOS, FSIN, FSINCOS, FPTAN	Undefined		1=source operand out of range.	Roundup or #IS (Undefined if C2=1)
FABS, FBLD, FCHS, FDECSTP, FILD, FINCSTP, FLD, Load Constants, FSTP (ext. real), FXCH, FXTRACT	Undefined			0 or #IS
FLDENV, FRSTOR	Each bit loaded from memory			
FFREE, FLDCW, FCLEX/FNCLEX, FNOP, FSTCW/FNSTCW, FSTENV/FNSTENV, FSTSW/FNSTSW,	Undefined			
FINIT/FNINIT, FSAVE/FNSAVE	0	0	0	0

The C2 condition code flag is used by the FPREM and FPREM1 instructions to indicate an incomplete reduction (or partial remainder). When a successful reduction has been completed, the C0, C3, and C1 condition code flags are set to the three least-significant bits of the quotient (Q2, Q1, and Q0, respectively). See Chapter 11, "FPREM—Partial Remainder" or Chapter 11, "FPREM1—Partial Remainder" for more information on how these instructions use the condition code flags.

The FPTAN, FSIN, FCOS, and FSINCOS instructions set the C2 flag to 1 to indicate that the source operand is beyond the allowable range of $\pm2^{63}$.

Where the state of the condition code flags are listed as undefined in Table 7-3, do not rely on any specific value in these flags.

7.3.2.3.   EXCEPTION FLAGS

The 6 exception flags (bits 0 through 5) of the status word and the exception summary status (ES) flag (bit 7) indicate that one or more floating-point exceptions has been detected since the bits were last cleared. The individual exception flags (IE, DE, ZE, OE, UE, and PE) are described in detail in Section 7.7., "Floating-Point Exception Handling". Each of the exception flags can be masked by an exception mask bit in the FPU control word (see Section 7.3.4., "FPU Control Word"). The ES flag is set when any of the unmasked exception bits are set. The exception flags are "sticky" bits, meaning that once set, they remain set until explicitly cleared. They can be cleared by executing the FCLEX/FNCLEX (clear exceptions) instructions, by reinitializing the FPU with the FINIT/FNINIT or FSAVE/FNSAVE instructions, or by overwriting the flags with an FRSTOR or FLDENV instruction.

The B-bit (bit 15) is included for 8087 compatibility only. It reflects the contents of the ES flag.

7.3.2.4.   STACK FAULT FLAG

The stack fault flag (bit 6 of the FPU status word) indicates that stack overflow or stack underflow has occurred. The FPU explicitly sets the SF flag when it detects a stack overflow or underflow condition, but it does not explicitly clear the flag when it detects an invalid-arithmetic-operand condition. When this flag is set, the condition code flag C1 indicates the nature of the fault: overflow (C1 = 1) and underflow (C1 = 0). The SF flag is a "sticky" flag, meaning that after it is set, the processor does not clear it until it is explicitly instructed to do so (for example, by an FINIT/FNINIT or FSAVE/FNSAVE instruction).

See Section 7.3.6., "FPU Tag Word" for more information on FPU stack faults.

7.3.3.   Branching and Conditional Moves on FPU Condition Codes

The Pentium Pro processor supports two mechanisms for branching and performing conditional moves according to comparisons of two floating-point values. These mechanism are referred to here as the "old mechanism" and the "new mechanism."

The old mechanism is available in FPU's prior to the Pentium Pro processor and in the Pentium Pro processor. This mechanism uses the floating-point compare instructions (FCOM, FCOMP, FCOMPP, FTST, FUCOMPP, FICOM, and FICOMP) to compare two floating-point values and set the condition code flags (C0 through C3) according to the results. The contents of the condition code flags are then copied into the status flags of the EFLAGS register using a two step process (see Figure 7-9):

1.   The FSTSW AX instruction moves the FPU status word into the AX register.

2.   The SAHF instruction copies the upper 8 bits of the AX register, which includes the condition code flags, into the lower 8 bits of the EFLAGS register.

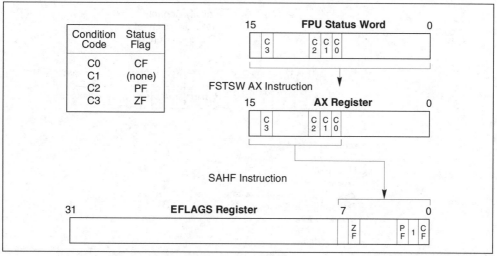

Figure 7-9. Moving the FPU Condition Codes to the EFLAGS Register

When the condition code flags have been loaded into the EFLAGS register, conditional jumps or conditional moves can be performed based on the new settings of the status flags in the EFLAGS register.

The new mechanism is available only in the Pentium Pro processor. Using this mechanism, the new floating-point compare and set EFLAGS instructions (FCOMI, FCOMIP, FUCOMI, and FUCOMIP) compare two floating-point values and set the ZF, PF, and CF flags in the EFLAGS register directly. A single instruction thus replaces a three instructions, using the old mechanism.

Note also that the FCMOV*cc* instructions (also new in the Pentium Pro processor) allow conditional moves of floating-point values (values in the FPU data registers) based on the setting of the status flags (ZF, PF, and CF) in the EFLAGS register. These instructions eliminate the need for an IF statement to perform conditional moves of floating-point values.

7.3.4. FPU Control Word

The 16-bit FPU control word (see in Figure 7-10) controls the precision of the FPU and rounding method used. It also contains the exception-flag mask bits. The control word is cached in the FPU in the FPU control register. The contents of this register can be loaded with the FLDCW instruction and stored in memory with the FSTCW/FNSTCW instructions.

When the FPU is initialized with either an FINIT/FNINIT or FSAVE/FNSAVE instruction, the FPU control word is set to 037FH, which masks all floating-point exceptions, sets rounding to nearest, and sets the FPU precision to 64 bits.

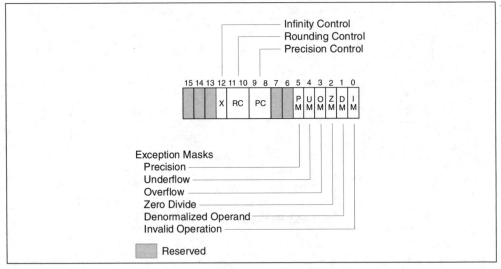

Figure 7-10. FPU Control Word

7.3.4.1. EXCEPTION-FLAG MASKS

The exception-flag mask bits (bits 0 through 5 of the FPU control word) mask the 6 exception flags in the FPU status word (also bits 0 through 5). When one of these mask bits is set, its corresponding floating-point exception is inhibited from being generated.

7.3.4.2. PRECISION CONTROL FIELD

The precision-control (PC) field (bits 8 and 9 of the FPU control word) determines the precision (64, 53, or 24 bits) of floating-point calculations made by the FPU (see Table 7-4). The default precision is extended precision, which uses the full 64-bit significand available with the extended-real format of the FPU data registers. This setting is best suited for most applications, because it allows applications to take full advantage of the precision of the extended-real format.

Table 7-4. Precision Control Field (PC)

Precision	PC Field
Single Precision (24-Bits*)	00B
Reserved	01B
Double Precision (53-Bits*)	10B
Extended Precision (64-Bits)	11B

NOTE:

*Includes the implied integer bit.

The double precision and single precision settings, reduce the size of the significand to 53 bits and 24 bits, respectively. These settings are provided to support the IEEE standard and to provide compatibility with the earlier Intel Architecture NPXs. Using these settings nullifies the advantages of the extended-real format's 64-bit significand length. When reduced precision is specified, the rounding of the significand value clears the unused bits on the right to zeros.

The precision-control bits only affect the results of the following floating-point instructions: FADD, FADDP, FSUB, FSUBP, FSUBR, FSUBRP, FMUL, FMULP, FDIV, FDIVP, FDIVR, FDIVRP, and FSQRT.

7.3.4.3. ROUNDING CONTROL FIELD

The rounding-control (RC) field of the FPU control register (bits 10 and 11) controls how the results of floating-point instructions are rounded. Four rounding modes are supported (see Table 7-5): round to nearest, round up, round down, and round toward zero. Round to nearest is the default rounding mode and is suitable for most applications. It provides the most accurate and statistically unbiased estimate of the true result.

Table 7-5. Rounding Control Field (RC)

Rounding Mode	RC Field Setting	Description
Round to nearest (even)	00B	Rounded result is the closest to the infinitely precise result. If two values are equally close, the result is the even value (that is, the one with the least-significant bit of zero).
Round down (toward −∞)	01B	Rounded result is close to but no greater than the infinitely precise result.
Round up (toward +∞)	10B	Rounded result is close to but no less than he infinitely precise result.
Round toward zero (Truncate)	11B	Rounded result is close to but no greater in absolute value than the infinitely precise result.

The round up and round down modes are termed *directed rounding* and can be used to implement interval arithmetic. Interval arithmetic is used to determine upper and lower bounds for the true result of a multistep computation, when the intermediate results of the computation are subject to rounding.

The round toward zero mode (sometimes called the "chop" mode) is commonly used when performing integer arithmetic with the FPU.

Whenever possible, the FPU produces an infinitely precise result in the destination format (single, double, or extended real). However, it is often the case that the infinitely precise result of an arithmetic or store operation cannot be encoded exactly in the format of the destination operand. For example, the following value (a) has a 24-bit fraction. The least-significant bit of this fraction (the underlined bit) cannot be encoded exactly in the single-real format (which has only a 23-bit fraction):

(a) 1.0001 0000 1000 0011 1001 0111$\underline{1}$E$_2$ 101

To round this result (a), the FPU first selects two representable fractions b and c that most closely bracket a in value ($b < a < c$).

(b) 1.0001 0000 1000 0011 1001 011E$_2$ 101

(c) 1.0001 0000 1000 0011 1001 100E$_2$ 101

The FPU then sets the result to b or to c according to the rounding mode selected in the RC field. Rounding introduces an error in a result that is less than one unit in the last place to which the result is rounded.

The rounded result is called the inexact result. When the FPU produces an inexact result, the floating-point precision (inexact) flag (PE) is set in the FPU status word.

When the infinitely precise result is between the largest positive finite value allowed in a particular format and $+\infty$, the FPU rounds the result as shown in Table 7-6.

Table 7-6. Rounding of Positive Numbers

Rounding Mode	Result
Rounding to nearest (even)	$+\infty$
Rounding toward zero (Truncate)	Maximum, positive finite value
Rounding up (toward $+\infty$)	$+\infty$
Rounding down) (toward $-\infty$)	Maximum, positive finite value

When the infinitely precise result is between the largest negative finite value allowed in a particular format and $-\infty$, the FPU rounds the result as shown in Table 7-7.

Table 7-7. Rounding of Negative Numbers

Rounding Mode	Result
Rounding to nearest (even)	-∞
Rounding toward zero (Truncate)	Maximum, negative finite value
Rounding up (toward +∞)	Maximum, negative finite value
Rounding down) (toward −∞)	-∞

The rounding modes have no effect on comparison operations, operations that produce exact results, or operations that produce NaN results.

7.3.5. Infinity Control Flag

The infinity control flag (bit 12 of the FPU control word) is provided for compatibility with the Intel287™ Math Coprocessor; it is not meaningful for the Pentium Pro processor FPU or for the Pentium processor FPU, the Intel486 processor FPU, or Intel387™ processor NPX. See Section 7.2.3.3., "Signed Infinities" for information on how the Pentium Pro processor handles infinity values.

7.3.6. FPU Tag Word

The 16-bit tag word (see in Figure 7-11) indicates the contents of each the 8 registers in the FPU data-register stack (one 2-bit tag per register). The tag codes indicate whether a register contains a valid number, zero, or a special floating-point number (NaN, infinity, denormal, or unsupported format), or whether it is empty. The FPU tag word is cached in the FPU in the FPU tag word register. When the FPU is initialized with either an FINIT/FNINIT or FSAVE/FNSAVE instruction, the FPU tag word is set to FFFFH, which marks all the FPU data registers as empty.

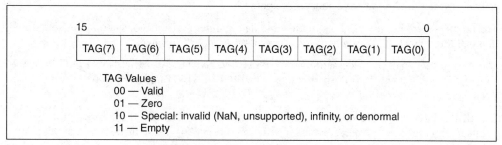

Figure 7-11. FPU Tag Word

Each tag in the FPU tag word corresponds to a physical register (numbers 0 through 7). The current top-of-stack (TOP) pointer stored in the FPU status word can be used to associate tags with registers relative to ST(0).

The FPU uses the tag values to detect stack overflow and underflow conditions. Stack overflow occurs when the TOP pointer is decremented (due to a register load or push operation) to point to a non-empty register. Stack underflow occurs when the TOP pointer is incremented (due to a save or pop operation) to point to an empty register or when an empty register is also referenced as a source operand. A non-empty register is defined as a register containing a zero (01), a valid value (00), or an special (10) value.

Application programs and exception handlers can use this tag information to check the contents of an FPU data register without performing complex decoding of the actual data in the register. To read the tag register, it must be stored in memory using either the FSTENV/FNSTENV or FSAVE/FNSAVE instructions. The location of the tag word in memory after being saved with one of these instructions is shown in Figure 7-13 through Figure 7-14.

Software cannot directly load or modify the tags in the tag register. The FLDENV and FRSTOR instructions load an image of the tag register into the FPU; however, the FPU uses those tag values only to determine if the data registers are empty (11B) or non-empty (00B, 01B, or 10B). If the tag register image indicates that a data register is empty, the tag in the tag register for that data register is marked empty (11B); if the tag register image indicates that the data register is non-empty, the FPU reads the actual value in the data register and sets the tag for the register accordingly. This action prevents a program from setting the values in the tag register to incorrectly represent the actual contents of non-empty data registers.

7.3.7. The Floating-Point Instruction and Data Pointers

The FPU stores pointers to the instruction and data (operand) for the last non-control instruction executed in two 48-bit registers: the FPU instruction pointer and FPU data pointer registers (see Figure 7-5). (This information is saved to provide state information for exception handlers.)

The contents of the FPU instruction and data pointer registers remain unchanged when any of the control instructions (FINIT/FNINIT, FCLEX/FNCLEX, FLDCW, FSTCW/FNSTCW, FSTSW/FNSTSW, FSTENV/FNSTENV, FLDENV, FSAVE/FNSAVE, FRSTOR, and WAIT/FWAIT) are executed. The contents of the data register are undefined if the prior non-control instruction did not have a memory operand.

The pointers stored in the FPU instruction and data pointer registers consist of an offset (stored in bits 0 through 31) and a segment selector (stored in bits 32 through 47).

These registers can be accessed by the FSTENV/FNSTENV, FLDENV, FINIT/FNINIT, FSAVE/FNSAVE and FRSTOR instructions. The FINIT/FNINIT and FSAVE/FNSAVE instructions clear these registers.

For all the Intel Architecture FPUs and NPXs except the 8087, the FPU instruction pointer points to any prefixes that preceded the instruction. For the 8087, the instruction pointer points only to the actual opcode.

7.3.8.   Last Instruction Opcode

The FPU stores the opcode of the last non-control instruction executed in an 11-bit FPU opcode register. (This information provides state information for exception handlers.) Only the first and second opcode bytes (after all prefixes) are stored in the FPU opcode register. Figure 7-12 shows the encoding of these two bytes. Since the upper 5 bits of the first opcode byte are the same for all floating-point opcodes (11011B), only the lower 3 bits of this byte are stored in the opcode register.

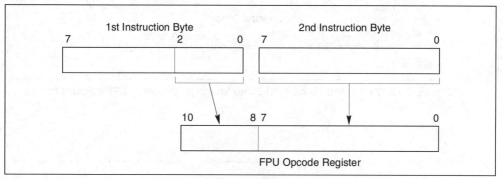

Figure 7-12. Contents of FPU Opcode Registers

7.3.9.   Saving the FPU's State

The FSTENV/FNSTENV and FSAVE/FNSAVE instructions store FPU state information in memory for use by exception handlers and other system and application software. The FSTENV/FNSTENV instruction saves the contents of the status, control, tag, instruction pointer, data pointer, and opcode registers. The FSAVE instruction stores that information plus the contents of the FPU data registers.

The manner in which this information is stored in memory depends on the operating mode of the processor (protected mode or real-address mode) and on the operand-size attribute in effect (32-bit or 16-bit). See Figures 7-13 through 7-16. In virtual-8086 mode, the real-address mode formats are used.

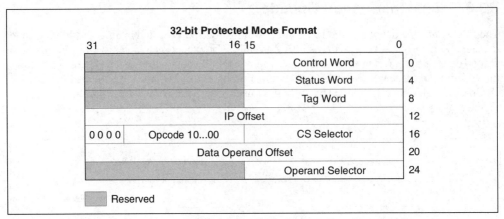

Figure 7-13. Protected-Mode FPU State Image in Memory, 32-Bit Format

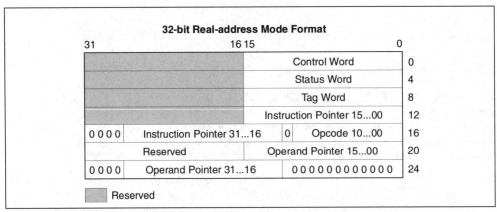

Figure 7-14. Real Mode FPU State Image in Memory, 32-Bit Format

16-bit Protected Mode Format

15 0	
Control Word	0
Status Word	2
Tag Word	4
IP Offset	6
CS Selector	8
Operand Offset	10
Operand Selector	12

Figure 7-15. Protected-Mode FPU State Image in Memory, 16-Bit Format

**16-bit Real-address Mode and
Virtual 8086 Mode Format**

15 0	
Control Word	0
Status Word	2
Tag Word	4
Instruction Pointer 15...00	6
IP 19...16	0	Opcode 10...00	8
Operand Pointer 15...00	10
DP 19...16	0	0 0 0 0 0 0 0 0 0 0 0 0	12

Figure 7-16. Real Mode FPU State Image in Memory, 16-Bit Format

The FLDENV and FRSTOR instructions allow FPU state information to be loaded from memory into the FPU. Here, the FLDENV instruction loads only the status, control, tag, instruction pointer, data pointer, and opcode registers, and the FRSTOR instruction loads all the FPU registers, including the data registers.

7.4.   FLOATING-POINT DATA TYPES AND FORMATS

The Pentium Pro processor's FPU recognizes and operates on 7 data types, divided into three groups: reals, integers, and packed BCD integers. Figure 7-17 shows the data formats for each of the FPU data types. Table 7-8 gives the length, precision, and approximate normalized range that can be represented of each FPU data type. Denormal values are also supported in each of the real types, as required by IEEE Std. 854.

With the exception of the 80-bit extended-real format, all of these data types exist in memory only. When they are loaded into FPU data registers, they are converted into extended-real format and operated on in that format.

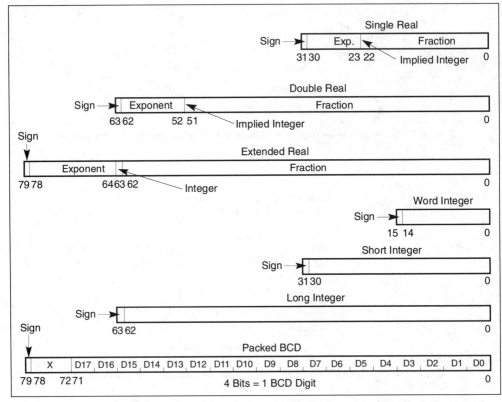

Figure 7-17. Floating-Point Unit Data Type Formats

When stored in memory, the least significant byte an FPU data-type value is stored at the initial address specified for the value. Successive bytes from the value are then stored in successively higher addresses in memory. The floating-point instructions load and store memory operands using only the initial address of the operand.

7.4.1. Real Numbers

The FPU's three real data types (single-real, double-real, and extended-real) correspond directly to the single-precision, double-precision, and double-extended-precision formats in the IEEE standard. The extended-precision format is the format used by the data registers in the FPU. Table 7-8 gives the precision and range of these data types and Figure 7-17 gives the formats.

For the single-real and double-real formats, only the fraction part of the significand is encoded. The integer is assumed to be 1 for all numbers except 0 and denormalized finite numbers. For the extended-real format, the integer is contained in bit 63, and the most-significant fraction bit is bit 62. Here, the integer is explicitly set to 1 for normalized numbers, infinities, and NaNs, and to 0 for zero and denormalized numbers.

Table 7-8. Length, Precision, and Range of FPU Data Types

Data Type	Length	Precision (Bits)	Approximate Normalized Range	
			Binary	Decimal
Binary Real Single real	32	24	2^{-126} to 2^{127}	1.18×10^{-38} to 3.40×10^{38}
Double real	64	53	2^{-1022} to 2^{1023}	2.23×10^{-308} to 1.79×10^{308}
Extended real	80	64	2^{-16382} to 2^{16383}	3.37×10^{-4932} to 1.18×10^{4932}
Binary Integer Word integer	16	15	-2^{15} to $2^{15} - 1$	$-32,768$ to $32,767$
Short integer	32	31	-2^{31} to $2^{31} - 1$	-2.14×10^9 to 2.14×10^9
Long integer	64	63	-2^{63} to $2^{63} - 1$	-9.22×10^{18} to 9.22×10^{18}
Packed BCD Integers	80	18 (decimal digits)	Not Pertinent	$(-10^{18} + 1)$ to $(10^{18} - 1)$

The exponent of each real data type is encoded in biased format. The biasing constant is 127 for the single-real format, 1023 for the double-real format, and 16,383 for the extended-real format.

Table 7-9 shows the encodings for all the classes of real numbers (that is, zero, denormalized-finite, normalized-finite, and ∞) and NaNs for each of the three real data-types. It also gives the format for the real indefinite value.

When storing real values in memory, single-real values are stored in 4 consecutive bytes in memory; double-real values are stored in 8 consecutive bytes; and extended-real values are stored in 10 consecutive bytes.

As a general rule, values should be stored in memory in double-real format. This format provides sufficient range and precision to return correct results with a minimum of programmer attention. The single-real format is appropriate for applications that are constrained by memory; however, it provides less precision and a greater chance of overflow. The single-real format is also useful for debugging algorithms, because rounding problems will manifest themselves more quickly in this format. The extended-real format is normally reserved for holding intermediate results in the FPU registers and constants. Its extra length is designed to shield final results from the effects of rounding and overflow/underflow in intermediate calculations. However, when an application requires the maximum range and precision of the FPU (for data storage, computations, and results), values can be stored in memory in extended-real format.

The real indefinite value is a QNaN encoding that is stored by several floating-point instructions in response to a masked floating-point invalid-operation exception (see Table 7-20).

Table 7-9. Real Number and NaN Encodings

Class		Sign	Biased Exponent	Significand	
				Integer[1]	Fraction
Positive	+∞	0	11..11	1	00..00
	+Normals	0	11..10	1	11..11
		.	.	.	.
		0	00..01	1	00..00
	+Denormals	0	00..00	0	11.11
		.	.	.	.
		0	00..00	0	00..01
	+Zero	0	00..00	0	00..00
Negative	−Zero	1	00..00	0	00..00
	−Denormals	1	00..00	0	00..01
		.	.	.	.
		1	00..00	0	11..11
	−Normals	1	00..01	1	00..00
		.	.	.	.
		1	11..10	1	11..11
	−∞	1	11..11	1	00..00
NaNs	SNaN	X	11..11	1	0X..XX[2]
	QNaN	X	11..11	1	1X..XX
	Real Indefinite (QNaN)	1	11..11	1	10..00
	Single-Real: Double-Real: Extended-Real		⟵ 8 Bits ⟶ ⟵ 11 Bits ⟶ ⟵ 15 Bits ⟶		⟵ 23 Bits ⟶ ⟵ 52 Bits ⟶ ⟵ 63 Bits ⟶

NOTES:

1. Integer bit is implied and not stored for single-real and double-real formats.

2. The fraction for SNaN encodings must be non-zero.

7.4.2. Binary Integers

The FPU's three binary integer data types (word, short, and long) have identical formats, except for length. Table 7-8 gives the precision and range of these data types and Figure 7-17 gives the formats. Table 7-10 gives the encodings of the three binary integer types.

Table 7-10. Binary Integer Encodings

Class		Sign	Magnitude
Positive	Largest	0	11..11
		.	.
		.	.
		.	.
	Smallest	0	00..01
Zero		0	00..00
Negative	Smallest	1	11..11
		.	.
		.	.
		.	.
		.	.
	Largest	1	00..00
Integer Indefinite		1	00..00
	Word Integer:		← 15 bits →
	Short Integer:		← 31 Bits →
	Long Integer:		← 63 Bits →

The most significant bit of each format is the sign bit (0 for positive and 1 for negative). Negative values are represented in standard two's complement notation. The quantity zero is represented with all bits (including the sign bit) set to zero. Note that the FPU's word-integer data type is identical to the word-integer data type used by the processor's integer unit and the short-integer format is identical to the integer unit's doubleword-integer data type.

Word-integer values are stored in 2 consecutive bytes in memory; short-integer values are stored in 4 consecutive bytes; and long-integer values are stored in 8 consecutive bytes. When loaded into the FPU's data registers, all the binary integers are exactly representable in the extended-real format.

The binary integer encoding 100..00B represents either of two things, depending on the circumstances of its use:

- The largest negative number supported by the format (-2^{15}, -2^{31}, or -2^{63}).

- The *integer indefinite* value.

If this encoding is used as a source operand (as in an integer load or integer arithmetic instruction), the FPU interprets it as the largest negative number representable in the format being used. If the FPU detects an invalid operation when storing an integer value in memory with an FIST/FISTP instruction and the invalid-operation exception is masked, the FPU stores the integer indefinite encoding in the destination operand as a masked response to the exception. In situations where the origin of a value with this encoding may be ambiguous, the invalid-operation exception flag can be examined to see if the value was produced as a response to an exception.

If the integer indefinite is stored in memory and is later loaded back into an FPU data register, it is interpreted as the largest negative number supported by the format.

7.4.3. Decimal Integers

Decimal integers are stored in a 10-byte, packed BCD format. Table 7-8 gives the precision and range of this data type and Figure 7-17 shows the format. In this format, the first 9 bytes hold 18 BCD digits, 2 digits per byte (see Section 5.2.3., "BCD Integers"). The least-significant digit is contained in the lower half-byte of byte 0 and the most-significant digit is contained in the upper half-byte of byte 9. The most significant bit of byte 10 contains the sign bit (0 = positive and 1 = negative). (Bits 0 through 6 of byte 10 are don't care bits.) Negative decimal integers are not stored in two's complement form; they are distinguished from positive decimal integers only by the sign bit.

Table 7-11 gives the possible encodings of value in the decimal integer data type.

Table 7-11. Packed Decimal Integer Encodings

Class	Sign		Magnitude					
			digit	digit	digit	digit	...	digit
Positive Largest	0	0000000	1001	1001	1001	1001	...	1001
	.	.			.			
	.	.			.			
	0	0000000	0000	0000	0000	0000	...	0001
Smallest								
Zero	0	0000000	0000	0000	0000	0000	...	0000
Negative Zero	1	0000000	0000	0000	0000	0000	...	0000
	1	0000000	0000	0000	0000	0000	...	0001
Smallest								
	.	.			.			
	.	.			.			
Largest	1	0000000	1001	1001	1001	1001	...	1001
Decimal Integer Indefinite	1	1111111	1111	1111	UUUU*	UUUU	...	UUUU
		← 1 byte →		← 9 bytes →					

NOTE:

* UUUU means bit values are undefined and may contain any value.

The decimal integer format exists in memory only. When a decimal integer is loaded in a data register in the FPU, it is automatically converted to the extended-real format. All decimal integers are exactly representable in extended-real format.

The *packed decimal indefinite* encoding is stored by the FBSTP instruction in response to a masked floating-point invalid-operation exception. Attempting to load this value with the FBLD instruction produces an undefined result.

7.4.4. Unsupported Extended-Real Encodings

The extended-real format permits many encodings that do not fall into any of the categories shown in Table 7-9. Table 7-12 shows these unsupported encodings. Some of these encodings were supported by the Intel287 math coprocessor; however, most of them are not supported by the Intel387 math coprocessor, or the internal FPUs in the Intel486, Pentium, or Pentium Pro processors. These encodings are no longer supported due to changes made in the final version of IEEE Std. 754 that eliminated these encodings.

The categories of encodings formerly known as pseudo-NaNs, pseudo-infinities, and un-normal numbers are not supported. The Intel387 math coprocessor and the internal FPUs in the Intel486, Pentium, and Pentium Pro processors generate the invalid-operation exception when they are encountered as operands.

The encodings formerly known as pseudo-denormal numbers are not generated by the Pentium Pro processor; however, they are used correctly when encountered as operands. The exponent is treated as if it were 00..01B and the mantissa is unchanged. The denormal exception is generated.

7.5. FPU INSTRUCTION SET

The floating-point instruction set available on the Pentium Pro processor's FPU can be grouped into six functional categories:

- Data transfer instructions

- Basic arithmetic instructions

- Comparison instructions

- Transcendental instructions

- Load constant instructions

- FPU control instructions

See Section 6.2.2., "Floating-Point Instructions" for a list of the floating-point instructions by category.

The following section briefly describes the instructions in each category. Detailed descriptions of the floating-point instructions are given in Chapter 11, *Instruction Set Reference*.

Table 7-12. Unsupported Extended-Real Encodings

Class		Sign	Biased Exponent	Significand	
				Integer	Fraction
Positive Pseudo-NaNs	Quiet	0 . 0	11..11 . 11..11	0	11..11 . 10..00
	Signaling	0 . 0	11..11 . 11..11	0	01..11 . 00..01
Positive Reals	Pseudo-infinity	0	11..11	0	00..00
	Unnormals	0 . 0	11..10 . 00..01	0	11..11 . 00..00
	Pseudo-denormals	0 . 0	00..00 . 00..00	1	11..11 . 00..00
Negative Reals	Pseudo-denormals	1 . 1	00..00 . 00..00	1	11..11 . 00..00
	Unnormals	1 . 1	11..10 . 00..01	0	11..01 . 00..00
	Pseudo-infinity	1	11..11	0	00..00
Negative Pseudo-NaNs	Signaling	1 . 1	11..11 . 11..11	0	01..11 . 00..01
	Quiet	1 . 1	11..11 . 11..11	0	11..11 . 10..00
			← 15 bits →		← 63 bits →

7.5.1.   Escape (ESC) Instructions

All of the instructions in the FPU instruction set fall into a class of instructions known as escape (ESC) instructions. All of these instructions have a common opcode format, which is slightly different from the format used by the integer and operating-system instructions.

7.5.2.   FPU Instruction Operands

Most floating-point instructions require one or two operands, which are located on the FPU data-register stack or in memory. (None of the floating-point instructions accept immediate operands.)

When an operand is located in a data register, it is referenced relative to the ST(0) register (the register at the top of the register stack), rather than by a physical register number. Often the ST(0) register is an implied operand.

Operands in memory can be referenced using the same operand addressing methods available for the integer and system instructions.

7.5.3. Data Transfer Instructions

The data transfer instructions (see Table 7-13) perform the following operations:

* Load real, integer, or packed BCD operands from memory into the ST(0) register.

* Store the value in the ST(0) register in memory in real, integer, or packed BCD format.

* Move values between registers in the FPU register stack.

Table 7-13. Data Transfer Instructions

Real		Integer		Packed Decimal	
FLD	Load Real	FILD	Load Integer	FBLD	Load Packed Decimal
FST	Store Real	FIST	Store Integer		
FSTP	Store Real and Pop	FISTP	Store Integer and Pop	FBSTP	Store Packed Decimal and Pop
FXCH	Exchange Register Contents				
FCMOV*cc*	Conditional Move				

Operands are normally stored in the FPU data registers in extended-real format (see Section 7.3.4.2., "Precision Control Field"). The FLD (load real) instruction pushes a real operand from memory onto the top of the FPU data-register stack. If the operand is in single- or double-real format, it is automatically converted to extended-real format. This instruction can also be used to push the value in a selected FPU data register onto the top of the register stack.

The FILD (load integer) instruction converts an integer operand in memory into extended-real format and pushes the value onto the top of the register stack. The FBLD (load packed decimal) instruction performs the same load operation for a packed BCD operand in memory.

The FST (store real) and FIST (store integer) instructions store the value in register ST(0) in memory in the destination format (real or integer, respectively). Again, the format conversion is carried out automatically.

The FSTP (store real and pop), FISTP (store integer and pop), and FBSTP (store packed decimal and pop) instructions store the value in the ST(0) registers into memory in the destination format (real, integer, or packed BCD), then performs a *pop* operation on the register stack. A pop operation causes the ST(0) register to be marked empty and the stack pointer (TOP) in the FPU control work to be incremented by 1. The FSTP instruction can also be used to copy the value in the ST(0) register to another FPU register [ST(*i*)].

The FXCH (exchange register contents) instruction exchanges the value in a selected register in the stack [ST(*i*)] with the value in ST(0).

The FCMOV*cc* (conditional move) instructions move the value in a selected register in the stack [ST(*i*)] to register ST(0). These instructions move the value only if the conditions specified with a condition code (*cc*) are satisfied (see Table 7-14). The conditions being tested with the FCMOV*cc* instructions are represented by the status flags in the EFLAGS register. The condition code mnemonics are appended to the letters "FCMOV" to form the mnemonic for a FCMOV*cc* instruction.

Table 7-14. Floating-Point Conditional Move Instructions

Instruction Mnemonic	Status Flag States	Condition Description
FCMOVB	CF=1	Below
FCMOVNB	CF=0	Not below
FCMOVE	ZF=1	Equal
FCMOVNE	ZF=0	Not equal
FCMOVBE	(CF or ZF)=1	Below or equal
FCMOVNBE	(CF or ZF)=0	Not below nor equal
FCMOVU	PF=1	Unordered
FCMOVNU	PF=0	Not unordered

Like the CMOV*cc* instructions, the FCMOV*cc* instructions are useful for optimizing small IF constructions. They also help eliminate branching overhead for IF operations and the possibility of branch mispredictions by the processor.

NOTE

The FCMOV*cc* instructions may not be supported on some processors in the Pentium Pro processor family. Software can check if the FCMOV*cc* instructions are supported by checking the processor's feature information with the CPUID instruction (see Chapter 11, "CPUID—CPU Identification").

7.5.4. Load Constant Instructions

The following instructions push commonly used constants onto the top [ST(0)] of the FPU register stack:

FLDZ	Load +0.0
FLD1	Load +1.0
FLDPI	Load π

FLDL2T	Load $\log_2 10$
FLDL2E	Load $\log_2 e$
FLDLG2	Load $\log_{10} 2$
FLDLN2	Load $\log_e 2$

The constant values have full extended-real precision (64 bits) and are accurate to approximately 19 decimal digits. They are stored internally in a format more precise than extended real. When loading the constant, the FPU rounds the more precise internal constant according to the RC (rounding control) field of the FPU control word. See Section 7.5.8., "Pi" for information on the π constant.

7.5.5. Basic Arithmetic Instructions

The following floating-point instructions perform basic arithmetic operations on real numbers. Where applicable, these instructions match IEEE Standard 754:

FADD/FADDP	Add real
FIADD	Add integer to real
FSUB/FSUBP	Subtract real
FISUB	Subtract integer from real
FSUBR/FSUBRP	Reverse subtract real
FISUBR	Reverse subtract real from integer
FMUL/FMULP	Multiply real
FIMUL	Multiply integer by real
FDIV/FDIVP	Divide real
FIDIV	Divide real by integer
FDIVR/FDIVRP	Reverse divide
FIDIVR	Reverse divide integer by real
FABS	Absolute value
FCHS	Change sign
FSQRT	Square root
FPREM	Partial remainder
FPREM1	IEEE partial remainder
FRNDINT	Round to integral value
FXTRACT	Extract exponent and significand

The add, subtract, multiply and divide instructions operate on the following types of operands:

- Two FPU register values.

- A register value and a real or integer value in memory.

Operands in memory can be in single-real, double-real, short-integer, or word-integer format. They are converted to extended-real format automatically.

Reverse versions of the subtract and divide instructions are provided to foster efficient coding. For example, the FSUB instruction subtracts the value in a specified FPU register [ST(i)] from the value in register ST(0); whereas, the FSUBR instruction subtracts the value in ST(0) from the value in ST(i). The results of both operations are stored in register ST(0). These instructions eliminate the need to exchange values between register ST(0) and another FPU register to perform a subtraction or division.

The pop versions of the add, subtract, multiply and divide instructions pop the FPU register stack following the arithmetic operation.

The FPREM instruction computes the remainder from the division of two operands in the manner used by the Intel 8087 and Intel287 math coprocessors; the FPREM1 instructions computes the remainder is the manner specified in the IEEE specification.

The FSQRT instruction computes the square root of the source operand.

The FRNDINT instructions rounds a real value to its nearest integer value, according to the current rounding mode specified in the RC field of the FPU control word. This instruction performs a function similar to the FIST/FISTP instructions, except that the result is saved in a real format.

The FABS, FCHS, and FXTRACT instructions perform convenient arithmetic operations. The FABS instruction produces the absolute value of the source operand. The FCHS instruction changes the sign of the source operand. The FXTRACT instruction separates the source operand into its exponent and fraction and stores each value in a register in real format.

7.5.6.   Comparison and Classification Instructions

The following instructions compare or classify real values:

FCOM/FCOMP/FCOMPP	Compare real and set FPU condition code flags.
FUCOM/FUCOMP/FUCOMPP	Unordered compare real and set FPU condition code flags.
FICOM/FICOMP	Compare integer and set FPU condition code flags.
FCOMI/FCOMIP	Compare real and set EFLAGS status flags.
FUCOMI/FUCOMIP	Unordered compare real and set EFLAGS status flags.
FTST	Test (compare real with 0.0).
FXAM	Examine.

Comparison of real values differ from comparison of integers because real values have four (rather than three) mutually exclusive relationships: less than, equal, greater than, and unordered.

The unordered relationship is true when at least one of the two values being compared is a NaN or in an undefined format. This additional relationship is required because, by definition, NaNs are not numbers, so they cannot have less than, equal, or greater than relationships with other real values.

The FCOM, FCOMP, and FCOMPP instructions compare the value in register ST(0) with a real source operand and set the condition code flags (C0, C2, and C3) in the FPU status word according to the results (see Table 7-15). If an unordered condition is detected (one or both of the values is a NaN or in an undefined format), a floating-point invalid-operation exception is generated.

The pop versions of the instruction pop the FPU register stack once or twice after the comparison operation is complete.

The FUCOM, FUCOMP, and FUCOMPP instructions operate the same as the FCOM, FCOMP, and FCOMPP instructions. The only difference is that with the FUCOM, FUCOMP, and FUCOMPP instructions, if an unordered condition is detected because one or both of the operands is a QNaN, the floating-point invalid-operation exception is not generated.

Table 7-15. Setting of FPU Condition Code Flags for Real Number Comparisons

Condition	C3	C2	C0
ST(0) > Source Operand	0	0	0
ST(0) < Source Operand	0	0	1
ST(0) = Source Operand	1	0	0
Unordered	1	1	1

The FICOM and FICOMP instructions also operate the same as the FCOM and FCOMP instructions, except that the source operand is an integer value in memory. The integer value is automatically converted into an extended real value prior to making the comparison. The FICOMP instruction pops the FPU register stack following the comparison operation.

The FTST instruction performs the same operation as the FCOM instruction, except that the value in register ST(0) is always compared with the value 0.0.

The FCOMI and FCOMIP instructions are new in the Intel Pentium Pro processor. They perform the same comparison as the FCOM and FCOMP instructions, except that they set the status flags (ZF, PF, and CF) in the EFLAGS register to indicate the results of the comparison (see Table 7-16) instead of the FPU condition code flags. The FCOMI and FCOMIP instructions allow condition branch instructions (Jcc) to be executed directly from the results of their comparison.

Table 7-16. Setting of EFLAGS Status Flags for Real Number Comparisons

Comparison Results	ZF	PF	CF
ST0 > ST(i)	0	0	0
ST0 < ST(i)	0	0	1
ST0 = ST(i)	1	0	0
Unordered	1	1	1

The FUCOMI and FUCOMIP instructions operate the same as the FCOMI and FCOMIP instructions, except that they do not generate a floating-point invalid-operation exception if the unordered condition is the result of one or both of the operands being a QNaN. The FCOMIP and FUCOMIP instructions pop the FPU register stack following the comparison operation.

The FXAM instruction determines the classification of the real value in the ST(0) register (that is, whether the value is zero, a denormal number, a normal finite number, ∞, a NaN, or an unsupported format) or that the register is empty. It sets the FPU condition code flags to indicate the classification (see Chapter 11, "FXAM—Examine"). It also sets the C1 flag to indicate the sign of the value.

7.5.6.1.   BRANCHING ON THE FPU CONDITION CODES

The processor does not offer any control-flow instructions that branch on the setting of the condition code flags (C0, C2, and C3) in the FPU status word. To branch on the state of these flags, the FPU status word must first be moved to the AX register in the integer unit. The FSTSW AX (store status word) instruction can be used for this purpose. When these flags are in the AX register, the TEST instruction can be used to control conditional branching as follows:

1.   Check for an unordered result. Use the TEST instruction to compare the contents of the AX register with the constant 0400H (see Table 7-17). This operation will clear the ZF flag in the EFLAGS register if the condition code flags indicate an unordered result; otherwise, the ZF flag will be set. The JNZ instruction can then be used to transfer control (if necessary) to a procedure for handling unordered operands.

Table 7-17. TEST Instruction Constants for Conditional Branching

Order	Constant	Branch
ST(0) > Source Operand	4500H	JZ
ST(0) < Source Operand	0100H	JNZ
ST(0) = Source Operand	4000H	JNZ
Unordered	0400H	JNZ

2.   Check ordered comparison result. Use the constants given in Table 7-17 in the TEST instruction to test for a less than, equal to, or greater than result, then use the corresponding conditional branch instruction to transfer program control to the appropriate procedure or section of code.

If a program or procedure has been thoroughly tested and it incorporates periodic checks for QNaN results, then it is not necessary to check for the unordered result every time a comparison is made.

Some non-comparison FPU instructions update the condition code flags in the FPU status word. To ensure that the status word is not altered inadvertently, store it immediately following a comparison operation.

7.5.7.   Trigonometric Instructions

The following instructions perform four common trigonometric functions:

FSIN	Sine
FCOS	Cosine
FSINCOS	Sine and cosine
FPTAN	Tangent
FPATAN	Arctangent

These instructions operate on the top one or two registers of the FPU register stack and they return their results to the stack. The source operands must be given in radians.

The FSINCOS instruction returns both the sine and the cosine of a source operand value. It operates faster than executing the FSIN and FCOS instructions in succession.

The FPATAN instruction computes the arctangent of ST(1) divided by ST(0). It is useful for converting rectangular coordinates to polar coordinates.

7.5.8.   Pi

When the argument (source operand) of a trigonometric function is within the range of the function, the argument is automatically reduced by the appropriate multiple of 2π through the same reduction mechanism used by the FPREM and FPREM1 instructions. The internal value of π that the Pentium Pro processor uses for argument reduction and other computations is as follows:

$\pi = 0.f * 2^e$

where:

f = C90FDAA2 2168C234 C

e = 2 if the significand is 0.f

(The spaces in the fraction above indicate 32-bit boundaries.)

This internal π value has a 66-bit mantissa, which is 2 bits more than is allowed in the significand of an extended-real value. (Since 66 bits is not an even number of hexadecimal digits, two additional zeros have been added to the value so that it can be represented in hexadecimal format. The least-significant hexadecimal digit (C) is thus 1100B, where the two least-significant bits represent bits 67 and 68 of the mantissa.)

This value of π has been chosen to guarantee no loss of significance in a source operand, provided the operand is within the specified range for the instruction.

If the results of computations that explicitly use π are to be used in the FSIN, FCOS, FSINCOS, or FPATAN instructions, the full 66-bit fraction of π should be used. This insures that the results are consistent with the argument-reduction algorithms that these instructions use. Using a rounded version of π can cause inaccuracies in result values, which if propagated through several calculations, might result in meaningless results.

A common method of representing the full 66-bit fraction of π is to separate the value into two numbers. For example, the following two double-real values (given in hexadecimal) added together give the value for π shown earlier in this section with the full 66-bit fraction:

$\pi = \text{high}\pi + \text{low}\pi$

where:

highπ = 400921FB 54400000

lowπ = 3DD0B4661 1A600000

Here highπ gives the most-significant 33 bits of π and lowπ gives the least-significant 33 bits. Similar versions of π can also be written in extended-real format.

When using this two-part π value in an algorithm, parallel computations should be performed on each part, with the results kept separate. When all the computations are complete, the two results can be added together to form the final result.

The complications of maintaining a consistent value of π for argument reduction can be avoided, either by applying the trigonometric functions only to arguments within the range of the automatic reduction mechanism, or by performing all argument reductions (down to a magnitude less than π/4) explicitly in software.

7.5.9. Logarithmic, Exponential, and Scale

The following instructions provide two different logarithmic functions, an exponential function, and a scale function.

FYL2X	Compute log (y * $\log_2 x$)
FYL2XP1	Compute log epsilon (y * $\log_2(x + 1)$)
F2XM1	Compute exponential ($2^x - 1$)
FSCALE	Scale

The FYL2X and FYL2XP1 instructions perform two different base 2 logarithmic operations. The FYL2X instruction computes the log of (y * $\log_2 x$). This operation permits the calculation of the log of any base using the following equation:

$\log_b x = (1/\log_2 b) * \log_2 x$

The FYEXP1 instruction computes the log epsilon of (y * $\log_2 (x + 1)$). This operation provides optimum accuracy for values of epsilon (ε) that are close to 0.

The F2XM1 instruction computes the exponential ($2^x - 1$). This instruction only operates on source values in the range −1.0 to +1.0.

The FSCALE instruction multiplies the source operand by a power of 2.

7.5.10. Transcendental Instruction Accuracy

The algorithms that the Intel Pentium and Pentium Pro processors use for the transcendental instructions (FSIN, FCOS, FSINCOS, FPTAN, FPATAN, F2XM1, FYL2X, and FYL2XP1) allow a higher level of accuracy than was possible in earlier Intel Architecture math coprocessors and FPUs. The accuracy of these instructions is measured in terms of *units in the last place* (*ulp*). For a given argument x, let $f(x)$ and $F(x)$ be the correct and computed (approximate) function values, respectively. The error in ulps is defined to be:

$$error = \left| \frac{f(x) - F(x)}{2^{k-63}} \right|$$

where k is an integer such that $1 \le 2^{-k} f(x) < 2$.

With the Pentium Pro processor, the worst case error on transcendental functions is less than 1 ulp when rounding to the nearest-even and less than 1.5 ulps when rounding in other modes. The functions are guaranteed to be monotonic, with respect to the input operands, throughout the domain supported by the instruction.

7.5.11. FPU Control Instructions

The following instructions control the state and modes of operation of the FPU. They also allow the status of the FPU to be examined:

FINIT/FNINIT	Initialize FPU
FLDCW	Load FPU control word
FSTCW/FNSTCW	Store FPU control word
FSTSW/FNSTSW	Store FPU status word
FCLEX/FNCLEX	Clear FPU exception flags
FLDENV	Load FPU environment
FSTENV/FNSTENV	Store FPU environment
FRSTOR	Restore FPU state
FSAVE/FNSAVE	Save FPU state
FINCSTP	Increment FPU register stack pointer
FDECSTP	Decrement FPU register stack pointer
FFREE	Free FPU register
FNOP	No operation
WAIT/FWAIT	Check for and handle pending unmasked FPU exceptions

The FINIT/FNINIT instructions initialize the FPU and its internal registers to default values.

The FLDCW instructions loads the FPU control word register with a value from memory. The FSTCW/FNSTCW and FSTSW/FNSTSW instructions store the FPU control and status words, respectively, in memory (or for an FSTSW/FNSTSW instruction in a general-purpose register).

The FSTENV/FNSTENV and FSAVE/FNSAVE instructions save the FPU environment and state, respectively, in memory. The FPU environment includes all the FPU's control and status registers; the FPU state includes the FPU environment and the data registers in the FPU register stack. The FLDENV and FRSTOR instructions load the FPU environment and state, respectively, from memory into the FPU. These instructions are commonly used when switching tasks or contexts.

The WAIT/FWAIT instructions are synchronization instructions. (They are actually mnemonics for the same opcode.) These instructions check FPU status word for pending unmasked FPU exceptions. If any pending unmasked FPU exceptions are found, they are handled before the processor resumes execution of the instructions (integer, floating-point, or system instruction) in the instruction stream. The WAIT/FWAIT instructions are provided to allow synchronization of instruction execution between the FPU and the processor's integer unit. See Section 7.9., "Floating-Point Exception Synchronization" for more information on the use of the WAIT/FWAIT instructions.

7.5.12. Waiting Vs. Non-Waiting Instructions

All of the floating-point instructions except a few special control instructions perform a wait operation (similar to the WAIT/FWAIT instructions), to check for and handle pending unmasked FPU exceptions, before they perform their primary operation (such as adding two real numbers). These instructions are called *waiting* instructions. Some of the FPU control instructions, such as FSTSW/FNSTSW, have both a waiting and a non-waiting versions. The version waiting version (with the "F" prefix) executes a wait operation before it performs its primary operation; whereas, the non-waiting version (with the "FN" prefix) ignores pending unmasked exceptions. Non-waiting instructions allow software to save the current FPU state without first handling pending exceptions or to reset or reinitialize the FPU without regard for pending exceptions.

7.5.13. Unsupported FPU Instructions

The Intel 8087 instructions FENI and FDISI and the Intel287 math coprocessor instruction FSETPM perform no function in the Pentium Pro processor. If these opcodes are detected in the instruction stream, the FPU performs no specific operation and no internal FPU states are affected.

7.6. OPERATING ON NANS

As was described in Section 7.2.3.4., "NaNs", the FPU supports two types of NaNs: SNaNs and QNaNs. An SNaN is any NaN value with its most-significant fraction bit set to 0 and at least one other fraction bit set to 1. (If all the fraction bits are set to 0, the value is an ∞.) A QNaN is any NaN value with the most-significant fraction bit set to 1. The sign bit of a NaN is not interpreted.

As a general rule, when a QNaN is used in one or more arithmetic floating-point instructions, it is allowed to propagate through a computation. An SNaN on the other hand causes a floating-point invalid-operation exception to be signaled. SNaNs are typically used to trap or invoke an exception handler.

The floating-point invalid-operation exception has a flag and a mask bit associated with it in the FPU status and control registers, respectively (see Section 7.7., "Floating-Point Exception Handling"). The mask bit determines how the FPU handles an SNaN value. If the floating-point invalid-operation mask bit is set, the SNaN is convert to a QNaN by setting the most-significant fraction bit of the value to 1. The result is then stored in the destination operand and the floating-point invalid-operation flag is set. If the invalid-operation mask is clear, a floating-point invalid-operation fault is signaled and no result is stored in the destination operand.

When a real operation or exception delivers a QNaN result, the value of the result depends on the source operands, as shown in Table 7-18.

Except for the rules given at the beginning of this section for encoding SNaNs and QNaNs, software is free to use the bits in the significand of a NaN for any purpose. Both SNaNs and QNaNs can be encoded to carry and store data, such as diagnostic information.

Table 7-18. Rules for Generating QNaNs

Source Operands	QNaN Result
An SNaN and a QNaN.	The QNaN source operand.
Two SNaNs.	The SNaN with the larger significand converted into a QNaN.
Two QNaNs.	The QNaN with the larger significand.
An SNaN and a real value.	The SNaN converted into a QNaN.
A QNaN and a real value.	The QNaN source operand.
Neither source operand is a NaN and a floating-point invalid-operation exception is signaled.	The default QNaN *real indefinite*.

7.7. FLOATING-POINT EXCEPTION HANDLING

The FPU detects six classes of exception conditions while executing floating-point instructions:

- Invalid operation (#I)
  - Stack overflow or underflow (#IS)
  - Invalid arithmetic operation (#IA)
- Divide-by-zero (#Z)
- Denormalized operand (#D)
- Numeric overflow (#O)
- Numeric underflow (#U)
- Inexact result (precision) (#P)

The nomenclature of "#" symbol followed by one or two letters (for example, #IS) is used in this manual to indicate exception conditions. It is merely a short-hand form and is not related to assembler mnemonics.

Each of the six exception classes has a corresponding flag bit in the FPU status word and a mask bit in the FPU control word (see Section 7.3.2., "FPU Status Register" and Section 7.3.4., "FPU Control Word", respectively). In addition, the exception summary (ES) flag in the status word indicates when any of the exceptions has been detected, and the stack fault (SF) flag (also in the status word) distinguishes between the two types of invalid-operation exceptions.

When the FPU detects a floating-point exception, it sets the appropriate flags in the FPU status word, then takes one of two possible courses of action:

- Handles the exception automatically, producing a predefined (and often times usable result), while allowing program execution to continue undisturbed.

- Invokes a software exception handler to handle the exception.

The following sections describe how the FPU handles exceptions (either automatically or by calling a software exception handler), how the FPU detects the various floating-point exceptions, and the automatic (masked) response to the floating-point exceptions.

7.7.1. Arithmetic vs. Non-Arithmetic Instructions

When dealing with floating-point exceptions, it is useful to distinguish between *arithmetic instructions* and *non-arithmetic instructions*. Non-arithmetic instructions have no operands or do not make substantial changes to their operands. Arithmetic instructions do make significant changes to their operands; in particular, they make changes that could result in a floating-point exception being signaled. Table 7-19 lists the non-arithmetic and arithmetic instructions. It should be noted that some non-arithmetic instructions can signal a floating-point stack (fault) exception, but this exception is not the result of an operation on an operand.

7.7.2. Automatic Exception Handling

If the FPU detects an exception condition for a masked exception (an exception with its mask bit set), it delivers a predefined (default) response and continues executing instructions. The masked (default) responses to exceptions have been chosen to deliver a reasonable result for each exception condition and are generally satisfactory for most floating-point applications. By masking or unmasking specific floating-point exceptions in the FPU control word, programmers can delegate responsibility for most exceptions to the FPU and reserve the most severe exception conditions for software exception handlers.

Because the exception flags are "sticky," they provide a cumulative record of the exceptions that have occurred since they were last cleared. A programmer can thus mask all exceptions, run a calculation, and then inspect the exception flags to see if any exceptions were detected during the calculation.

Note that when exceptions are masked, the FPU may detect multiple exceptions in a single instruction, because it continues executing the instruction after performing its masked response. For example, the FPU can detect a denormalized operand, perform its masked response to this exception, and then detect numeric underflow.

7.7.3. Software Exception Handling

If the FPU detects an exception condition for an unmasked exception (an exception with its mask bit cleared), a software exception handler is invoked immediately before execution of any of the following instructions in the processor's instruction stream:

*   The next floating-point instruction, unless it is one of the non-waiting instructions (FNINIT, FNCLEX, FNSTSW, FNSTCW, FNSTENV, and FNSAVE).

*   The next WAIT/FWAIT instruction.

Table 7-19. Arithmetic and Non-Arithmetic Instructions

Non-arithmetic Instructions	Arithmetic Instructions
FABS	F2XM1
FCHS	FADD/FADDP
FCLEX	FBLD
FDECSTP	FBSTP
FFREE	FCOM/FCOMP/FCOMPP
FINCSTP	FCOS
FINIT/FNINIT	FDIV/FDIVP/FDIVR/FDIVRP
FLD (register-to-register)	FIADD
FLD (extended format from memory)	FICOM/FICOMP
FLD constant	FIDIV/FIDIVR
FLDCW	FILD
FLDENV	FIMUL
FNOP	FIST/FISTP
FRSTOR	FISUB/FISUBR
FSAVE/FNSAVE	FLD (conversion)
FST/FSTP (register-to-register)	FMUL/FMULP
FSTP (extended format to memory)	FPATAN
FSTCW/FNSTCW	FPREM/FPREM1
FSTENV/FNSTENV	FPTAN
FSTSW/FNSTSW	FRNDINT
WAIT/FWAIT	FSCALE
FXAM	FSIN
FXCH	FSINCOS
	FSQRT
	FST/FSTP (conversion)
	FSUB/FSUBP/FSUBR/FSUBRP
	FTST
	FUCOM/FUCOMP/FUCOMPP
	FXTRACT
	FYL2X/FYL2XP1

The method the processor uses to invoke the floating-point exception handler depends on the setting of the NE flag of the CR0 control register and the state of the processor's IGNNE# pin. If the NE flag is set, the exception handler is invoked through a floating-point-error exception (#MF, vector 16). (When the NE flag is set, the IGNNE# signal has no effect on the processor.)

If the NE flag is cleared, but the IGNNE# pin is asserted, the processor disregards the exception and continues executing instructions. (Here, the FPU never calls the floating-point exception handler, but still generates masked and unmasked exception responses.)

If the NE bit is cleared and the IGNNE# pin is deasserted, an unmasked floating-point exception causes the processor to do the following:

1. Stop instruction execution immediately before executing the next waiting floating-point instruction or WAIT/FWAIT instruction and wait for an external interrupt. (Waiting instructions are those floating-point instructions that cause the processor to check for and service pending unmasked interrupts before the instructions are executed.)

2. Assert its FERR# pin to generate a external interrupt.

When using this external interrupt mechanism, the FERR# pin must be connected to an input to an external interrupt controller. An external interrupt is then generated when the FERR# output drives the input to the interrupt controller. (Regardless of the value of NE, an unmasked floating-point exception always causes the FERR# pin to be asserted upon completion of the instruction that caused the exception.)

Error reporting by means of an external interrupt is provided to support PC-style error reporting. See Chapter 2, *System Architecture Overview*, in the *Pentium® Pro Family Developer's Manual, Volume 3* for more information about the NE bit.

After a floating-point exception handler is invoked, the processor handles the exception in the same manner that it handles non-FPU exceptions. (The floating-point exception handler is normally part of the operating system or executive software.) A typical action of the exception handler is to store FPU state information in memory (with the FSTENV/FNSTENV or FSAVE/FNSAVE instructions) so that it can evaluate the exception and formulate an appropriate response (see Section 7.3.9., "Saving the FPU's State"). Other typical exception handler actions include:

- Examine stored FPU state information (control, status, and tag words, and operand and instruction pointers) to determine the nature of the error.

- Taking action to correct the condition that caused the error.

- Clear the exception bits in the status word.

- Return to the interrupted program and resume normal execution.

If the faulting floating-point instruction is followed by one or more non-floating-point instructions, it may not be useful to re-execute the faulting instruction. See Section 7.9., "Floating-Point Exception Synchronization" for more information on synchronizing floating-point exceptions.

In cases where the handler needs to restart program execution with the faulting instruction, the IRET instruction cannot be used directly. The reason for this is that because the exception is not generated until the next floating-point or WAIT/FWAIT instruction following the faulting floating-point instruction, the return instruction pointer on the stack may not point to the faulting instruction. To restart program execution at the faulting instruction, the exception handler must obtain a pointer to the instruction from the saved FPU state information, load it into the return instruction pointer location on the stack, and then execute the IRET instruction.

In lieu of writing recovery procedures, the exception handler can do the following:

- Increment an exception counter for later display or printing.

- Print or display diagnostic information (such as, the FPU environment and registers).

- Halt further program execution.

7.8. FLOATING-POINT EXCEPTION CONDITIONS

The following sections describe the various conditions that cause a floating-point exception to be generated and the masked response of the FPU when these conditions are detected. Chapter 11, *Instruction Set Reference*, lists the floating-point exceptions that can be signaled for each floating-point instruction.

7.8.1. Invalid Operation Exception

The floating-point invalid-operation exception occurs in response to two general types of operations:

- Stack overflow or underflow (#IS).

- Invalid arithmetic operand (#IA).

The flag for this exception (IE) is bit 0 of the FPU status word, and the mask bit (IM) is bit 0 of the FPU control word. The stack fault flag (SF) of the FPU status word indicates the type of operation caused the exception. When the SF flag is set to 1, a stack operation has resulted in stack overflow or underflow; when the flag is cleared to 0, an arithmetic instruction has encountered an invalid operand. Note that the FPU explicitly sets the SF flag when it detects a stack overflow or underflow condition, but it does not explicitly clear the flag when it detects an invalid-arithmetic-operand condition. As a result, the state of the SF flag can be 1 following an invalid-arithmetic-operation exception, if it was not cleared from the last time a stack overflow or underflow condition occurred. See Section 7.3.2.4., "Stack Fault Flag" for more information about the SF flag.

7.8.1.1. STACK OVERFLOW OR UNDERFLOW EXCEPTION (#IS)

The FPU tag word keeps track of the contents of the registers in the FPU register stack (see Section 7.3.6., "FPU Tag Word"). It then uses this information to detect two different types of stack faults:

- Stack overflow—an instruction attempts to write a value into a non-empty FPU register

- Stack underflow—an instruction attempts to read a value from an empty FPU register.

When the FPU detects stack overflow or underflow, it sets the IE and SF flags in the FPU status word to 1. It then sets condition-code flag C1 in the FPU status word to 1 if stack overflow occurred or to 0 if stack underflow occurred.

If the invalid-operation exception is masked, the FPU then returns the real, integer, or BCD-integer indefinite value to the destination operand, depending on the instruction being executed. This value overwrites the destination register or memory location specified by the instruction.

If the invalid-operation exception is not masked, a software exception handler is invoked (see Section 7.7.3., "Software Exception Handling") and the top-of-stack pointer (TOP) and source operands remain unchanged.

The term stack overflow comes from the condition where the a program has pushed eight values onto the FPU register stack and the next value pushed on the stack causes a stack wraparound to a register that already contains a value. The term stack underflow refers to the opposite condition from stack overflow. Here, a program has popped eight values from the FPU register stack and the next value popped from the stack causes stack wraparound to an empty register.

A possible action of the invalid-operand exception handler for handling stack faults is to create and maintain an extension of the FPU register stack (a virtual stack) in memory. The handler can then adjust the stack contents by writing values to memory when stack overflow occurs or reading values from memory when stack underflow occurs.

7.8.1.2.   INVALID ARITHMETIC OPERAND EXCEPTION (#IA)

The FPU is able to detect a variety of invalid arithmetic operations that can be coded in a program. These operations generally indicate a programming error, such as dividing ∞ by ∞. Table 7-20 lists the invalid arithmetic operations that the FPU detects. This group includes the invalid operations defined in IEEE Std. 854.

When the FPU detects an invalid arithmetic operand, it sets the IE flag in the FPU status word to 1. If the invalid-operation exception is masked, the FPU then returns an indefinite value to the destination operand or sets the floating-point condition codes, as shown in Table 7-20. If the invalid-operation exception is not masked, a software exception handler is invoked (see Section 7.7.3., "Software Exception Handling") and the top-of-stack pointer (TOP) and source operands remain unchanged.

7.8.2.   Division-By-Zero Exception (#Z)

The FPU reports a floating-point zero-divide exception whenever an instruction attempts to divide a finite non-zero operand by 0. The flag (ZE) for this exception is bit 2 of the FPU status word, and the mask bit (ZM) is bit 2 of the FPU control word. The FDIV, FDIVP, FDIVR, FDIVRP, FIDIV, and FIDIVR instructions and the other instructions that perform division internally (FYL2X and FXTRACT) can report the divide-by-zero exception.

Table 7-20. Invalid Arithmetic Operations and the Masked Responses to Them

Condition	Masked Response
Any arithmetic operation on an operand that is in an unsupported format.	Return the real indefinite value to the destination operand.
Any arithmetic operation on a SNaN.	Return a QNaN to the destination operand (see Section 7.6., "Operating on NaNs").
Compare and test operations: one or both operands are NaNs.	Set the condition code flags (C0, C2, and C3) in the FPU status word to 111B (not comparable).
Addition: operands are opposite-signed infinities. Subtraction: operands are like-signed infinities.	Return the real indefinite value to the destination operand.
Multiplication: ∞ by 0; 0 by ∞.	Return the real indefinite value to the destination operand.
Division: ∞ by ∞; 0 by 0.	Return the real indefinite value to the destination operand.
Remainder instructions FPREM, FPREM1: modulus (divisor) is 0 or dividend is ∞.	Return the real indefinite; clear condition code flag C2 to 0.
Trigonometric instructions FCOS, FPTAN, FSIN, FSINCOS: source operand is ∞.	Return the real indefinite; clear condition code flag C2 to 0.
FSQRT: negative operand (except FSQRT (−0) = −0); FYL2X: negative operand (except FYL2X (−0) = −∞); FYL2XP1: operand more negative than −1.	Return the real indefinite value to the destination operand.
FBSTP: source register is empty or it contains a NaN, ∞, or a value that cannot be represented in 18 decimal digits.	Store BDC integer indefinite value in the destination operand.
FXCH: one or both registers are tagged empty.	Load empty registers with the real indefinite value, then perform the exchange.

When a divide-by-zero exception occurs and the exception is masked, the FPU sets the ZE flag and returns the values shown in Table 7-20. If the divide-by-zero exception is not masked, the ZE flag is set, a software exception handler is invoked (see Section 7.7.3., "Software Exception Handling"), and the top-of-stack pointer (TOP) and source operands remain unchanged.

Table 7-21. Divide-By-Zero Conditions and the Masked Responses to Them

Condition	Masked Response
Divide or reverse divide operation with a 0 divisor.	Returns an ∞ signed with the exclusive OR of the sign of the two operands to the destination operand.
FYL2X instruction.	Returns an ∞ signed with the opposite sign of the non-zero operand to the destination operand.
FXTRACT instruction.	ST(1) is set to −∞; ST(0) is set to 0 with the same sign as the source operand.

7.8.3. Denormal Operand Exception (#D)

The FPU signals the denormal-operand exception under the following conditions:

- If an arithmetic instruction attempts to operate on a denormal operand (see Section 7.2.3.2., "Normalized and Denormalized Finite Numbers").

- If an attempt is made to load a denormal single- or double-real value into an FPU register. (If the denormal value being loaded is an extended-real value, the denormal-operand exception is not reported.)

The flag (DE) for this exception is bit 1 of the FPU status word, and the mask bit (DM) is bit 1 of the FPU control word.

When a denormal-operand exception occurs and the exception is masked, the FPU sets the DE flag, then proceeds with the instruction. The denormal operand in single- or double-real format is automatically normalized when converted to the extended-real format. Operating on denormal numbers will produce results at least as good as, and often better than, what can be obtained when denormal numbers are flushed to zero. In fact, subsequent operations will benefit from the additional precision of the internal extended-real format. Most programmers mask this exception so that a computation may proceed, then analyze any loss of accuracy when the final result is delivered.

When a denormal-operand exception occurs and the exception is not masked, the DE flag is set and a software exception handler is invoked (see Section 7.7.3., "Software Exception Handling"). The top-of-stack pointer (TOP) and source operands remain unchanged. When denormal operands have reduced significance due to loss of low-order bits, it may be advisable to not operate on them. Precluding denormal operands from computations can be accomplished by an exception handler that responds to unmasked denormal-operand exceptions.

7.8.4. Numeric Overflow Exception (#O)

The FPU reports a floating-point numeric overflow exception (#O) whenever the rounded result of an arithmetic instruction exceeds the largest allowable finite value that will fit into the real format of the destination operand. For example, if the destination format is extended-real (80 bits), overflow occurs when the rounded result falls outside the unbiased range of $-1.0 * 2^{16384}$ to $1.0 * 2^{16384}$ (exclusive). Numeric overflow can occur on arithmetic operations where the result is stored in an FPU data register. It can also occur on store-real operations (with the FST and

FSTP instructions), where a within-range value in a data register is stored in memory in a single- or double-real format. The overflow threshold range for the single-real format is $-1.0 * 2^{128}$ to $1.0 * 2^{128}$; the range for the double-real format is $-1.0 * 2^{1024}$ to $1.0 * 2^{1024}$.

The numeric overflow exception cannot occur when overflow occurs when storing values in an integer or BCD integer format. Instead, the invalid-arithmetic-operand exception is signaled.

The flag (OE) for the numeric-overflow exception is bit 3 of the FPU status word, and the mask bit (OM) is bit 3 of the FPU control word.

When a numeric-overflow exception occurs and the exception is masked, the FPU sets the OE flag and returns one of the values shown in Table 7-22. The value returned depends on the current rounding mode of the FPU (see Section 7.3.4.3., "Rounding Control Field").

Table 7-22. Masked Responses to Numeric Overflow

Rounding Mode	Sign of True Result	Result
To nearest	+	$+\infty$
	−	$-\infty$
Toward $-\infty$	+	Largest finite positive number
	−	$-\infty$
Toward $+\infty$	+	$+\infty$
	−	Largest finite negative number
Toward zero	+	Largest finite positive number
	−	Largest finite negative number

The action that the FPU takes when numeric overflow occurs and the numeric-overflow exception is not masked, depends on whether the instruction is supposed to store the result in memory or on the register stack.

If the destination is a memory location, the OE flag is set and a software exception handler is invoked (see Section 7.7.3., "Software Exception Handling"). The top-of-stack pointer (TOP) and source operands remain unchanged.

If the destination is the register stack, the exponent of the rounded result is divided by 2^{24576} and stored with the significand in the destination operand. Condition code bit C1 in the FPU status word (called in this situation the "round-up bit") is set if the significand was rounded upward and cleared if the result is rounded toward 0. After the result is stored, the OE flag is set and a software exception handler is invoked.

The scaling bias value 24,576 is equal to $3 * 2^{13}$. Biasing the exponent by 24,576 normally translates the number as nearly as possible to the middle of the extended-real exponent range so that, if desired, it can be used in subsequent scaled operations with less risk of causing further exceptions.

When using the FSCALE instruction, massive overflow can occur, where the result is too large to be represented, even with a bias-adjusted exponent. Here, if overflow occurs again, after the result has been biased, a properly signed ∞ is stored in the destination operand.

7.8.5. Numeric Underflow Exception (#U)

The FPU reports a floating-point numeric underflow exception (#U) whenever the rounded result of an arithmetic instruction is tiny; that is, less than the smallest possible normalized, finite value that will fit into the real format of the destination operand. For example, if the destination format is extended-real (80 bits), underflow occurs when the rounded result falls in the unbiased range of $-1.0 * 2^{-16382}$ to $1.0 * 2^{-16382}$ (exclusive). Like numeric overflow, numeric underflow can occur on arithmetic operations where the result is stored in an FPU data register. It can also occur on store-real operations (with the FST and FSTP instructions), where a within-range value in a data register is stored in memory in a single- or double-real format. The underflow threshold range for the single-real format is $-1.0 * 2^{-126}$ to $1.0 * 2^{-126}$; the range for the double-real format is $-1.0 * 2^{-1022}$ to $1.0 * 2^{-1022}$. (The numeric underflow exception cannot occur when storing values in an integer or BCD integer format.)

The flag (UE) for the numeric-underflow exception is bit 4 of the FPU status word, and the mask bit (UM) is bit 4 of the FPU control word.

When a numeric-underflow exception occurs and the exception is masked, the FPU denormalizes the result (see Section 7.2.3.2., "Normalized and Denormalized Finite Numbers"). If the denormalized result is exact, FPU stores the result in the destination operand, without setting the UE flag. If the denormal result is inexact, the FPU sets the UE flag, then goes on to handle the inexact-result exception condition (see Section 7.8.6., "Inexact-Result (Precision) Exception (#P)"). It is important to note that if numeric-underflow is masked, a numeric-underflow exception is signaled only if the denormalized result is inexact. If the denormalized result is exact, no flags are set and no exceptions are signaled.

The action that the FPU takes when numeric underflow occurs and the numeric-underflow exception is not masked, depends on whether the instruction is supposed to store the result in memory or on the register stack.

If the destination is a memory location, the UE flag is set and a software exception handler is invoked (see Section 7.7.3., "Software Exception Handling"). The top-of-stack pointer (TOP) and source operands remain unchanged.

If the destination is the register stack, the exponent of the rounded result is multiplied by 2^{24576} and stored with the significand in the destination operand. Condition code bit C1 in the FPU the status register (acting here as a "round-up bit") is set if the significand was rounded upward and cleared if the result is rounded toward 0. After the result is stored, the UE flag is set and a software exception handler is invoked.

The scaling bias value 24,576 is the same as is used for the overflow exception and has the same effect, which is to translates the result as nearly as possible to the middle of the extended-real exponent range.

When using the FSCALE instruction, massive underflow can occur, where the result is too tiny to be represented, even with a bias-adjusted exponent. Here, if overflow occurs again, after the result has been biased, a properly signed 0 is stored in the destination operand.

7.8.6. Inexact-Result (Precision) Exception (#P)

The inexact-result exception (also called the precision exception) occurs if the result of an operation is not exactly representable in the destination format. For example, the fraction 1/3 cannot be precisely represented in binary form. This exception occurs frequently and indicates that some (normally acceptable) accuracy has been lost. The exception is supported for applications that need to perform exact arithmetic only. Because the rounded result is generally satisfactory for most applications, this exception is commonly masked. Note that the transcendental instructions [FSIN, FCOS, FSINCOS, FPTAN, FPATAN, F2XM1, FYL2X, and FYL2XP1] by nature produce inexact results.

The inexact-result exception flag (PE) is bit 4 of the FPU status word, and the mask bit (PM) is bit 4 of the FPU control word.

If the inexact-result exception is masked when an inexact-result condition occurs and a numeric overflow or underflow condition has not occurred, the FPU sets the PE flag and stores the rounded result in the destination operand. The current rounding mode determines the method used to round the result (see Section 7.3.4.3., "Rounding Control Field"). The C1 (round-up) bit in the FPU status word indicates whether the inexact result was rounded up (C1 is set) or "not rounded up" (C1 is cleared). In the "not rounded up" case (C1 is cleared), the least-significant bits of the inexact result are truncated so that the result fits in the destination format.

If the inexact-result exception is not masked when an inexact result occurs and numeric overflow or underflow has not occurred, the FPU performs the same operation described in the previous paragraph and, in addition, invokes a software exception handler (see Section 7.7.3., "Software Exception Handling").

If an inexact result occurs in conjunction with numeric overflow or underflow, one of the following operations is carried out:

- If an inexact result occurs along with masked overflow or underflow, the OE or UE flag and the PE flag are set and the result is stored as describe for the overflow or underflow exceptions (see Section 7.8.4., "Numeric Overflow Exception (#O)" or Section 7.8.5., "Numeric Underflow Exception (#U)"). If the inexact-result exception is unmasked, the FPU also invokes the software exception handler.

- If an inexact result occurs along with unmasked overflow or underflow and the destination operand is a register, the OE or UE flag and the PE flag are set, the result is stored as describe for the overflow or underflow exceptions, and the software exception handler is invoked.

- If an inexact result occurs along with unmasked overflow or underflow and the destination operand is a memory location, the inexact-result condition is ignored.

7.8.7. Exception Priority

The processor handles exceptions according to a predetermined precedence. When an instruction generates two or more exception conditions, the exception precedence sometimes results in the higher-priority exception being handled and the lower-priority exceptions being ignored. For example, dividing an SNaN by zero can potentially signal an invalid-arithmetic-operand exception (due to the SNaN operand) and a divide-by-zero exception. Here, if both exceptions are masked, the FPU handles the higher-priority exception only (the invalid-arithmetic-operand exception), returning a real indefinite to the destination. Alternately, a denormal-operand or inexact-result exception can accompany a numeric underflow or overflow exception, with both exceptions being handled.

The precedence for floating-point exceptions is as follows:

1. Invalid-operation exception, subdivided as follows:

   a. Stack underflow.

   b. Stack overflow.

   c. Operand of unsupported format.

   d. SNaN operand.

2. QNaN operand. Though this is not an exception, the handling of a QNaN operand has precedence over lower-priority exceptions. For example, a QNaN divided by zero results in a QNaN, not a zero-divide exception.

3. Any other invalid-operation exception not mentioned above or a divide-by-zero exception.

4. Denormal-operand exception. If masked, then instruction execution continues, and a lower-priority exception can occur as well.

5. Numeric overflow and underflow exceptions in conjunction with the inexact-result exception.

6. Inexact-result exception.

Invalid operation, zero divide, and denormal operand exceptions are detected before a floating-point operation begins, whereas overflow, underflow, and precision errors are not detected until a true result has been computed. When a *pre-operation* exception is detected, the FPU register stack and memory have not yet been updated, and appear as if the offending instructions has not been executed. When a *post-operation* exception is detected, the register stack and memory may be updated with a result (depending on the nature of the error).

7.9. FLOATING-POINT EXCEPTION SYNCHRONIZATION

Because the integer unit and FPU are separate execution units, it is possible for the processor to execute floating-point, integer, and system instructions concurrently. No special programming techniques are required to gain the advantages of concurrent execution. (Floating-point instructions are placed in the instruction stream along with the integer and system instructions.) However, concurrent execution can cause problems for floating-point exception handlers.

The root of this problem concerns the way the FPU signals the existence of unmasked floating-point exceptions. (Special exception synchronization is not required for masked floating-point exceptions, because the FPU always returns a masked result to the destination operand.)

When a floating-point exception is unmasked and the exception condition occurs, the FPU stops further execution of the floating-point instruction and signals the exception event. On the next occurrence of a floating-point instruction or a WAIT/FWAIT instruction in the instruction stream, the processor checks the ES flag in the FPU status word for pending floating-point exceptions. It floating-point exceptions are pending, the FPU makes an implicit call (traps) to the floating-point software exception handler. The exception handler can then execute recovery procedures for selected or all floating-point exceptions.

Synchronization problems occur in the time frame between when the exception is signaled and when it is actually handled. Because of concurrent execution, integer or system instructions can be executed during this time frame. It is thus possible for the source or destination operands for a floating-point instruction that faulted to be overwritten in memory, making it impossible for the exception handler to analyze or recovery from the exception.

To solve this problem, an exception synchronizing instruction (either a floating-point instruction or a WAIT/FWAIT instruction) can be placed immediately after any floating-point instruction that might present a situation where state information pertaining to a floating-point exception might be lost or corrupted. Floating-point instructions that store data in memory are prime candidates for synchronization. For example, the following three lines of code have the potential for exception synchronization problems:

```
FILD COUNT ; Floating-point instruction
INC COUNT  ; Integer instruction
FSQRT      ; Subsequent floating-point instruction
```

In this example, the INC instruction modifies the result of a floating-point instruction (FILD). If an exception is signaled during the execution of the FILD instruction, the result stored in the COUNT memory location might be overwritten before the exception handler is called.

Rearranging the instructions, as follows, so that the FSQRT instruction follows the FILD instruction, synchronizes the exception handling and eliminates the possibility of the exception being handled incorrectly.

```
FILD COUNT ; Floating-point instruction
FSQRT      ; Subsequent floating-point instruction synchronizes
           ; any exceptions generated by the FILD instruction.
INC COUNT  ; Integer instruction
```

The FSQRT instruction does not require any synchronization, because the results of this instruction are stored in the FPU data registers and will remain there, undisturbed, until the next floating-point or WAIT/FWAIT instruction is executed. To absolutely insure that any exceptions emanating from the FSQRT instruction are handled (for example, prior to a procedure call), a WAIT instruction can be placed directly after the FSQRT instruction.

Note that some floating-point instructions (non-waiting instructions) do not check for pending unmasked exceptions (see Section 7.5.11., "FPU Control Instructions"). They include the FNINIT, FNSTENV, FNSAVE, FNSTSW, FNSTCW, and FNCLEX instructions. When an

FNINIT, FNSTENV, FNSAVE, or FNCLEX instruction is executed, all pending exceptions are essentially lost (either the FPU status register is cleared or all exceptions are masked). The FNSTSW and FNSTCW instructions do not check for pending interrupts, but they do not modify the FPU status and control registers. A subsequent "waiting" floating-point instruction can then handle any pending exceptions.

intel®

8

Input/Output

intel

CHAPTER 8
INPUT/OUTPUT

In addition to transferring data to and from external memory, the Pentium Pro processor can also transfer data to and from input/output ports (I/O ports). I/O ports are created in system hardware by circuity that decodes the control, data, and address pins on the processor. These I/O ports are then configured to communicate with peripheral devices. An I/O port can be an input port, an output port, or a bidirectional port. Some I/O ports are used for transmitting data, such as to and from the transmit and receive registers, respectively, of a serial interface device. Other I/O ports are used to control peripheral devices, such as the control registers of a disk controller.

This chapter describes the processor's I/O architecture. The topics discussed include:

* I/O port addressing.
* I/O instructions.
* The I/O protection mechanism.

8.1. I/O PORT ADDRESSING

The processor allows I/O ports to be accessed in either of two ways:

* Through a separate I/O address space.
* Through memory-mapped I/O.

Accessing I/O ports through the I/O address space is handled through a set of I/O instructions and a special I/O protection mechanism. Accessing I/O ports through memory-mapped I/O is handled with the processors general-purpose move and string instructions, with protection provided through segmentation or paging. I/O ports can be mapped so that they appear in the I/O address space or the physical-memory address space (memory mapped I/O) or both.

One benefit of using the I/O address space is that writes to I/O ports are guaranteed to be completed before the next instruction in the instruction stream is executed. Thus, I/O writes to control system hardware cause the hardware to be set to its new state before any other instructions are executed. See Section 8.6., "Ordering I/O" for more information on serializing of I/O operations.

8.2. I/O PORT HARDWARE

From a hardware point of view, I/O is handled through the processor's address lines. A special memory-I/O transaction on the system bus indicates whether the address lines are being driven with a memory address or an I/O address. When the separate I/O address space is selected, it is the responsibility of the hardware to decode the memory-I/O bus transaction to select I/O ports rather than memory.

Data is transmitted between the processor and an I/O device through the data lines.

8.3. I/O ADDRESS SPACE

The processor's I/O address space is separate and distinct from the physical-memory address space. The I/O address space consists of 2^{16} (64K) individually addressable 8-bit I/O ports, numbered 0 through FFFFH. I/O port addresses 0F8H through 0FFH are reserved. Do not assign I/O ports to these addresses.

Any two consecutive 8-bit ports can be treated as a 16-bit port, and any four consecutive ports can be a 32-bit port. In this manner, the processor can transfer 8, 16, or 32 bits to or from a device in the I/O address space. Like words in memory, 16-bit ports should be aligned to even addresses (0, 2, 4, ...) so that all 16 bits can be transferred in a single bus cycle. Likewise, 32-bit ports should be aligned to addresses that are multiples of four (0, 4, 8, ...). The processor supports data transfers to unaligned ports, but there is a performance penalty because one or more extra bus cycle must be used.

The exact order of bus cycles used to access unaligned ports is undefined and is not guaranteed to remain the same in future Intel Architecture processors. If hardware or software requires that I/O ports be written to in a particular order, that order must be specified explicitly. For example, to load a word-length I/O port at address 2H and then another word port at 4H, two word-length writes must be used, rather than a single doubleword write at 2H.

Note that the processor does not mask parity errors for bus cycles to the I/O address space. Accessing I/O ports through the I/O address space is thus a possible source of parity errors.

8.3.1. Memory-Mapped I/O

I/O devices that respond like memory components can be accessed through the processor's physical-memory address space (see Figure 8-1). When using memory-mapped I/O, any of the processor's instructions that reference memory can be used to access an I/O port located at a physical-memory address. For example, the MOV instruction can transfer data between any register and a memory-mapped I/O port. The AND, OR, and TEST instructions may be used to manipulate bits in the control and status registers of a memory-mapped peripheral devices.

If caching is enabled in real-address mode, caching of I/O accesses can be prevented by using MTRRs to map the I/O address space as uncacheable (UC). See Chapter 11, *Memory Cache Control*, in the *Pentium® Pro Family Developer's Manual, Volume 3* for a complete discussion of the MTRRs.

8.4. I/O INSTRUCTIONS

The processor's I/O instructions provide access to I/O ports through the I/O address space. (These instructions cannot be used to access memory-mapped I/O ports). There are two groups of I/O instructions:

- Those which transfer a single item (byte, word, or doubleword) between an I/O port and a general-purpose register.

- Those which transfer strings of items (strings of bytes, words, or doublewords) between an I/O port and memory.

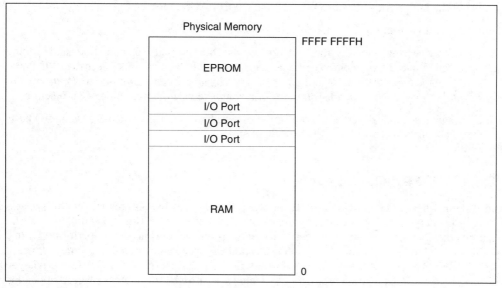

Figure 8-1. Memory-Mapped I/O

The register I/O instructions IN (input from I/O port) and OUT (output to I/O port) move data between I/O ports and the EAX register (32-bit I/O), the AX register (16-bit I/O), or the AL (8-bit I/O) register. The address of the I/O port can be given with an immediate value or a value in the DX register.

The string I/O instructions INS (input string from I/O port) and OUTS (output string to I/O port) move data between an I/O port and a memory location. The address of the I/O port being accesses is given in the DX register; the source or destination memory address is given in the DS:ESI or ES:EDI register, respectively.

When used with one of the repeat prefixes (such as REP), the INS and OUTS instructions perform string (or block) input or output operations. The repeat prefix REP modifies the INS and OUTS instructions to transfer blocks of data between an I/O port and memory. Here, the ESI or EDI register is incremented or decremented (according to the setting of the DF flag in the EFLAGS register) after each byte, word, or doubleword is transferred between the selected I/O port and memory.

See the individual references for the IN, INS, OUT, and OUTS instructions in Chapter 11, *Instruction Set Reference*, for more information on these instructions.

8.5.   PROTECTED-MODE I/O

When the processor is running in protected mode, the following protection mechanisms regulate access to I/O ports:

*   When accessing I/O ports through the I/O address space, two protection devices control access:

    —   The I/O privilege level (IOPL) field in the EFLAGS register.

    —   The I/O permission bit map of a task state segment (TSS).

*   When accessing memory-mapped I/O ports, the normal segmentation and paging protection and the memory type range registers (MTRRs) also affect access to I/O ports. See Chapter 4, *Protection*, and Chapter 11, *Memory Cache Control*, in *Pentium® Pro Family Developer's Manual, Volume 3* for a complete discussion of memory protection.

The following sections describe the protection mechanisms available when accessing I/O ports in the I/O address space with the I/O instructions.

8.5.1.   I/O Privilege Level

In systems where I/O protection is used, the IOPL field in the EFLAGS register controls access to the I/O address space by restricting use of selected instructions. This protection mechanism permits the operating system or executive to set the privilege level needed to perform I/O. In a typical protection ring model, access to the I/O address space is restricted to privilege levels 0 and 1. Here, kernel and the device drivers are allowed to perform I/O, while less privileged device drivers and application programs are denied access to the I/O address space. Application programs must then make calls to the operating system to perform I/O.

The following instructions can be executed only if the current privilege level (CPL) of the program or task currently executing is less than or equal to the IOPL: IN, INS, OUT, OUTS, CLI (clear interrupt-enable flag), and STI (set interrupt-enable flag). These instructions are called *I/O sensitive* instructions, because they are sensitive to the IOPL field. Any attempt by a less privileged program or task to use an I/O sensitive instruction results in a general-protection exception (#GP) being signaled. Because each task has its own copy of the EFLAGS register, each task can have a different IOPL.

The I/O permission bit map in the TSS can be used to modify the effect of the IOPL on I/O sensitive instructions, allowing access to some I/O ports by less privileged programs or tasks (see Section 8.5.2., "I/O Permission Bit Map").

A program or task can change its IOPL only with the POPF and IRET instructions; however, such changes are privileged. No procedure may change the current IOPL unless it is running at privilege level 0. An attempt by a less privileged procedure to change the IOPL does not result in an exception; the IOPL simply remains unchanged.

The POPF instruction also may be used to change the state of the IF flag (as can the CLI and STI instructions); however, the POPF instruction in this case is also I/O sensitive. A procedure may use the POPF instruction to change the setting of the IF flag only if the CPL is less than or equal to the current IOPL. An attempt by a less privileged procedure to change the IF flag does not result in an exception; the IF flag simply remains unchanged.

8.5.2. I/O Permission Bit Map

The I/O permission bit map is a device for permitting limited access to I/O ports by less privileged programs or tasks and for tasks operating in virtual-8086 mode. The I/O permission bit map is located in the TSS (see Figure 8-2) for the currently running task or program. The address of the first byte of the I/O permission bit map is given in the I/O map base address field of the TSS. The size of the I/O permission bit map and its location in the TSS are variable.

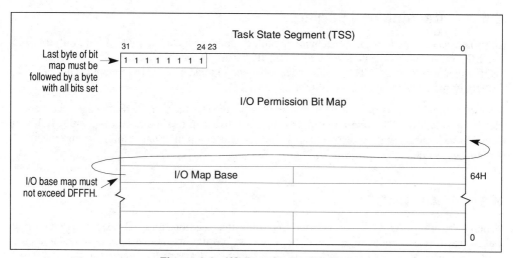

Figure 8-2. I/O Permission Bit Map

Because each task has its own TSS, each task has its own I/O permission bit map. Access to individual I/O ports can thus be granted to individual tasks.

If in protected mode the CPL is less than or qual to the current IOPL, the processor allows all I/O operations to proceed. If the CPL is greater than the IOPL or if the processor is operating in virtual-8086 mode, the processor checks the I/O permission bit map to determine if access to a particular I/O port is allowed. Each bit in the map corresponds to an I/O port byte address. For example, the control bit for I/O port address 29H in the I/O address space is found at bit position 1 of the sixth byte in the bit map. Before granting I/O access, the processor tests all the bits corresponding to the I/O port being addressed. For a doubleword access, for example, the processors tests the four bits corresponding to the four adjacent 8-bit port addresses. If any tested bit is set, a general-protection exception (#GP) is signaled. If all tested bits are clear, the I/O operation is allows to proceed.

Because I/O port addresses are not necessarily aligned to word and doubleword boundaries, the processor read two bytes from the I/O permission bit map for every access to an I/O port. To prevent exceptions from being generated when the ports with the highest addresses are accessed, an extra byte needs to included in the TSS immediately after the table. This byte must have all of its bits set, and it must be within the segment limit.

It is not necessary for the I/O permission bit map to represent all the I/O addresses. I/O addresses not spanned by the map are treated as if they had set bits in the map. For example, if the TSS segment limit is 10 bytes past the bit-map base address, the map has 11 bytes and the first 80 I/O ports are mapped. Higher addresses in the I/O address space generate exceptions.

If the I/O bit map base address is greater than or equal to the TSS segment limit, there is no I/O permission map, and all I/O instructions generate exceptions when the CPL is greater than the current IOPL. The I/O bit map base address must be less than or equal to DFFFH.

8.5.3. Caching and Paging

In protected mode, the paging mechanism can be used to control caching of data buffers used for I/O and memory-mapped I/O addresses. If caching is enabled, either the MTRRs or the paging mechanism (the PCD bit in the page table entry) must be used to prevent caching of data buffers or memory-mapped I/O addresses.

The segmentation or paging mechanism can also be used to manage the data space accessed by the I/O mechanism. The operating system or executive can use the AVL (available) fields in segment descriptors or page table entries to mark pages containing data buffers as unrelocatable and unswappable.

8.6. ORDERING I/O

When controlling I/O devices it is often important that memory and I/O operations be carried out in precisely the order programmed. For example, a program may write a command to an I/O port, then read the status of the I/O device from another I/O port. It is important that the status returned be the status of the device *after* it receives the command, not *before*.

When using memory-mapped I/O, caution should be taken to avoid situations in which the programmed order is not preserved by the processor. To optimize performance, the processor allows memory reads to be reordered ahead of buffered writes in most situations. Internally, processor reads (cache hits) can be reordered around buffered writes. Memory reordering does not occur externally at the pins, reads (cache misses) and writes appear in-order. Using memory-mapped I/O, therefore, creates the possibility that an I/O read might be performed before the memory write of a previous instruction. The recommended method of enforcing program ordering of I/O accesses with the Pentium Pro processor, is to use the MTRRs to make the memory mapped I/O address space uncacheable. This operation insures that reads and writes of I/O devices are carried out in program order. See Chapter 11, *Memory Cache Control*, in the *Pentium® Pro Family Developer's Manual, Volume 3* for more information on using MTRRs.

Another method of enforcing program order is to insert one of the serializing instructions, such as the CPUID instruction, between operations. See Chapter 7, *Multiple Processor Management*, in the *Pentium® Pro Family Developer's Manual, Volume 3* for more information on serialization of instructions.

When the I/O address space is used instead of memory-mapped I/O, the situation is different in two respects:

- I/O writes are never buffered. Therefore, strict ordering of I/O operations is enforced by the processor.

- The processor synchronizes I/O instruction execution with external bus activity (see Table 8-1).

Table 8-1. I/O Instruction Serialization

Instruction Being Executed	Processor Delays Execution of ...		Until Completion of ...	
	Current Instruction?	Next Instruction?	Pending Stores?	Current Store?
IN	Yes		Yes	
INS	Yes		Yes	
REP INS	Yes		Yes	
OUT		Yes	Yes	Yes
OUTS		Yes	Yes	Yes
REP OUTS		Yes	Yes	Yes

intel®

9

Processor Identification and Feature Determination

CHAPTER 9
PROCESSOR IDENTIFICATION AND FEATURE DETERMINATION

When writing software intended to run on several different processors in the Intel Architecture family, it is generally necessary to identify the type of processor present in a system and the processor features that are available to an application. This chapter describes how to identify the processor that is executing the code and determine the features the processor supports. It also shows how to determine if an FPU or NPX is present. See Chapter 10, *Intel Architecture Compatibility*, for a complete list of the features that are available for the different Intel Architecture processors.

9.1. PROCESSOR IDENTIFICATION

The CPUID instruction returns the processor type for the processor that executes the instruction. It also indicates the features that are present in the processor, including the existence of an on-chip FPU. The following information can be obtained with this instruction:

- The highest operand value the instruction responds to (2 for the Pentium Pro processor).

- The processor's family identification (ID) number, model ID, and stepping ID.

- The presence of an on-chip FPU.

- Support for or the presence of the following architectural extensions and enhancements:

  — Virtual-8086 mode enhancements.

  — Debugging extensions.

  — Page-size extensions.

  — Read time stamp counter (RDTSC) instruction.

  — Read model specific registers (RDMSR) and write model specific registers (WRMSR) instructions.

  — Physical address extension.

  — Machine check exceptions.

  — Compare and exchange 8 bytes instruction (CMPXCHG8B).

  — On-chip, advanced programmable interrupt controller (APIC).

  — Memory-type range registers (MTRRs).

  — Page global flag.

> — Machine check architecture.
>
> — Conditional move instruction (CMOV*cc*).

- Cache information.

To use this instruction, a source operand value of 0, 1 or 2 is placed in the EAX register. Processor identification and feature information is then returned in the EAX, EBX, ECX, and EDX registers. See Chapter 11, "CPUID—CPU Identification" for more detailed information about the instruction.

9.2. IDENTIFICATION OF EARLIER INTEL ARCHITECTURE PROCESSORS

The CPUID instruction is only available in the Pentium Pro and Pentium processors. For the Intel486 and earlier Intel Architecture processors, several other architectural features can be exploited to identify the processor.

The settings of bits 12 and 13 (IOPL), 14 (NT), and 15 (reserved) in the EFLAGS register (see Figure 3-7) is different for Intel's 32-bit processors than for the Intel 8086 and Intel 286 processors. By examining the settings of these bits (with the PUSHF/PUSHFD and POP/POPFD instructions), an application program can determine whether the processor is an 8086, Intel286, or one of the Intel 32-bit processors:

- 8086 processor — Bits 12 through 15 of the EFLAGS register are always set.

- Intel 286 processor — Bits 12 through 15 are always clear in real-address mode.

- 32-bit processors — In real-address mode, bit 15 is always clear and bits 12 through 14 have the last value loaded into them. In protected mode, bit 15 is always clear, bit 14 has the last value loaded into it, and the IOPL bits depends on the current privilege level (CPL). The IOPL field can be changed only if the CPL is 0.

Other EFLAG register bits that can be used to differentiate between the 32-bit processors:

- Bit 18 (AC) — Implemented only on the Pentium Pro, Pentium, and Intel486 processors. The inability to set or clear this bit distinguishes an Intel386 processor from the other Intel 32-bit processors.

- Bit 21 (ID) — Determines if the processor is able to execute the CPUID instruction. The ability to set and clear this bit indicates that the processor is either a Pentium Pro or a Pentium processor.

To determine whether an FPU or NPX is present in a system, applications can write to the FPU/NPX status and control registers using the FNINIT instruction and then verify the correct values are read back using the FNSTENV instruction.

After determining that an FPU or NPX is present, its type can then be determined. In most cases, the processor type will determine the type of FPU or NPX; however, an Intel386 processor is compatible with either an Intel287 or Intel387 math coprocessor. The method the coprocessor uses to represent ∞ indicates which coprocessor is present. The Intel287 math coprocessor uses the same bit representation for +∞ and −∞; whereas, the Intel387 math coprocessor uses different representations for +∞ and −∞.

See "Intel Application Note 485 — Intel Processor Identification With the CPUID Instruction" for more information on identifying Intel Architecture processors. This application note also provides example source code for using the CPUID instruction and the other processor identification techniques.

intel®

10

Intel Architecture Compatibility

CHAPTER 10
INTEL ARCHITECTURE COMPATIBILITY

The Pentium Pro processor is fully binary compatible with all Intel Architecture processors, including the Pentium, Intel486 DX and SX, Intel386 DX and SX, Intel 286, and the 8086/8088 processors. Compatibility means that, within certain limited constraints, programs that execute on previous generations of Intel Architecture processors will produce identical results when executed on the Pentium Pro processor. The compatibility constraints and any implementation differences between the Intel Architecture processors are described in this chapter and in Chapter 15, *Intel Architecture Compatibility*, in the *Pentium® Pro Family Developer's Manual, Volume 3*. The compatibility issues described in this chapter deal with new instructions, the basic execution environment, and the floating-point unit (FPU) and math coprocessors. Compatibility issues regarding the system architecture of the processors are covered in the *Pentium® Pro Family Developer's Manual, Volume 3*.

The Pentium Pro processor also includes extensions to the registers, instruction set, and control functions found in earlier Intel Architecture processors. Those extensions have been defined with consideration for compatibility with previous and future processors. This chapter also summarizes the compatibility considerations for those extensions.

10.1. RESERVED BITS

Throughout this manual, certain bits are marked as reserved in many register and memory layout descriptions. When bits are marked as undefined or reserved, it is essential for compatibility with future processors that software treat these bits as having a future, though unknown effect. Software should follow these guidelines in dealing with reserved bits:

- Do not depend on the states of any reserved bits when testing the values of registers or memory locations that contain such bits. Mask out the reserved bits before testing.

- Do not depend on the states of any reserved bits when storing them to memory or to a register.

- Do not depend on the ability to retain information written into any reserved bits.

- When loading a register, always load the reserved bits with the values indicated in the documentation, if any, or reload them with values previously read from the same register.

Avoid any software dependence upon the state of reserved Pentium Pro processor bits. Depending on the values of reserved bits will make software dependent upon the unspecified manner in which the Pentium Pro processor handles these bits. Depending upon reserved values risks incompatibility with future processors.

Software written for an Pentium, Intel486, or Intel386 processor that handles reserved bits correctly will port to the Pentium Pro processor without generating protection exceptions.

10.2. ENABLING NEW FUNCTIONS AND MODES

Most of the new control functions defined for the Pentium Pro processor are enabled by new mode flags in the control registers (primarily register CR4). This register is undefined for Intel Architecture processors earlier than the Pentium processor. Attempting to access this register with an Intel486 or earlier Intel Architecture processor results in an invalid-opcode exception (#UD). Consequently, programs that execute correctly on the Intel486 or earlier Intel Architecture processor cannot erroneously enable these functions. Attempting set a reserved bit in register CR4 to a value other than its original value results in a general-protection exception (#GP). So, programs that execute on the Pentium Pro processor cannot erroneously enable functions that may be implemented in future processors.

The Pentium Pro processor does not check for attempts to set reserved bits in model-specific registers. It is the obligation of the software writer to enforce this discipline. These reserved bits may be used in future Intel processors.

10.3. DETECTING THE PRESENCE OF NEW FEATURES THROUGH SOFTWARE

Software can check for the presence of new architectural features and extensions in either of two ways:

- Test for the presence of the feature or extension — Software can test for the presence of new flags in the EFLAGS register and control registers. If these flags are reserved (meaning not present in the processor executing the test), an exception is generated. Likewise, software can attempt to execute a new instruction, which results in an invalid-opcode exception (#UD) being generated if it is not supported.

- Execute the CPUID instruction — The CPUID instruction (added to the Intel Architecture in the Pentium processor) indicates the presence of new features directly.

See Chapter 9, *Processor Identification and Feature Determination*, for detailed information on detecting new processor features and extensions.

10.4. NEW INSTRUCTIONS

This section identifies the introduction of new instructions for the 32-bit Intel Architecture processors.

10.4.1. New Pentium® Pro Processor Instructions

The following instructions are new in the Pentium Pro processor:

- CMOV*cc* (conditional move) instruction, see Chapter 11, "CMOVcc—Conditional Move".

- FCMOV*cc* (floating-point conditional move) instructions, see Chapter 11, "FCMOVcc—Floating-Point Conditional Move".

- FCOMI (floating-point compare and set EFLAGS) instructions, see Chapter 11, "FCOMI/FCOMIP/ FUCOMI/FUCOMIP—Compare Real and Set EFLAGS".

- RDPMC (read performance monitoring counters) instruction, see Chapter 11, "RDPMC—Read Performance-Monitoring Counters". This instruction was available in the Pentium processor, but was undocumented.

- UD2 (undefined) instruction, see Chapter 11, "UD2—Undefined Instruction".

10.4.2. New Pentium® Processor Instructions

The following instructions are new in the Pentium processor:

- CMPXCHG8B (compare and exchange 8 bytes) instruction.

- CPUID (CPU identification) instruction.

- RDTSC (read time-stamp counter) instruction.

- RDMSR (read model-specific register) instruction.

- WRMSR (write model-specific register) instruction.

- RSM (resume from SSM) instruction.

The form of the MOV instruction used to access the test registers has been removed on the Pentium and future Intel Architecture processors.

10.4.3. New Intel486™ Processor Instructions

The following instructions are new in the Intel486 processor:

- BSWAP (byte swap) instruction.

- XADD (exchange and add) instruction.

- CMPXCHG (compare and exchange) instruction.

- INVD (invalidate cache) instruction.

- WBINVD (write-back and invalidate cache) instruction.

- INVLPG (invalidate TLB entry) instruction.

10.4.4. New Intel386™ Processor Instructions

The following instructions are new in the Intel386 processor:

- LSS, LFS, and LGS (load SS, FS, and GS registers)
- Long-displacement conditional jumps.
- Single-bit instructions.
- Bit scan instructions.
- Double-shift instructions.
- Byte set on condition instruction.
- Move with sign/zero extension.
- Generalized multiply instruction.
- MOV to and from control registers.
- MOV to and from test registers (now obsolete).
- MOV to and from debug registers.

10.5. OBSOLETE INSTRUCTIONS

The MOV to and from test registers instructions were removed the Pentium and future Intel Architecture processors. Execution of these instructions generates an invalid-opcode exception (#UD).

10.6. UNDEFINED OPCODES

All new instructions defined for Intel Architecture processors use binary encodings that were reserved on earlier-generation processors. Attempting to execute a reserved opcode always results in an invalid-opcode (#UD) exception being generated. Consequently, programs that execute correctly on earlier-generation processors cannot erroneously execute these instructions and thereby produce unexpected results when executed on later Intel Architecture processors.

10.7. NEW FLAGS IN THE EFLAGS REGISTER

Figure 3-7 shows the configuration of flags in the EFLAGS register for the Pentium Pro processor. No new flags have been added to this register in the Pentium Pro processor. The flags added to this register in the Pentium and Intel486 processors are described in the following sections.

10.7.1. New Pentium® Processor Flags

The following flags were added to the EFLAGS register in the Pentium processor:

- VIF (virtual interrupt flag), bit 19.

- VIP (virtual interrupt pending), bit 20.

- ID (identification flag), bit 21.

10.7.2. New Intel486™ Processor Flags

The AC flag (bit 18) was added to the EFLAGS register in the Intel486 processor.

10.7.3. Using EFLAGS Flags to Distinguish Between 32-Bit Intel Architecture Processors

The following bits in the EFLAGS register that can be used to differentiate between the 32-bit Intel Architecture processors:

- Bit 18 (the AC flag) can be used to distinguish an Intel386 processor from the Pentium Pro, Pentium, and Intel486 processors. Since it is not implemented on the Intel386 processor, it will always be clear.

- Bit 21 (the ID flag) indicates whether an application can execute the CPUID instruction. The ability to set and clear this bit indicates that the processor is a Pentium Pro or Pentium processor. The CPUID instruction can then be used to determine which processor.

- Bits 19 (the VIF flag) and 20 (the VIP flag) will always be zero on processors that do not support virtual mode extensions, which includes all 32-bit processors prior to the Pentium processor.

See Chapter 9, *Processor Identification and Feature Determination*, for more information on identifying processors.

10.8. STACK OPERATIONS

This section identifies the differences in stack implementation between the various Intel Architecture processors.

10.8.1. PUSH SP

The Pentium Pro, Pentium, Intel486, Intel386, and Intel 286 processors push a different value on the stack for a PUSH SP instruction than the 8086 processor. The 32-bit processors push the value of the SP register before it is decremented as part of the push operation; the 8086 processor pushes the value of the SP register after it is decremented. If the value pushed is important, replace PUSH SP instructions with the following three instructions:

```
PUSH BP
MOV  BP, SP
XCHG BP, [BP]
```

This code functions as the 8086 processor PUSH SP instruction on the Pentium Pro, Pentium, Intel486, Intel386, and Intel 286 processors.

10.8.2. EFLAGS Pushed On The Stack

The setting of the stored values of bits 12 through 15 (which includes the IOPL field and the NT flag) in the EFLAGS register by the PUSHF instruction, by interrupts, and by exceptions is different with the 32-bit Intel Architecture processors than with the 8086 and Intel 286 processors. The differences are as follows:

- 8086 processor—bits 12 through 15 are always set.

- Intel 286 processor—bits 12 through 15 are always cleared in real-address mode.

- 32-bit processors in real-address mode—bit 15 (reserved) is always cleared, and bits 12 through 14 have the last value loaded into them.

10.9. FPU

This section addresses the issues that must be faced when porting floating-point software designed to run on earlier Intel Architecture processors and math coprocessors to a Pentium Pro processor with integrated FPU. To software, the Pentium Pro processor looks very much like a Pentium processor. Floating-point software which runs on the Pentium or Intel486 DX processor, or on an Intel486 SX processor/Intel487 SX math coprocessor system or an Intel386 processor/Intel387 math coprocessor system, will run with at most minor modifications on the Pentium Pro processor. To port code directly from an Intel 286 processor/Intel287 math coprocessor system or an Intel 8086 processor/8087 math coprocessor system to the Pentium Pro processor, certain additional issues must be addressed.

In the following sections, the term "32-bit Intel Architecture FPUs" refers to the Pentium Pro, Pentium, and Intel486 DX processors, and to the Intel487 SX and Intel387 math coprocessors; the term "16-bit Intel Architecture math coprocessors" refers to the Intel287 and 8087 math coprocessors.

10.9.1. Control Register CR0 Flags

The ET, NE, and MP flags in control register CR0 control the interface between the integer unit of an Intel Architecture processor and either its internal FPU or an external math coprocessor. The effect of these flags in the various Intel Architecture processors are described in the following paragraphs.

The ET (extension type) flag (bit 4 of the CR0 register) is used in the Intel386 processor to indicate whether the math coprocessor in the system is an Intel287 math coprocessor (flag is clear) or an Intel387 DX math coprocessor (flag is set). This bit is hardwired to 1 in the Pentium Pro, Pentium, and Intel486 processors.

The NE (Numeric Exception) flag (bit 5 of the CR0 register) is used in the Pentium Pro, Pentium, and Intel486 processors to determine whether unmasked floating-point exceptions are reported internally through interrupt vector 16 (flag is set) or externally through an external interrupt (flag is clear). On a hardware reset, the NE flag is initialized to 0, so software using the automatic internal error-reporting mechanism must set this flag to 1. This flag is nonexistent on the Intel386 processor.

As on the Intel 286 and Intel386 processors, the MP (monitor coprocessor) flag (bit 1 of register CR0) determines whether the WAIT/FWAIT instructions or waiting-type floating-point instructions trap when the context of the FPU is different from that of the currently-executing task. If the MP and TS flag are set, then a WAIT/FWAIT instruction and waiting instructions will cause a device-not-available exception (interrupt vector 7). The MP flag is used on the Intel 286 and Intel386 processors to support the use of a WAIT/FWAIT instruction to wait on a device other than a math coprocessor. The device reports its status through the BUSY# pin. Since the Pentium Pro, Pentium, and Intel486 processors do not have such a pin, the MP flag has no relevant use and should be set to 1 for normal operation.

10.9.2. FPU Status Word

This section identifies differences to the FPU status word for the different Intel Architecture processors and math coprocessors, the reason for the differences, and their impact on software.

10.9.2.1. CONDITION CODE FLAGS (C0 THROUGH C3)

The following information pertains to differences in the use of the condition code flags (C0 through C3) located in bits 8, 9, 10, and 14 of the FPU status word.

After execution of an FINIT instruction or a hardware reset on a 32-bit Intel Architecture FPU, the condition code flags are set to 0. The same operations on a 16-bit Intel Architecture math coprocessor leave these flags intact (they contain their prior value). This difference in operation has no impact on software and provides a consistent state after reset.

Transcendental instruction results in the core range of the Pentium Pro and Pentium processors (see Section 7.5.10., "Transcendental Instruction Accuracy") may differ from the Intel486 DX processor and Intel487 SX math coprocessor by 2 to 3 units in the last place (ulps). As a result, the value saved in the C1 flag may also differ.

After an incomplete FPREM/FPREM1 instruction, the C0, C1, and C3 flags are set to 0 on the 32-bit Intel Architecture FPUs. After the same operation on a 16-bit Intel Architecture math coprocessor, these flags are left intact.

On the 32-bit Intel Architecture FPUs, the C2 flag serves as an incomplete flag for the FTAN instruction. On the 16-bit Intel Architecture math coprocessors, the C2 flag is undefined for the FPTAN instruction. This difference has no impact on software, because Intel287 or 8087 programs do not check C2 after an FPTAN instruction. The use of this flag on later processors allows fast checking of operand range.

10.9.2.2. STACK FAULT FLAG

When unmasked stack overflow or underflow occurs on a 32-bit Intel Architecture FPU, the IE flag (bit 0) and the SF flag (bit 6) of the FPU status word are set to indicate a stack fault and condition code flag C1 is set or cleared to indicate overflow or underflow, respectively. When unmasked stack overflow or underflow occurs on a 16-bit Intel Architecture math coprocessor, only the IE flag is set. Bit 6 is reserved on these processors. The addition of the SF flag on a 32-bit Intel Architecture FPU has no impact on software. Existing exception handlers need not change, but may be upgraded to take advantage of the additional information.

10.9.3. FPU Control Word

Only affine closure is supported for infinity control on a 32-bit Intel Architecture FPU. The infinity control flag (bit 12 of the FPU control word) remains programmable on these processors, but has no effect. This change was made to conform to IEEE Standard 754. On a 16-bit Intel Architecture math coprocessor, both affine and projective closures are supported, as determined by the setting of bit 12. After a hardware reset, the default value of bit 12 is projective. Software that requires projective infinity arithmetic may give different results.

10.9.4. FPU Tag Word

When loading the tag word of a 32-bit Intel Architecture FPU, using an FLDENV or FRSTOR instruction, the processor examines the incoming tag and classifies the location only as empty or non-empty. Thus, tag values of 00, 01, and 10 are interpreted by the processor to indicate a non-empty location. The tag value of 11 is interpreted by the processor to indicate an empty location. Subsequent operations on a non-empty register always examine the value in the register, not the value in its tag. The FSTENV and FSAVE instructions examine the non-empty registers and put the correct values in the tags before storing the tag word.

The corresponding tag for a 16-bit Intel Architecture math coprocessor is checked before each register access to determine the class of operand in the register; the tag is updated after every change to a register so that the tag always reflects the most recent status of the register. Software can load a tag with a value that disagrees with the contents of a register (for example, the register contains a valid value, but the tag says special). Here, the 16-bit Intel Architecture math coprocessors honor the tag and do not examine the register.

Software written to run on a 16-bit Intel Architecture math coprocessor may not operate correctly on a 16-bit Intel Architecture FPU, if it uses FLDENV or FRSTOR to change tags to values (other than to empty) that are different from actual register contents.

The encoding in the tag word for the 32-bit Intel Architecture FPUs for unsupported data formats (including pseudo-zero and unnormal) is special (10B), to comply with the IEEE Standard 754 standard. The encoding in the 16-bit Intel Architecture math coprocessors for pseudo-zero and unnormal is valid (00B) and the encoding for other unsupported data formats is special (10B). Code that recognizes the pseudo-zero or unnormal format as valid must therefore be changed if it is ported to a 32-bit Intel Architecture FPU.

10.9.5. Data Types

This section discusses the differences of data types for the various Intel Architecture FPUs and math coprocessors.

10.9.5.1.   NANS

The 32-bit Intel Architecture FPUs distinguish between signaling NaNs (SNaNs) and quiet NaNs (QNaNs). These FPUs only generate QNaNs and normally do not generate an exception upon encountering a QNaN. An invalid-operation exception (#I) is generated only upon encountering a SNaN, except for the FCOM, FIST, and FBSTP instructions, which also generates an invalid-operation exceptions for a QNaNs. This behavior matches the IEEE Standard 754.

The 16-bit Intel Architecture math coprocessors only generate one kind of NaN (the equivalent of a QNaN), but the raise an invalid-operation exception upon encountering any kind of NaN.

When porting software written to run on a 16-bit Intel Architecture math coprocessor to a 32-bit Intel Architecture FPU, uninitialized memory locations that contain QNaNs should be changed to SNaNs to cause the FPU or math coprocessor to fault when uninitialized memory locations are referenced.

10.9.5.2.   PSEUDO-ZERO, PSEUDO-NAN, PSEUDO-INFINITY, AND UNNORMAL FORMATS

The 32-bit Intel Architecture FPUs neither generate nor support the pseudo-zero, pseudo-NaN, pseudo-infinity, and unnormal formats. Whenever they encounter them in an arithmetic operation, they raise an invalid-operation exception. The 16-bit Intel Architecture math coprocessors define and support special handling for these formats. Support for these formats was dropped to conform with the IEEE Standard 754.

This change should not impact software ported from 16-bit Intel Architecture math coprocessors to 32-bit Intel Architecture FPUs. The 32-bit Intel Architecture FPUs do not generate these formats, and therefore will not encounter them unless software explicitly loads them in the data registers. The only affect may be in how software handles the tags in the tag word (see Section 10.9.4., "FPU Tag Word").

10.9.6. Floating-Point Exceptions

This section identifies the implementation differences in exception handling for floating-point instructions in the various Intel Architecture FPUs and math coprocessors.

10.9.6.1. DENORMAL OPERAND EXCEPTION (#D)

When the denormal operand exception is masked, the 32-bit Intel Architecture FPUs automatically normalize denormalized numbers when possible; whereas, the 16-bit Intel Architecture math coprocessors return a denormal result. A program written to run on a 16-bit Intel Architecture math coprocessor that uses the denormal exception solely to normalize denormalized operands is redundant when run on the 32-bit Intel Architecture FPUs. If such a program is run on 32-bit Intel Architecture FPUs, performance can be improved by masking the denormal exception. Floating-point programs run faster when the FPU performs normalization of denormalized operands.

The denormal operand exception is not raised for transcendental instructions and the FXTRACT instruction on the 16-bit Intel Architecture math coprocessors. This exception is raised for these instructions on the 32-bit Intel Architecture FPUs. The exception handlers ported to these latter processors need to be changed only if the handlers gives special treatment to different opcodes.

10.9.6.2. NUMERIC OVERFLOW EXCEPTION (#O)

On the 32-bit Intel Architecture FPUs, when the numeric overflow exception is masked and the rounding mode is set to chop (toward 0), the result is the largest positive or smallest negative number. The 16-bit Intel Architecture math coprocessors do not signal the overflow exception when the masked response is not ∞; that is, they signal overflow only when the rounding control is not set to round to 0. If rounding is set to chop (toward 0), the result is positive or negative ∞. Under the most common rounding modes, this difference has no impact on existing software.

If rounding is toward 0 (chop), a program on a 32-bit Intel Architecture FPU produces, under overflow conditions, a result that is different in the least significant bit of the significand, compared to the result on a 16-bit Intel Architecture math coprocessor. The reason for this difference is IEEE Standard 754 compatibility.

When the overflow exception is not masked, the precision exception is flagged on the 32-bit Intel Architecture FPUs. When the result is stored in the stack, the significand is rounded according to the precision control (PC) field of the FPU control word or according to the opcode. On the 16-bit Intel Architecture math coprocessors, the precision exception is not flagged and the significand is not rounded. The impact on existing software is that if the result is stored on the stack, a program running on a 32-bit Intel Architecture FPU produces a different result under overflow conditions than on a 16-bit Intel Architecture math coprocessor. The difference is apparent only to the exception handler. This difference is for IEEE Standard 754 compatibility.

10.9.6.3. NUMERIC UNDERFLOW EXCEPTION (#U)

When the underflow exception is masked on the 32-bit Intel Architecture FPUs, the underflow exception is signaled when both the result is tiny and denormalization results in a loss of accuracy. When the underflow exception is unmasked and the instruction is supposed to store the result on the stack, the significand is rounded to the appropriate precision (according to the PC flag in the FPU control word, for those instructions controlled by PC, otherwise to extended precision), after adjusting the exponent.

When the underflow exception is masked on the 16-bit Intel Architecture math coprocessors and rounding is toward 0, the underflow exception flag is raised on a tiny result, regardless of loss of accuracy. When the underflow exception is not masked and the destination is the stack, the significand is not rounded, but instead is left as is.

When the underflow exception is masked, this difference has no impact on existing software. The underflow exception occurs less often when rounding is toward 0.

When the underflow exception not masked. A program running on a 32-bit Intel Architecture FPU produces a different result during underflow conditions than on a 16-bit Intel Architecture math coprocessor if the result is stored on the stack. The difference is only in the least significant bit of the significand and is apparent only to the exception handler.

10.9.6.4. EXCEPTION PRECEDENCE

There is no difference in the precedence of the denormal-operand exception on the 32-bit Intel Architecture FPUs, whether it be masked or not. When the denormal-operand exception is not masked on the 16-bit Intel Architecture math coprocessors, it takes precedence over all other exceptions. This difference causes no impact on existing software, but some unneeded normalization of denormalized operands is prevented on the Intel486 processor and Intel387 math coprocessor.

10.9.6.5. CS AND EIP FOR FPU EXCEPTIONS

On the Intel 32-bit Intel Architecture FPUs, the values from the CS and EIP registers saved for floating-point exceptions point to any prefixes that come before the floating-point instruction. On the 8087 math coprocessor, the saved CS and IP registers points to the floating-point instruction.

10.9.6.6. FPU ERROR SIGNALS

The floating-point error signals to the Pentium Pro, Pentium, and Intel486 processors do not pass through an interrupt controller; an INT# signal from an Intel387, Intel287 or 8087 math coprocessors does. If an 8086 processor uses another exception for the 8087 interrupt, both exception vectors should call the floating-point-error exception handler. Some instructions in a floating-point-error exception handler may need to be deleted if they use the interrupt controller. The Pentium Pro, Pentium, and Intel486 processors have signals that, with the addition of external logic, support reporting for emulation of the interrupt mechanism used in many personal computers.

On the Pentium Pro, Pentium, and Intel486 processors, an undefined floating-point opcode will cause an invalid-opcode exception (#UD, interrupt vector 6). Undefined floating-point opcodes, like legal floating-point opcodes, cause a device not available exception (#NM, interrupt vector 7) when either the TS or EM flag in control register CR0 is set. The Pentium Pro, Pentium, and Intel486 processors do not check for floating-point error conditions on encountering an undefined floating-point opcode.

10.9.6.7.   ASSERTION OF THE FERR# PIN

When using this external interrupt mechanism, the FERR# pin must be connected to an input to an external interrupt controller. An external interrupt is then generated when the FERR# output drives the input to the interrupt controller. For the Pentium Pro and Intel386 processors, an unmasked floating-point exception always causes the FERR# pin to be asserted upon completion of the instruction that caused the exception; for the Pentium and Intel486 processors, an unmasked floating-point exception always causes the FERR# pin to be asserted prior to executing the next waiting floating-point instruction. See Section 7.7.3., "Software Exception Handling" for more information on the use of the FERR# pin.

10.9.6.8.   INVALID OPERATION EXCEPTION ON DENORMALS

An invalid-operation exception is not generated on the 32-bit Intel Architecture FPUs upon encountering a denormal value when executing a FSQRT, FDIV, or FPREM instruction or upon conversion to BCD or to integer. The operation proceeds by first normalizing the value. On the 16-bit Intel Architecture math coprocessors, upon encountering this situation, the invalid-operation exception is generated. This difference has no impact on existing software. Software running on the 32-bit Intel Architecture FPUs continues to execute in cases where the 16-bit Intel Architecture math coprocessors trap. The reason for this change was to eliminate an exception from being raised.

10.9.6.9.   ALIGNMENT CHECK EXCEPTIONS (#AC)

If alignment checking is enabled, a misaligned data operand on the Pentium Pro, Pentium, and Intel486 processors causes an alignment check exception (#AC) when a program or procedure is running at privilege-level 3, except for the stack portion of the FSAVE/FNSAVE and FRSTOR instructions.

10.9.6.10.   SEGMENT NOT PRESENT EXCEPTION DURING FLDENV

On the Intel486 processor, when a segment not present exception (#NP) occurs in the middle of an FLDENV instruction, it can happen that part of the environment is loaded and part not. In such cases, the FPU control word is left with a value of 007FH. The Pentium Pro and Pentium processors ensures the internal state is correct at all times by attempting to read the first and last bytes of the environment before updating the internal state.

10.9.6.11.   DEVICE NOT AVAILABLE EXCEPTION (#NM)

The device-not-available exception (#NM, interrupt 7) will occur in the Pentium Pro, Pentium, and Intel486 processors when they encounter a floating-point instruction while either the TS or EM flag in control register CR0 is set. If the TS and MP flags are set, then a WAIT/FWAIT instruction will also cause a device-not-available exception. An exception handler should be included in Pentium Pro, Pentium, or Intel486 processor code to handle these situations.

10.9.6.12.   COPROCESSOR SEGMENT OVERRUN EXCEPTION

The coprocessor segment overrun exception (interrupt 9) does not occur in the Pentium Pro, Pentium, and Intel486 processors. In situations where the Intel387 math coprocessor would cause an interrupt 9, the Pentium Pro, Pentium, and Intel486 processors simply abort the instruction. To avoid undetected segment overruns, it is recommended that the floating-point save area be placed in the same page as the TSS. This placement will prevent the FPU environment from being lost is a page fault occurs during the execution of an FLDENV or FRSTOR instruction while the operating system is performing a task switch.

10.9.6.13.   GENERAL PROTECTION EXCEPTION (#GP)

A general-protection exception (#GP, interrupt 13) occurs if the starting address of a floating-point operand falls outside a segment's size. An exception handler should be included to report these programming errors.

10.9.6.14.   FLOATING-POINT ERROR EXCEPTION (#MF)

In real mode and protected mode (not including virtual 8086 mode), interrupt vector 16 must point to the floating-point exception handler. In virtual 8086 mode, the virtual-8086 monitor can be programmed to accommodate a different location of the interrupt vector for floating-point exceptions.

10.9.7.   Changes to Floating-Point Instructions

This section identifies the differences in floating-point instructions for the various Intel FPU and math coprocessor architectures, the reason for the differences, and their impact on software.

10.9.7.1.   NEW FLOATING-POINT INSTRUCTIONS IN THE INTEL PENTIUM® PRO PROCESSOR

The following floating-point instructions are new in the Pentium Pro processor:

- FCMOV*cc* (floating-point conditional move) instructions, see Chapter 11, "FCMOVcc—Floating-Point Conditional Move".

- FCOMI (floating-point compare and set EFLAGS) instructions, see Chapter 11, "FCOM/FCOMP/FCOMPP—Compare Real".

10.9.7.2. FDIV, FPREM, AND FSQRT INSTRUCTIONS

The 32-bit Intel Architecture FPUs support operations on denormalized operands and, when detected, an underflow exception can occur, for compatibility with the IEEE Standard 754. The 16-bit Intel Architecture math coprocessors do not operate on denormalized operands or return underflow results. Instead, they generate an invalid-operation exception when they detect an underflow condition. An existing underflow exception handler will require change only if it gives different treatment to different opcodes. Also, it is possible that fewer invalid-operation exceptions will occur.

10.9.7.3. FSCALE INSTRUCTION

With the 32-bit Intel Architecture FPUs, the range of the scaling operand is not restricted. If $(0 < | ST(1) < 1)$, the scaling factor is 0; therefore, $ST(0)$ remains unchanged. If the rounded result is not exact or if there was a loss of accuracy (masked underflow), the precision exception is signaled. With the 16-bit Intel Architecture math coprocessors, the range of the scaling operand is restricted. If $(0 < | ST(1) | < 1)$, the result is undefined and no exception is signaled. The impact of this difference on exiting software is that different results are delivered on the 32-bit and 16-bit FPUs and math coprocessors when $(0 < | ST(1) | < 1)$.

10.9.7.4. FPREM1 INSTRUCTION

The 32-bit Intel Architecture FPUs compute a partial remainder according to the IEEE Standard 754 standard. This instruction does not exist on the 16-bit Intel Architecture math coprocessors. The availability of the FPREM1 instruction has is no impact on existing software.

10.9.7.5. FPREM INSTRUCTION

On the 32-bit Intel Architecture FPUs, the condition code flags C0, C3, C1 in the status word correctly reflect the three low-order bits of the quotient following execution of the FPREM instruction. On the 16-bit Intel Architecture math coprocessors, the quotient bits are incorrect when performing a reduction of $(64^N + M)$ when $(N \geq 1)$ and M is 1 or 2. This difference does not affect existing software; software that works around the bug should not be affected.

10.9.7.6. FUCOM, FUCOMP, AND FUCOMPP INSTRUCTIONS

When executing the FUCOM, FUCOMP, and FUCOMPP instructions, the 32-bit Intel Architecture FPUs perform unordered compare according to IEEE Standard 754 standard. These instructions do not exist on the 16-bit Intel Architecture math coprocessors. The availability of these new instructions has no impact on existing software.

10.9.7.7. FPTAN INSTRUCTION

On the 32-bit Intel Architecture FPUs, the range of the operand for the FPTAN instruction is much less restricted $(| ST(0) | < 2^{63})$ than on earlier math coprocessors. The instruction reduces the operand internally using an internal $\pi/4$ constant that is more accurate. The range of the operand is restricted to ($| ST(0) | < \pi/4$) on the 16-bit Intel Architecture math coprocessors; the operand must be reduced to this range using FPREM. This change has no impact on existing software.

10.9.7.8.   STACK OVERFLOW

On the 32-bit Intel Architecture FPUs, if a stack overflow occurs when the invalid-operation exception is masked, both the ST(0) and ST(1) registers will contain QNaNs. On the 16-bit Intel Architecture math coprocessors, the original operand remains unchanged following a stack overflow, but it is loaded into register ST(1). This difference has no impact on existing software.

10.9.7.9.   FSIN, FCOS, AND FSINCOS INSTRUCTIONS

On the 32-bit Intel Architecture FPUs, these instructions perform three common trigonometric functions. These instructions do not exist on the 16-bit Intel Architecture math coprocessors. The availability of these instructions has no impact on existing software, but using them provides a performance upgrade.

10.9.7.10.   FPATAN INSTRUCTION

On the 32-bit Intel Architecture FPUs, the range of operands for the FPATAN instruction is unrestricted. On the 16-bit Intel Architecture math coprocessors, the absolute value of the operand in register ST(0) must be smaller than the absolute value of the operand in register ST(1). This difference has impact on existing software.

10.9.7.11.   F2XM1 INSTRUCTION

The 32-bit Intel Architecture FPUs support a wider range of operands ($-1 < ST(0) < +1$) for the F2XM1 instruction. The supported operand range for the 16-bit Intel Architecture math coprocessors is ($0 \leq ST(0) \leq 0.5$). This difference has no impact on existing software.

10.9.7.12.   FLD INSTRUCTION

On the 32-bit Intel Architecture FPUs, when using the FLD instruction to load an extended-real value, a denormal-operand exception is not generated because the instruction is not arithmetic. The 16-bit Intel Architecture math coprocessors do report a denormal-operand exception in this situation. This difference does not affect existing software.

On the 32-bit Intel Architecture FPUs, loading a denormal value that is in single- or double-real format causes the value to be converted to extended-real format. Loading a denormal value on the 16-bit Intel Architecture math coprocessors causes the value to be converted to an unnormal. If the next instruction is FXTRACT or FXAM, the 32-bit Intel Architecture FPUs will give a different result than the 16-bit Intel Architecture math coprocessors. This change was made for IEEE Standard 754 compatibility.

On the 32-bit Intel Architecture FPUs, loading an SNaN that is in single- or double-real format causes the FPU to generate an invalid-operation exception. The 16-bit Intel Architecture math coprocessors do not raise an exception when loading a signaling NaN. The invalid-operation exception handler for 16-bit math coprocessor software needs to be updated to handle this condition when porting software to 32-bit FPUs. This change was made for IEEE Standard 754 compatibility.

10.9.7.13. FXTRACT INSTRUCTION

On the 32-bit Intel Architecture FPUs, if the operand is 0 for the FXTRACT instruction, the divide-by-zero exception is reported and $-\infty$ is delivered to register ST(1). If the operand is $+\infty$, no exception is reported. If the operand is 0 on the 16-bit Intel Architecture math coprocessors, 0 is delivered to register ST(1) and no exception is reported. If the operand is $+\infty$, the invalid-operation exception is reported. These differences have no impact on existing software. Software usually bypasses 0 and ∞. This change is due to the IEEE 754 recommendation to fully support the "logb" function.

10.9.7.14. LOAD CONSTANT INSTRUCTIONS

On 32-bit Intel Architecture FPUs, rounding control is in effect for the load constant instructions. Rounding control is not in effect for the 16-bit Intel Architecture math coprocessors. Results for the FLDPI, FLDLN2, FLDLG2, and FLDL2E instructions are the same as for the 16-bit Intel Architecture math coprocessors when rounding control is set to round to nearest or round to $+\infty$. They are the same for the FLDL2T instruction when rounding control is set to round to nearest, round to $-\infty$, or round to zero. Results are different from the 16-bit Intel Architecture math coprocessors in the least significant bit of the mantissa if rounding control is set to round to $-\infty$ or round to 0 for the FLDPI, FLDLN2, FLDLG2, and FLDL2E instructions; they are different for the FLDL2T instruction if round to $+\infty$ is specified. These changes were implemented for compatibility with IEEE 754 recommendations.

10.9.7.15. FSETPM INSTRUCTION

With the 32-bit Intel Architecture FPUs, the FSETPM instruction is treated as FNOP (no operation). This instruction informs the Intel287 math coprocessor that the processor is in protected mode. This change has no impact on existing software. The 32-bit Intel Architecture FPUs handle all addressing and exception-pointer information, whether in protected mode or not.

10.9.7.16. FXAM INSTRUCTION

With the 32-bit Intel Architecture FPUs, if the FPU encounters an empty register when executing the FXAM instruction, it not generate combinations of C0 through C3 equal to 1101 or 1111. The 16-bit Intel Architecture math coprocessors may generate these combinations, among others. This difference has no impact on existing software; it provides a performance upgrade to provide repeatable results.

10.9.7.17. FSAVE AND FSTENV INSTRUCTIONS

With the 32-bit Intel Architecture FPUs, the address of a memory operand pointer stored by FSAVE or FSTENV is undefined if the previous floating-point instruction did not refer to memory

10.9.8. Transcendental Instructions

The floating-point results of the Pentium Pro and Pentium processors for transcendental instructions in the core range may differ from the Intel486 processors by about 2 or 3 ulps (see Section 7.5.10., "Transcendental Instruction Accuracy"). Condition code flag C1 of the status word may differ as a result. The exact threshold for underflow and overflow will vary by a few ulps. The Pentium Pro and Pentium processor's results will have a worst case error of less than 1 ulp when rounding to the nearest-even and less than 1.5 ulps when rounding in other modes. The transcendental instructions are guaranteed to be monotonic, with respect to the input operands, throughout the domain supported by the instruction.

Transcendental instructions may generate different results in the round-up flag (C1) on the 32-bit Intel Architecture FPUs. The round-up flag is undefined for these instructions on the 16-bit Intel Architecture math coprocessors. This difference has no impact on existing software.

10.9.9. Obsolete Instructions

The 8087 math coprocessor instructions FENI and FDISI and the Intel287 math coprocessor instruction FSETPM are treated as integer NOP instructions in the 32-bit Intel Architecture FPUs. If these opcodes are detected in the instruction stream, no specific operation is performed and no internal states are affected.

10.9.10. WAIT/FWAIT Prefix Differences

On the Intel486 processor, when a WAIT/FWAIT instruction precedes a floating-point instruction (one which itself automatically synchronizes with the previous floating-point instruction), the WAIT/FWAIT instruction is treated as a no-op. Pending floating-point exceptions from a previous floating-point instruction are processed not on the WAIT/FWAIT instruction but on the floating-point instruction following the WAIT/FWAIT instruction. In such a case, the report of a floating-point exception may appear one instruction later on the Intel486 processor than on a Pentium Pro or Pentium FPU, or on Intel387 math coprocessor.

10.9.11. Operands Split Across Segments and/or Pages

On the Pentium Pro, Pentium, and Intel486 processor FPUs, when the first half of an operand to be written is inside a page or segment and the second half is outside, a memory fault can cause the first half to be stored but not the second half. In this situation, the Intel387 math coprocessor stores nothing.

10.9.12. FPU Instruction Synchronization

On the 32-bit Intel Architecture FPUs, all floating-point instructions are automatically synchronized; that is, the processor automatically waits until the previous floating-point instruction has completed before completing the next floating-point instruction. No explicit WAIT/FWAIT instructions are required to assure this synchronization. For the 8087 math coprocessors, explicit waits are required before each floating-point instruction to ensure synchronization. Although 8087 programs having explicit WAIT instructions execute perfectly on the 32-bit Intel Architecture processors without reassembly, these WAIT instructions are unnecessary.

Since the 32-bit Intel Architecture FPU's do not require WAIT/FWAIT instructions before each floating-point instruction, 32-bit Intel Architecture assemblers do not automatically generate these WAIT instructions. The ASM86 assembler, however, automatically precedes every floating-point instruction with a WAIT instruction. Although floating-point routines generated using the ASM86 assembler will generally execute correctly on the 32-bit Intel Architecture FPU's, reassembly using a 32-bit Intel Architecture assembler may result in a more compact code image and faster execution. The control instructions for the 32-bit Intel Architecture FPU's can be coded using either a wait or non-wait form of the mnemonic. The wait forms of these instructions cause a 32-bit Intel Architecture assembler to precede the floating-point instruction with a WAIT instruction, in the identical manner as does ASM86.

intel

11

Instruction Set Reference

CHAPTER 11
INSTRUCTION SET REFERENCE

This chapter describes the complete Pentium Pro processor instruction set, including the integer, floating-point, and system instructions. The instruction descriptions are arranged in alphabetical order. For each instruction, the forms are given for each operand combination, including the opcode, operands required, and a description. Also given for each instruction are a description of the instruction and its operands, an operational description, a description of the effect of the instructions on flags in the EFLAGS register, and a summary of the exceptions that can be generated.

The following sections describe the instruction format for all Intel Architecture processors and a description of the information contained in the various sections of the instruction descriptions.

11.1. INSTRUCTION FORMAT

All instruction encodings are subsets of the general instruction format shown in Figure 11-1. Instructions consist of optional instruction prefixes (in any order), one or two primary opcode bytes, an addressing-form specifier (if required) consisting of the ModR/M byte and the SIB (Scale-Index-Base) byte, a displacement (if required), and an immediate data field (if required).

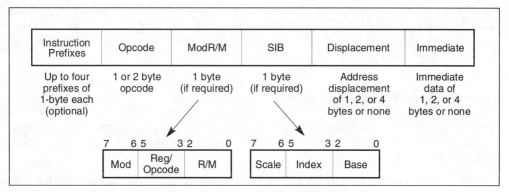

Figure 11-1. Instruction Format

11.1.1. Instruction Prefixes

The instruction prefixes are divided into four groups, each with a set of allowable prefix codes:

- Lock and repeat prefixes.
    - F0H—LOCK prefix.
    - F2H—REPNE/REPNZ prefix (used only with string instructions).

— F3H—REP prefix (used only with string instructions).

— F3H—REPE/REPZ prefix (used only with string instructions).

- Segment override.

  — 2EH—CS segment override prefix.

  — 36H—SS segment override prefix.

  — 3EH—DS segment override prefix.

  — 26H—ES segment override prefix.

  — 64H—FS segment override prefix.

  — 65H—GS segment override prefix.

- Operand-size override, 66H

- Address-size override, 67H

For each instruction, one prefix may be used from each of these groups and be placed in any order. The effect of redundant prefixes (more than one prefix from a group) is undefined and may vary from processor to processor.

11.1.2. Opcode

The primary opcode is either 1 or 2 bytes. An additional 3-bit opcode field is sometimes encoded in the ModR/M byte. Smaller encoding fields can be defined within the primary opcode. These fields define the direction of the operation, the size of displacements, the register encoding, condition codes, or sign extension. The encoding of fields in the opcode varies, depending on the class of operation.

11.1.3. ModR/M and SIB Bytes

Most instructions that refer to an operand in memory have an addressing-form specifier byte (called the ModR/M byte) following the primary opcode. The ModR/M byte contains three fields of information:

- The *mod* field combines with the r/m field to form 32 possible values: eight registers and 24 addressing modes.

- The *reg/opcode* field specifies either a register number or three more bits of opcode information. The purpose of the reg/opcode field is specified in the first byte of the primary opcode.

- The *r/m* field can specify a register as an operand or can be combined with the mod field to encode an addressing mode.

Certain encodings of the ModR/M byte require a second addressing byte, the SIB byte, to fully specify the addressing form. The base-plus-index and scale-plus-index forms of 32-bit addressing require the SIB byte. The SIB byte includes the following fields:

- The *scale* field specifies the scale factor.

- The *index* field specifies the register number of the index register.

- The *base* field specifies the register number of the base register.

The values and the corresponding addressing forms of the ModR/M and SIB bytes are shown in Table 11-1 through Table 11-3. The 16-bit addressing forms specified by the ModR/M byte are in Table 11-1. The 32-bit addressing forms specified by the ModR/M byte are in Table 11-2. Table 11-3 shows the 32-bit addressing forms specified by the SIB byte.

11.1.4. Displacement and Immediate Bytes

Some addressing forms include a displacement immediately following either the ModR/M or SIB byte. If a displacement is required, it can be 1, 2, or 4 bytes.

If the instruction specifies an immediate operand, the operand always follows any displacement bytes. An immediate operand can be 1, 2 or 4 bytes.

Table 11-1. 16-Bit Addressing Forms with the ModR/M Byte

r8(/r)			AL	CL	DL	BL	AH	CH	DH	BH
r16(/r)			AX	CX	DX	BX	SP	BP[1]	SI	DI
r32(/r)			EAX	ECX	EDX	EBX	ESP	EBP	ESI	EDI
/digit (Opcode)			0	1	2	3	4	5	6	7
REG =			000	001	010	011	100	101	110	111
Effective Address	**Mod**	**R/M**	\multicolumn{8}{c}{**ModR/M Values in Hexadecimal**}
[BX+SI]	00	000	00	08	10	18	20	28	30	38
[BX+DI]		001	01	09	11	19	21	29	31	39
[BP+SI]		010	02	0A	12	1A	22	2A	32	3A
[BP+DI]		011	03	0B	13	1B	23	2B	33	3B
[SI]		100	04	0C	14	1C	24	2C	34	3C
[DI]		101	05	0D	15	1D	25	2D	35	3D
disp16[2]		110	06	0E	16	1E	26	2E	36	3E
[BX]		111	07	0F	17	1F	27	2F	37	3F
[BX+SI]+disp8[3]	01	000	40	48	50	58	60	68	70	78
[BX+DI]+disp8		001	41	49	51	59	61	69	71	79
[BP+SI]+disp8		010	42	4A	52	5A	62	6A	72	7A
[BP+DI]+disp8		011	43	4B	53	5B	63	6B	73	7B
[SI]+disp8		100	44	4C	54	5C	64	6C	74	7C
[DI]+disp8		101	45	4D	55	5D	65	6D	75	7D
[BP]+disp8		110	46	4E	56	5E	66	6E	76	7E
[BX]+disp8		111	47	4F	57	5F	67	6F	77	7F
[BX+SI]+disp16	10	000	80	88	90	98	A0	A8	B0	B8
[BX+DI]+disp16		001	81	89	91	99	A1	A9	B1	B9
[BP+SI]+disp16		010	82	8A	92	9A	A2	AA	B2	BA
[BP+DI]+disp16		011	83	8B	93	9B	A3	AB	B3	BB
[SI]+disp16		100	84	8C	94	9C	A4	AC	B4	BC
[DI]+disp16		101	85	8D	95	9D	A5	AD	B5	BD
[BP]+disp16		110	86	8E	96	9E	A6	AE	B6	BE
[BX]+disp16		111	87	8F	97	9F	A7	AF	B7	BF
EAX/AX/AL	11	000	C0	C8	D0	D8	E0	E8	F0	F8
ECX/CX/CL		001	C1	C9	D1	D9	EQ	E9	F1	F9
EDX/DX/DL		010	C2	CA	D2	DA	E2	EA	F2	FA
EBX/BX/BL		011	C3	CB	D3	DB	E3	EB	F3	FB
ESP/SP/AH		100	C4	CC	D4	DC	E4	EC	F4	FC
EBP/BP/CH		101	C5	CD	D5	DD	E5	ED	F5	FD
ESI/SI/DH		110	C6	CE	D6	DE	E6	EE	F6	FE
EDI/DI/BH		111	C7	CF	D7	DF	E7	EF	F7	FF

NOTES:

1. The default segment register is SS for the effective addresses containing a BP index, DS for other effective addresses.

2. The "disp16" nomenclature denotes a 16-bit displacement following the ModR/M byte, to be added to the index.

3. The "disp8" nomenclature denotes an 8-bit displacement following the ModR/M byte, to be sign-extended and added to the index.

Table 11-2. 32-Bit Addressing Forms with the ModR/M Byte

r8(/r)			AL	CL	DL	BL	AH	CH	DH	BH
r16(/r)			AX	CX	DX	BX	SP	BP	SI	DI
r32(/r)			EAX	ECX	EDX	EBX	ESP	EBP	ESI	EDI
/digit (Opcode)			0	1	2	3	4	5	6	7
REG =			000	001	010	011	100	101	110	111
Effective Address	Mod	R/M	ModR/M Values in Hexadecimal							
[EAX]	00	000	00	08	10	18	20	28	30	38
[ECX]		001	01	09	11	19	21	29	31	39
[EDX]		010	02	0A	12	1A	22	2A	32	3A
[EBX]		011	03	0B	13	1B	23	2B	33	3B
[--][--][1]		100	04	0C	14	1C	24	2C	34	3C
disp32[2]		101	05	0D	15	1D	25	2D	35	3D
[ESI]		110	06	0E	16	1E	26	2E	36	3E
[EDI]		111	07	0F	17	1F	27	2F	37	3F
disp8[EAX][3]	01	000	40	48	50	58	60	68	70	78
disp8[ECX]		001	41	49	51	59	61	69	71	79
disp8[EDX]		010	42	4A	52	5A	62	6A	72	7A
disp8[EBX];		011	43	4B	53	5B	63	6B	73	7B
disp8[--][--]		100	44	4C	54	5C	64	6C	74	7C
disp8[EBP]		101	45	4D	55	5D	65	6D	75	7D
disp8[ESI]		110	46	4E	56	5E	66	6E	76	7E
disp8[EDI]		111	47	4F	57	5F	67	6F	77	7F
disp32[EAX]	10	000	80	88	90	98	A0	A8	B0	B8
disp32[ECX]		001	81	89	91	99	A1	A9	B1	B9
disp32[EDX]		010	82	8A	92	9A	A2	AA	B2	BA
disp32[EBX]		011	83	8B	93	9B	A3	AB	B3	BB
disp32[--][--]		100	84	8C	94	9C	A4	AC	B4	BC
disp32[EBP]		101	85	8D	95	9D	A5	AD	B5	BD
disp32[ESI]		110	86	8E	96	9E	A6	AE	B6	BE
disp32[EDI]		111	87	8F	97	9F	A7	AF	B7	BF
EAX/AX/AL	11	000	C0	C8	D0	D8	E0	E8	F0	F8
ECX/CX/CL		001	C1	C9	D1	D9	E1	E9	F1	F9
EDX/DX/DL		010	C2	CA	D2	DA	E2	EA	F2	FA
EBX/BX/BL		011	C3	CB	D3	DB	E3	EB	F3	FB
ESP/SP/AH		100	C4	CC	D4	DC	E4	EC	F4	FC
EBP/BP/CH		101	C5	CD	D5	DD	E5	ED	F5	FD
ESI/SI/DH		110	C6	CE	D6	DE	E6	EE	F6	FE
EDI/DI/BH		111	C7	CF	D7	DF	E7	EF	F7	FF

NOTES:

1. The [--][--] nomenclature means a SIB follows the ModR/M byte.

2. The disp32 nomenclature denotes a 32-bit displacement following the SIB byte, to be added to the index.

3. The disp8 nomenclature denotes an 8-bit displacement following the SIB byte, to be sign-extended and added to the index.

Table 11-3. 32-Bit Addressing Forms with the SIB Byte

r32 Base = Base =			EAX 0 000	ECX 1 001	EDX 2 010	EBX 3 011	ESP 4 100	[*] 5 101	ESI 6 110	EDI 7 111
Scaled Index	SS	Index	SIB Values in Hexadecimal							
[EAX]	00	000	00	01	02	03	04	05	06	07
[ECX]		001	08	09	0A	0B	0C	0D	0E	0F
[EDX]		010	10	11	12	13	14	15	16	17
[EBX]		011	18	19	1A	1B	1C	1D	1E	1F
none		100	20	21	22	23	24	25	26	27
[EBP]		101	28	29	2A	2B	2C	2D	2E	2F
[ESI]		110	30	31	32	33	34	35	36	37
[EDI]		111	38	39	3A	3B	3C	3D	3E	3F
[EAX*2]	01	000	40	41	42	43	44	45	46	47
[ECX*2]		001	48	49	4A	4B	4C	4D	4E	4F
[ECX*2]		010	50	51	52	53	54	55	56	57
[EBX*2]		011	58	59	5A	5B	5C	5D	5E	5F
none		100	60	61	62	63	64	65	66	67
[EBP*2]		101	68	69	6A	6B	6C	6D	6E	6F
[ESI*2]		110	70	71	72	73	74	75	76	77
[EDI*2]		111	78	79	7A	7B	7C	7D	7E	7F
[EAX*4]	10	000	80	81	82	83	84	85	86	87
[ECX*4]		001	88	89	8A	8B	8C	8D	8E	8F
[EDX*4]		010	90	91	92	93	94	95	96	97
[EBX*4]		011	98	89	9A	9B	9C	9D	9E	9F
none		100	A0	A1	A2	A3	A4	A5	A6	A7
[EBP*4]		101	A8	A9	AA	AB	AC	AD	AE	AF
[ESI*4]		110	B0	B1	B2	B3	B4	B5	B6	B7
[EDI*4]		111	B8	B9	BA	BB	BC	BD	BE	BF
[EAX*8]	11	000	C0	C1	C2	C3	C4	C5	C6	C7
[ECX*8]		001	C8	C9	CA	CB	CC	CD	CE	CF
[EDX*8]		010	D0	D1	D2	D3	D4	D5	D6	D7
[EBX*8]		011	D8	D9	DA	DB	DC	DD	DE	DF
none		100	E0	E1	E2	E3	E4	E5	E6	E7
[EBP*8]		101	E8	E9	EA	EB	EC	ED	EE	EF
[ESI*8]		110	F0	F1	F2	F3	F4	F5	F6	F7
[EDI*8]		111	F8	F9	FA	FB	FC	FD	FE	FF

NOTE:

1. The [*] nomenclature means a disp32 with no base if MOD is 00, [EBP] otherwise. This provides the following addressing modes:

    disp32[index]   (MOD=00).
    disp8[EBP][index]   (MOD=01).
    disp32[EBP][index]   (MOD=10).

11.2. INTERPRETING THE INSTRUCTION REFERENCE PAGES

This section describes the information contained in the various sections of the instruction reference pages that make up the majority of this chapter. It also explains the notational conventions and abbreviations used in these sections.

11.2.1. Instruction Format

The following is an example of the format used for each processor instruction description in this chapter:

CMC—Complement Carry Flag

Opcode	Instruction	Description
F5	CMC	Complement carry flag

11.2.1.1. OPCODE COLUMN

The "Opcode" column gives the complete object code produced for each form of the instruction. When possible, the codes are given as hexadecimal bytes, in the same order in which they appear in memory. Definitions of entries other than hexadecimal bytes are as follows:

- **/digit**—A digit between 0 and 7 indicates that the ModR/M byte of the instruction uses only the r/m (register or memory) operand. The reg field contains the digit that provides an extension to the instruction's opcode.

- **/r**—Indicates that the ModR/M byte of the instruction contains both a register operand and an r/m operand.

- **cb, cw, cd, cp**—A 1-byte (cb), 2-byte (cw), 4-byte (cd), or 6-byte (cp) value following the opcode that is used to specify a code offset and possibly a new value for the code segment register.

- **ib, iw, id**—A 1-byte (ib), 2-byte (iw), or 4-byte (id) immediate operand to the instruction that follows the opcode, ModR/M bytes or scale-indexing bytes. The opcode determines if the operand is a signed value. All words and doublewords are given with the low-order byte first.

- **+rb, +rw, +rd**—A register code, from 0 through 7, added to the hexadecimal byte given at the left of the plus sign to form a single opcode byte. The register codes are given in Table 11-4.

- **+i**—A number used in floating-point instructions when one of the operands is ST(i) from the FPU register stack. The number i (which can range from 0 to 7) is added to the hexadecimal byte given at the left of the plus sign to form a single opcode byte.

Table 11-4. Register Encodings Associates With the +rb, +rw, and +rd Nomenclature

rb			rw			rd		
AL	=	0	AX	=	0	EAX	=	0
CL	=	1	CX	=	1	ECX	=	1
DL	=	2	DX	=	2	EDX	=	2
BL	=	3	BX	=	3	EBX	=	3
rb			rw			rd		
AH	=	4	SP	=	4	ESP	=	4
CH	=	5	BP	=	5	EBP	=	5
DH	=	6	SI	=	6	ESI	=	6
BH	=	7	DI	=	7	EDI	=	7

11.2.1.2. INSTRUCTION COLUMN

The "Instruction" column gives the syntax of the instruction statement as it would appear in an ASM386 program. The following is a list of the symbols used to represent operands in the instruction statements:

- **rel8**—A relative address in the range from 128 bytes before the end of the instruction to 127 bytes after the end of the instruction.

- **rel16 and rel32**—A relative address within the same code segment as the instruction assembled. The rel16 symbol applies to instructions with an operand-size attribute of 16 bits; the rel32 symbol applies to instructions with an operand-size attribute of 32 bits.

- **ptr16:16 and ptr16:32**—A far pointer, typically in a code segment different from that of the instruction. The notation *16:16* indicates that the value of the pointer has two parts. The value to the left of the colon is a 16-bit selector or value destined for the code segment register. The value to the right corresponds to the offset within the destination segment. The ptr16:16 symbol is used when the instruction's operand-size attribute is 16 bits; the ptr16:32 symbol is used with the 32-bit attribute.

- **r8**—One of the byte registers AL, CL, DL, BL, AH, CH, DH, or BH.

- **r16**—One of the word registers AX, CX, DX, BX, SP, BP, SI, or DI.

- **r32**—One of the doubleword registers EAX, ECX, EDX, EBX, ESP, EBP, ESI, or EDI.

- **imm8**—An immediate byte value. The imm8 symbol is a signed number between –128 and +127 inclusive. For instructions in which imm8 is combined with a word or doubleword operand, the immediate value is sign-extended to form a word or doubleword. The upper byte of the word is filled with the topmost bit of the immediate value.

- **imm16**—An immediate word value used for instructions whose operand-size attribute is 16 bits. This is a number between –32,768 and +32,767 inclusive.

- **imm32**—An immediate doubleword value used for instructions whose operand-size attribute is 32 bits. It allows the use of a number between +2,147,483,647 and –2,147,483,648 inclusive.

- **r/m8**—A byte operand that is either the contents of a byte register (AL, BL, CL, DL, AH, BH, CH, and DH), or a byte from memory.

- **r/m16**—A word register or memory operand used for instructions whose operand-size attribute is 16 bits. The word registers are: AX, BX, CX, DX, SP, BP, SI, and DI. The contents of memory are found at the address provided by the effective address computation.

- **r/m32**—A doubleword register or memory operand used for instructions whose operand-size attribute is 32 bits. The doubleword registers are: EAX, EBX, ECX, EDX, ESP, EBP, ESI, and EDI. The contents of memory are found at the address provided by the effective address computation.

- **m**—A 16- or 32-bit memory operand.

- **m8**—A memory byte addressed by DS:[E]SI or ES:[E]DI (used only by string instructions).

- **m16**—A memory word addressed by DS:[E]SI or ES:[E]DI (used only by string instructions).

- **m32**—A memory doubleword addressed by DS:[E]SI or ES:[E]DI (used only by string instructions).

- **m64**—A memory quadword (used only by the CMPXCHG8B instruction).

- **m16:16, m16:32**—A memory operand containing a far pointer composed of two numbers. The number to the left of the colon corresponds to the pointer's segment selector. The number to the right corresponds to its offset.

- **m16&32, m16&16, m32&32**—A memory operand consisting of data item pairs whose sizes are indicated on the left and the right side of the ampersand. All memory addressing modes are allowed. The m16&16 and m32&32 operands are used by the BOUND instruction to provide an operand containing an upper and lower bounds for array indices. The m16&32 operand is used by LIDT and LGDT to provide a word with which to load the limit field, and a doubleword with which to load the base field of the corresponding GDTR and IDTR registers.

- **moffs8, moffs16, moffs32**—A simple memory variable (memory offset) of type BYTE, WORD, or DWORD used by some variants of the MOV instruction. The actual address is given by a simple offset relative to the segment base. No ModR/M byte is used in the instruction. The number shown with moffs indicates its size, which is determined by the address-size attribute of the instruction.

- **Sreg**—A segment register. The segment register bit assignments are ES=0, CS=1, SS=2, DS=3, FS=4, and GS=5.

- **m32real, m64real, m80real**—A single-, double-, and extended-real (respectively) floating-point operand in memory.

- **m16int, m32int, m64int**—A word-, short-, and long-integer (respectively) floating-point operand in memory.

- **ST or ST(0)**—The top element of the FPU register stack.

- **ST(*i*)**—The ith element from the top of the FPU register stack. (*i* = 0 through 7)

11.2.1.3.   DESCRIPTION COLUMN

The "Description" column following the "Instruction" column briefly explains the various forms of the instruction. The following Description and Operation sections contain more details of the instruction's operation.

11.2.1.4.   DESCRIPTION

The "Description" section describes the purpose of the instructions and the required operands. It also discusses the effect of the instruction on flags.

11.2.2.   Operation

The "Operation" section contains an algorithmic description (written in pseudo-code) of the instruction. The pseudo-code uses a notation similar to the Algol or Pascal language. The algorithms are composed of the following elements:

- Comments are enclosed within the symbol pairs "(*" and "*)".

- Compound statements are enclosed in keywords, such as IF, THEN, ELSE, and FI for an if statement, DO and OD for a do statement, or CASE ... OF and ESAC for a case statement.

- A register name implies the contents of the register. A register name enclosed in brackets implies the contents of the location whose address is contained in that register. For example, ES:[DI] indicates the contents of the location whose ES segment relative address is in register DI. [SI] indicates the contents of the address contained in register SI relative to SI's default segment (DS) or overridden segment.

- Brackets are also used for memory operands, where they mean that the contents of the memory location is a segment-relative offset. For example, [SRC] indicates that the contents of the source operand is a segment-relative offset.

- A ← B; indicates that the value of B is assigned to A.

- The symbols =, ≠ , ≥, and ≤ are relational operators used to compare two values, meaning equal, not equal, greater or equal, less or equal, respectively. A relational expression such as A = B is TRUE if the value of A is equal to B; otherwise it is FALSE.

The following identifiers are used in the algorithmic descriptions:

- **OperandSize and AddressSize**—The OperandSize identifier represents the operand-size attribute of the instruction, which is either 16 or 32 bits. The AddressSize identifier represents the address-size attribute, which is either 16 or 32 bits. For example, the following pseudo-code indicates that the operand-size attribute depends on the form of the CMPS instruction used.

```
IF instruction = CMPSW
    THEN OperandSize ← 16;
    ELSE
        IF instruction = CMPSD
            THEN OperandSize ← 32;
        FI;
FI;
```

See Section 3.8., "Operand-Size and Address-Size Attributes" for general guidelines on how these attributes are determined.

- **StackAddrSize**—Represents the stack address-size attribute associated with the instruction, which has a value of 16 or 32 bits (see Section 4.2.2., "Address-Size Attribute for Stack").

- **SRC**—Represents the source operand.

- **DEST**—Represents the destination operand.

The following functions are used in the algorithmic descriptions:

- **ZeroExtend(value)**—Returns a value zero-extended to the operand-size attribute of the instruction. For example, if the operand-size attribute is 32, zero extending a byte value of –10 converts the byte from F6H to a doubleword value of 000000F6H. If the value passed to the ZeroExtend function and the operand-size attribute are the same size, ZeroExtend returns the value unaltered.

- **SignExtend(value)**—Returns a value sign-extended to the operand-size attribute of the instruction. For example, if the operand-size attribute is 32, sign extending a byte containing the value –10 converts the byte from F6H to a doubleword value of FFFFFFF6H. If the value passed to the SignExtend function and the operand-size attribute are the same size, SignExtend returns the value unaltered.

- **Push(value)**—Pushes a value onto the procedure stack. The number of bytes pushed is determined by the operand-size attribute of the instruction. See the Operation section in Chapter 11, "PUSH—Push Word or Doubleword Onto the Stack" for more information on the push operation.

- **Pop()** removes the value from the top of the procedure stack and returns it. The statement EAX ← Pop(); assigns to EAX the 32-bit value from the top of the stack. Pop will return either a word or a doubleword depending on the operand-size attribute. See the Operation section in Chapter 11, "POP—Pop a Value from the Stack" for more information on the pop operation.

- **PopRegisterStack**—Marks the FPU ST(0) register as empty and increments the FPU register stack pointer (TOP) by 1.

- **Switch-Tasks**—Performs a standard task switch.

- **Bit(BitBase, BitOffset)**—Returns the value of a bit within a bit string, which is a sequence of bits in memory or a register. Bits are numbered from low-order to high-order within registers and within memory bytes. If the base operand is a register, the offset can be in the range 0..31. This offset addresses a bit within the indicated register. An example, the function Bit[EAX, 21] is illustrated in Figure 11-2.

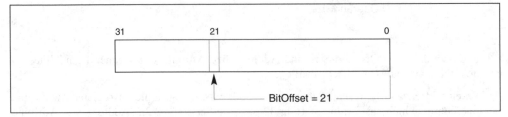

Figure 11-2. Bit Offset for BIT[EAX,21]

If BitBase is a memory address, BitOffset can range from –2 GBits to 2 GBits. The addressed bit is numbered (Offset MOD 8) within the byte at address (BitBase + (BitOffset DIV 8)), where DIV is signed division with rounding towards negative infinity, and MOD returns a positive number. This operation is illustrated in Figure 11-3.

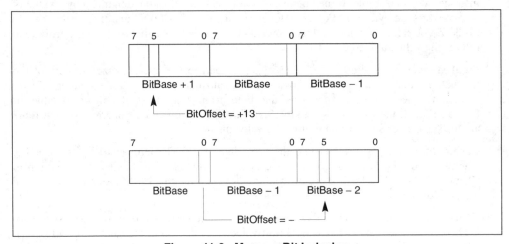

Figure 11-3. Memory Bit Indexing

11.2.3. Flags Affected

The "Flags Affected" section lists the flags in the EFLAGS register that are affected by the instruction. When a flag is cleared, it is set to 0; when it is set, it is set to 1. The arithmetic and logical instructions usually assign values to the status flags in a uniform manner (see Appendix A, *EFLAGS Cross-Reference*). Non-conventional assignments are described in the Operation section. The values of flags listed as *undefined* may be changed by the instruction in an indeterminate manner. Flags that are not listed are unchanged by the instruction.

11.2.4. FPU Flags Affected

The floating-point instructions have an "FPU Flags Affected" section that describes how each instruction can affect the four condition code flags of the FPU status word.

11.2.5. Protected Mode Exceptions

The "Protected Mode Exceptions" section lists the exceptions that can occur when the instruction is executed in protected mode and the reasons for the exceptions. Each exception is given a mnemonic that consists of a pound sign (#) followed by two letters and an optional error code in parentheses. For example, #GP(0) denotes a general protection exception with an error code of 0. Table 11-5 associates each two-letter mnemonic with the corresponding interrupt vector number and exception name. See Chapter 5, *Interrupt and Exception Handling*, in the *Pentium® Pro Family Developer's Manual, Volume 3* for a detailed description of the exceptions.

Table 11-5. Exception Mnemonics, Names, and Vector Numbers

Vector No.	Mnemonic	Name	Source
0	#DE	Divide Error	DIV and IDIV instructions.
1	#DB	Debug Exception	Any code or data reference.
3	#BP	Breakpoint	INT 3 instruction.
4	#OF	Overflow	INTO instruction.
5	#BR	BOUND Range Exceeded	BOUND instruction.
6	#UD	Invalid Opcode	UD2 instruction or reserved opcode.
7	#NM	Device Not Available	Floating-point or WAIT/FWAIT instruction.
8	#DF	Double Fault	Any instruction.
10	#TS	Invalid TSS	Task switch.
11	#NP	Segment Not Present	Loading segment registers or accessing system segments.
12	#SS	Stack Fault	Stack operations.
13	#GP	General Protection	Any memory reference.
14	#PF	Page Fault	Any memory reference.
16	#MF	Floating-Point Error	Floating-point or WAIT/FWAIT instruction.
17	#AC	Alignment Check	Any data reference in memory.
18	#MC	Machine Check	Model dependent.

Application programmers should consult the documentation provided with their operating systems to determine the actions taken when exceptions occur.

11.2.6. Real-Address Mode Exceptions

The "Real-Address Mode Exceptions" section lists the exceptions that can occur when the instruction is executed in real-address mode.

11.2.7. Virtual-8086 Mode Exceptions

The "Virtual-8086 Mode Exceptions" section lists the exceptions that can occur when the instruction is executed in virtual-8086 mode.

11.2.8. Floating-Point Exceptions

The "Floating-Point Exceptions" section lists additional exceptions that can occur when a floating-point instruction is executed in any mode. All of these exception conditions result in a floating-point error exception (#MF, vector 16) being generated. Table 11-6 associates each one- or two-letter mnemonic with the corresponding exception name. See Section 7.8., "Floating-Point Exception Conditions" for a detailed description of these exceptions.

Table 11-6. Floating-Point Exception Mnemonics and Names

Vector No.	Mnemonic	Name	Source
16	#IS #IA	Floating-point invalid operation: - Stack overflow or underflow - Invalid arithmetic operation	- FPU stack overflow or underflow - Invalid FPU arithmetic operation
16	#Z	Floating-point divide-by-zero	FPU divide-by-zero
16	#D	Floating-point denormalized operation	Attempting to operate on a denormal number
16	#O	Floating-point numeric overflow	FPU numeric overflow
16	#U	Floating-point numeric underflow	FPU numeric underflow
16	#P	Floating-point inexact result (precision)	Inexact result (precision)

11.3. INSTRUCTION REFERENCE

The remainder of this chapter provides detailed descriptions of each of the Pentium Pro processor instructions.

AAA—ASCII Adjust After Addition

Opcode	Instruction	Description
37	AAA	ASCII adjust AL after addition

Description

Adjusts the sum of two unpacked BCD values to create an unpacked BCD result. The AL register is the implied source and destination operand for this instruction. The AAA instruction is only useful when it follows an ADD instruction that adds (binary addition) two unpacked BCD values and stores a byte result in the AL register. The AAA instruction then adjusts the contents of the AL register to contain the correct 1-digit unpacked BCD result.

If the addition produces a decimal carry, the AH register is incremented by 1, and the CF and AF flags are set. If there was no decimal carry, the CF and AF flags are cleared and the AH register is unchanged. In either case, bits 4 through 7 of the AL register are cleared to 0.

Operation

```
IF ((AL AND FH) > 9) OR (AF = 1)
    THEN
        AL ← (AL + 6);
        AH ← AH + 1;
        AF ← 1;
        CF ← 1;
    ELSE
        AF ← 0;
        CF ← 0;
FI;
AL ←  AL AND FH;
```

Flags Affected

The AF and CF flags are set to 1 if the adjustment results in a decimal carry; otherwise they are cleared to 0. The OF, SF, ZF, and PF flags are undefined.

Exceptions (All Operating Modes)

None.

AAD—ASCII Adjust AX Before Division

Opcode	Instruction	Description
D5 0A	AAD	ASCII adjust AX before division

Description

Adjusts two unpacked BCD digits (the least-significant digit in the AL register and the most-significant digit in the AH register) so that a division operation performed on the result will yield a correct unpacked BCD value. The AAD instruction is only useful when it precedes a DIV instruction that divides (binary division) the adjusted value in the AL register by an unpacked BCD value.

The AAD instruction sets the value in the AL register to (AL + (10 * AH)), and then clears the AH register to 00H. The value in the AX register is then equal to the binary equivalent of the original unpacked two-digit number in registers AH and AL.

Operation

tempAL ← AL;
tempAH ← AH;
AL ← (tempAL + (tempAH * *imm8*)) AND FFH;
AH ← 0

The immediate value (*imm8*) is taken from the second byte of the instruction, which under normal assembly is 0AH (10 decimal). However, this immediate value can be changed to produce a different result.

Flags Affected

The SF, ZF, and PF flags are set according to the result; the OF, AF, and CF flags are undefined.

Exceptions (All Operating Modes)

None.

AAM—ASCII Adjust AX After Multiply

Opcode	Instruction	Description
D4 0A	AAM	ASCII adjust AX after multiply

Description

Adjusts the result of the multiplication of two unpacked BCD values to create a pair of unpacked BCD values. The AX register is the implied source and destination operand for this instruction. The AAM instruction is only useful when it follows an MUL instruction that multiplies (binary multiplication) two unpacked BCD values and stores a word result in the AX register. The AAM instruction then adjusts the contents of the AX register to contain the correct 2-digit unpacked BCD result.

Operation

tempAL ← AL;
AH ← tempAL / *imm8*;
AL ← tempAL MOD *imm8*;

The immediate value (*imm8*) is taken from the second byte of the instruction, which under normal assembly is 0AH (10 decimal). However, this immediate value can be changed to produce a different result.

Flags Affected

The SF, ZF, and PF flags are set according to the result. The OF, AF, and CF flags are undefined.

Exceptions (All Operating Modes)

None.

AAS—ASCII Adjust AL After Subtraction

Opcode	Instruction	Description
3F	AAS	ASCII adjust AL after subtraction

Description

Adjusts the result of the subtraction of two unpacked BCD values to create a unpacked BCD result. The AL register is the implied source and destination operand for this instruction. The AAS instruction is only useful when it follows a SUB instruction that subtracts (binary subtraction) one unpacked BCD value from another and stores a byte result in the AL register. The AAA instruction then adjusts the contents of the AL register to contain the correct 1-digit unpacked BCD result.

If the subtraction produced a decimal carry, the AH register is decremented by 1, and the CF and AF flags are set. If no decimal carry occurred, the CF and AF flags are cleared, and the AH register is unchanged. In either case, the AL register is left with its top nibble set to 0.

Operation

```
IF ((AL AND FH) > 9) OR (AF = 1)
THEN
    AL ← AL – 6;
    AH ← AH – 1;
    AF ← 1;
    CF ← 1;
ELSE
    CF ← 0;
    AF ← 0;
FI;
AL ← AL AND FH;
```

Flags Affected

The AF and CF flags are set to 1 if there is a decimal borrow; otherwise, they are cleared to 0. The OF, SF, ZF, and PF flags are undefined.

Exceptions (All Operating Modes)

None.

ADC—Add with Carry

Opcode	Instruction	Description
14 *ib*	ADC AL,*imm8*	Add with carry *imm8* to AL
15 *iw*	ADC AX,*imm16*	Add with carry *imm16* to AX
15 *id*	ADC EAX,*imm32*	Add with carry *imm32* to EAX
80 /2 *ib*	ADC *r/m8,imm8*	Add with carry *imm8* to *r/m8*
81 /2 *iw*	ADC *r/m16,imm16*	Add with carry *imm16* to *r/m16*
81 /2 *id*	ADC *r/m32,imm32*	Add with CF *imm32* to *r/m32*
83 /2 *ib*	ADC *r/m16,imm8*	Add with CF sign-extended *imm8* to *r/m16*
83 /2 *ib*	ADC *r/m32,imm8*	Add with CF sign-extended *imm8* into *r/m32*
10 /*r*	ADC *r/m8,r8*	Add with carry byte register to *r/m8*
11 /*r*	ADC *r/m16,r16*	Add with carry *r16* to *r/m16*
11 /*r*	ADC *r/m32,r32*	Add with CF *r32* to *r/m32*
12 /*r*	ADC *r8,r/m8*	Add with carry *r/m8* to byte register
13 /*r*	ADC *r16,r/m16*	Add with carry *r/m16* to *r16*
13 /*r*	ADC *r32,r/m32*	Add with CF *r/m32* to *r32*

Description

Adds the destination operand (first operand), the source operand (second operand), and the carry (CF) flag and stores the result in the destination operand. The destination operand can be a register or a memory location; the source operand can be an immediate, a register, or a memory location. The state of the CF flag represents a carry from a previous addition. When an immediate value is used as an operand, it is sign-extended to the length of the destination operand format.

The ADC instruction does not distinguish between signed or unsigned operands. Instead, the processor evaluates the result for both data types and sets the OF and CF flags to indicate a carry in the signed or unsigned result, respectively. The SF flag indicates the sign of the signed result.

The ADC instruction is usually executed as part of a multibyte or multiword addition in which an ADD instruction is followed by an ADC instruction.

Operation

DEST ← DEST + SRC + CF;

Flags Affected

The OF, SF, ZF, AF, CF, and PF flags are set according to the result.

Protected Mode Exceptions

#GP(0)	If the destination is located in a nonwritable segment.
	If a memory operand effective address is outside the CS, DS, ES, FS, or GS segment limit.
	If the DS, ES, FS, or GS register is used to access memory and it contains a null segment selector.
#SS(0)	If a memory operand effective address is outside the SS segment limit.
#PF(fault-code)	If a page fault occurs.
#AC(0)	If alignment checking is enabled and an unaligned memory reference is made while the current privilege level is 3.

Real Address Mode Exceptions

#GP	If a memory operand effective address is outside the CS, DS, ES, FS, or GS segment limit.
#SS	If a memory operand effective address is outside the SS segment limit.

Virtual 8086 Mode Exceptions

#GP(0)	If a memory operand effective address is outside the CS, DS, ES, FS, or GS segment limit.
#SS(0)	If a memory operand effective address is outside the SS segment limit.
#PF(fault-code)	If a page fault occurs.
#AC(0)	If alignment checking is enabled and an unaligned memory reference is made.

ADD—Add

Opcode	Instruction	Description
04 ib	ADD AL,imm8	Add imm8 to AL
05 iw	ADD AX,imm16	Add imm16 to AX
05 id	ADD EAX,imm32	Add imm32 to EAX
80 /0 ib	ADD r/m8,imm8	Add imm8 to r/m8
81 /0 iw	ADD r/m16,imm16	Add imm16 to r/m16
81 /0 id	ADD r/m32,imm32	Add imm32 to r/m32
83 /0 ib	ADD r/m16,imm8	Add sign-extended imm8 to r/m16
83 /0 ib	ADD r/m32,imm8	Add sign-extended imm8 to r/m32
00 /r	ADD r/m8,r8	Add r8 to r/m8
01 /r	ADD r/m16,r16	Add r16 to r/m16
01 /r	ADD r/m32,r32	Add r32 to r/m32
02 /r	ADD r8,r/m8	Add r/m8 to r8
03 /r	ADD r16,r/m16	Add r/m16 to r16
03 /r	ADD r32,r/m32	Add r/m32 to r32

Description

Adds the first operand (destination operand) and the second operand (source operand) and stores the result in the destination operand. The destination operand can be a register or a memory location; the source operand can be an immediate, a register, or a memory location. When an immediate value is used as an operand, it is sign-extended to the length of the destination operand format.

The ADD instruction does not distinguish between signed or unsigned operands. Instead, the processor evaluates the result for both data types and sets the OF and CF flags to indicate a carry in the signed or unsigned result, respectively. The SF flag indicates the sign of the signed result.

Operation

DEST ← DEST + SRC;

Flags Affected

The OF, SF, ZF, AF, CF, and PF flags are set according to the result.

Protected Mode Exceptions

#GP(0)   If the destination is located in a nonwritable segment.

If a memory operand effective address is outside the CS, DS, ES, FS, or GS segment limit.

If the DS, ES, FS, or GS register is used to access memory and it contains a null segment selector.

#SS(0)   If a memory operand effective address is outside the SS segment limit.

#PF(fault-code)   If a page fault occurs.

#AC(0)   If alignment checking is enabled and an unaligned memory reference is made while the current privilege level is 3.

Real Address Mode Exceptions

#GP   If a memory operand effective address is outside the CS, DS, ES, FS, or GS segment limit.

#SS   If a memory operand effective address is outside the SS segment limit.

Virtual 8086 Mode Exceptions

#GP(0)   If a memory operand effective address is outside the CS, DS, ES, FS, or GS segment limit.

#SS(0)   If a memory operand effective address is outside the SS segment limit.

#PF(fault-code)   If a page fault occurs.

#AC(0)   If alignment checking is enabled and an unaligned memory reference is made.

AND—Logical AND

Opcode	Instruction	Description
24 *ib*	AND AL,*imm8*	AL AND *imm8*
25 *iw*	AND AX,*imm16*	AX AND *imm16*
25 *id*	AND EAX,*imm32*	EAX AND *imm32*
80 /4 *ib*	AND r/m8,*imm8*	r/m8 AND *imm8*
81 /4 *iw*	AND r/m16,*imm16*	r/m16 AND *imm16*
81 /4 *id*	AND r/m32,*imm32*	r/m32 AND *imm32*
83 /4 *ib*	AND r/m16,*imm8*	r/m16 AND *imm8*
83 /4 *ib*	AND r/m32,*imm8*	r/m32 AND *imm8*
20 /r	AND r/m8,r8	r/m8 AND r8
21 /r	AND r/m16,r16	r/m16 AND r16
21 /r	AND r/m32,r32	r/m32 AND r32
22 /r	AND r8,r/m8	r8 AND r/m8
23 /r	AND r16,r/m16	r16 AND r/m16
23 /r	AND r32,r/m32	r32 AND r/m32

Description

Performs a bitwise AND operation on the destination (first) and source (second) operands and stores the result in the destination operand location. The source operand can be an immediate, a register, or a memory location; the destination operand can be a register or a memory location.

Operation

DEST ← DEST AND SRC;

Flags Affected

The OF and CF flags are cleared; the SF, ZF, and PF flags are set according to the result. The state of the AF flag is undefined.

Protected Mode Exceptions

#GP(0)	If the destination operand points to a nonwritable segment.
	If a memory operand effective address is outside the CS, DS, ES, FS, or GS segment limit.
	If the DS, ES, FS, or GS register contains a null segment selector.
#SS(0)	If a memory operand effective address is outside the SS segment limit.
#PF(fault-code)	If a page fault occurs.
#AC(0)	If alignment checking is enabled and an unaligned memory reference is made while the current privilege level is 3.

INSTRUCTION SET REFERENCE

Real Address Mode Exceptions

#GP   If a memory operand effective address is outside the CS, DS, ES, FS, or GS segment limit.

#SS   If a memory operand effective address is outside the SS segment limit.

Virtual 8086 Mode Exceptions

#GP(0)   If a memory operand effective address is outside the CS, DS, ES, FS, or GS segment limit.

#SS(0)   If a memory operand effective address is outside the SS segment limit.

#PF(fault-code)   If a page fault occurs.

#AC(0)   If alignment checking is enabled and an unaligned memory reference is made.

ARPL—Adjust RPL Field of Segment Selector

Opcode	Instruction	Description
63 /r	ARPL r/m16,r16	Adjust RPL of r/m16 to not less than RPL of r16

Description

Compares the RPL fields of two segment selectors. The first operand (the destination operand) contains one segment selector and the second operand (source operand) contains the other. (The RPL field is located in bits 0 and 1 of each operand.) If the RPL field of the destination operand is less than the RPL field of the source operand, the ZF flag is set and the RPL field of the destination operand is increased to match that of the source operand. Otherwise, the ZF flag is cleared and no change is made to the destination operand. (The destination operand can be a word register or a memory location; the source operand must be a word register.)

The ARPL instruction is provided for use by operating-system procedures (however, it can also be used by applications). It is generally used to adjust the RPL of a segment selector that has been passed to the operating system by an application program to match the privilege level of the application program. Here the segment selector passed to the operating system is placed in the destination operand and segment selector for the application program's code segment is placed in the source operand. (The RPL field in the source operand represents the privilege level of the application program.) Execution of the ARPL instruction then insures that the RPL of the segment selector received by the operating system is no lower (does not have a higher privilege) than the privilege level of the application program. (The segment selector for the application program's code segment can be read from the procedure stack following a procedure call.)

See "Checking Caller Access Privileges" in Chapter 4, *Protection*, of the *Pentium® Pro Family Developer's Manual, Volume 3* for more information about the use of this instruction.

Operation

```
IF DEST(RPL) < SRC(RPL)
THEN
    ZF ← 1;
    DEST(RPL) ← SRC(RPL);
ELSE
    ZF ← 0;
FI;
```

Flags Affected

The ZF flag is set to 1 if the RPL field of the destination operand is less than that of the source operand; otherwise, is cleared to 0.

Protected Mode Exceptions

#GP(0)	If the destination is located in a nonwritable segment.
	If a memory operand effective address is outside the CS, DS, ES, FS, or GS segment limit.
	If the DS, ES, FS, or GS register is used to access memory and it contains a null segment selector.
#SS(0)	If a memory operand effective address is outside the SS segment limit.
#PF(fault-code)	If a page fault occurs.
#AC(0)	If alignment checking is enabled and an unaligned memory reference is made while the current privilege level is 3.

Real Address Mode Exceptions

#UD	The ARPL instruction is not recognized in real address mode.

Virtual 8086 Mode Exceptions

#UD	The ARPL instruction is not recognized in virtual 8086 mode.

BOUND—Check Array Index Against Bounds

Opcode	Instruction	Description
62 /r	BOUND r16,m16&16	Check if r16 (array index) is within bounds specified by m16&16
62 /r	BOUND r32,m32&32	Check if r32 (array index) is within bounds specified by m16&16

Description

Determines if the first operand (array index) is within the bounds of an array specified the second operand (bounds operand). The array index is a signed integer located in a register. The bounds operand is a memory location that points to a pair of signed doubleword-integers (when the operand-size attribute is 32) or a pair of signed word-integers (when the operand-size attribute is 16). The first doubleword (or word) is the lower bound of the array and the second doubleword (or word) is the upper bound of the array. The array index must be greater than or equal to the lower bound and less than or equal to the upper bound plus the operand size in bytes. If the index is not within bounds, a BOUND range exceeded exception (#BR) is signaled. (When a this exception is generated, the saved return instruction pointer points to the BOUND instruction.)

The bounds limit data structure (two words or doublewords containing the lower and upper limits of the array) is usually placed just before the array itself, making the limits addressable via a constant offset from the beginning of the array. Because the address of the array already will be present in a register, this practice avoids extra bus cycles to obtain the effective address of the array bounds.

Operation

```
IF (ArrayIndex < LowerBound OR ArrayIndex > (UppderBound + OperandSize/8]))
    (* Below lower bound or above upper bound *)
    THEN
        #BR;
FI;
```

Flags Affected

None.

Protected Mode Exceptions

#BR	If the bounds test fails.
#UD	If second operand is not a memory location.
#GP(0)	If a memory operand effective address is outside the CS, DS, ES, FS, or GS segment limit.
	If the DS, ES, FS, or GS register contains a null segment selector.

#SS(0)   If a memory operand effective address is outside the SS segment limit.

#PF(fault-code)   If a page fault occurs.

#AC(0)   If alignment checking is enabled and an unaligned memory reference is made while the current privilege level is 3.

Real Address Mode Exceptions

#BR   If the bounds test fails.

#GP   If a memory operand effective address is outside the CS, DS, ES, FS, or GS segment limit.

#SS   If a memory operand effective address is outside the SS segment limit.

Virtual 8086 Mode Exceptions

#BR   If the bounds test fails.

#GP(0)   If a memory operand effective address is outside the CS, DS, ES, FS, or GS segment limit.

#SS(0)   If a memory operand effective address is outside the SS segment limit.

#PF(fault-code)   If a page fault occurs.

#AC(0)   If alignment checking is enabled and an unaligned memory reference is made.

BSF—Bit Scan Forward

Opcode	Instruction	Description
0F BC	BSF r16,r/m16	Bit scan forward on r/m16
0F BC	BSF r32,r/m32	Bit scan forward on r/m32

Description

Searches the source operand (second operand) for the least significant set bit (1 bit). If a least significant 1 bit is found, its bit index is stored in the destination operand (first operand). The source operand can be a register or a memory location; the destination operand is a register. The bit index is an unsigned offset from bit 0 of the source operand. If the contents source operand are 0, the contents of the destination operand is undefined.

Operation

```
IF SRC = 0
    THEN
        ZF ← 1;
        DEST is undefined;
    ELSE
        ZF ← 0;
        temp ← 0;
    WHILE Bit(SRC, temp) = 0
    DO
        temp ← temp + 1;
        DEST ← temp;
    OD;
FI;
```

Flags Affected

The ZF flag is set to 1 if all the source operand is 0; otherwise, the ZF flag is cleared. The CF, OF, SF, AF, and PF, flags are undefined.

Protected Mode Exceptions

#GP(0)	If a memory operand effective address is outside the CS, DS, ES, FS, or GS segment limit.
	If the DS, ES, FS, or GS register contains a null segment selector.
#SS(0)	If a memory operand effective address is outside the SS segment limit.
#PF(fault-code)	If a page fault occurs.
#AC(0)	If alignment checking is enabled and an unaligned memory reference is made while the current privilege level is 3.

Real Address Mode Exceptions

#GP   If a memory operand effective address is outside the CS, DS, ES, FS, or GS segment limit.

#SS   If a memory operand effective address is outside the SS segment limit.

Virtual 8086 Mode Exceptions

#GP(0)   If a memory operand effective address is outside the CS, DS, ES, FS, or GS segment limit.

#SS(0)   If a memory operand effective address is outside the SS segment limit.

#PF(fault-code) If a page fault occurs.

#AC(0)   If alignment checking is enabled and an unaligned memory reference is made.

BSR—Bit Scan Reverse

Opcode	Instruction	Description
0F BD	BSR r16,r/m16	Bit scan reverse on r/m16
0F BD	BSR r32,r/m32	Bit scan reverse on r/m32

Description

Searches the source operand (second operand) for the most significant set bit (1 bit). If a most significant 1 bit is found, its bit index is stored in the destination operand (first operand). The source operand can be a register or a memory location; the destination operand is a register. The bit index is an unsigned offset from bit 0 of the source operand. If the contents source operand are 0, the contents of the destination operand is undefined.

Operation

```
IF SRC = 0
    THEN
        ZF ← 1;
        DEST is undefined;
    ELSE
        ZF ← 0;
        temp ← OperandSize − 1;
    WHILE Bit(SRC, temp) = 0
    DO
        temp ← temp − 1;
        DEST ← temp;
    OD;
FI;
```

Flags Affected

The ZF flag is set to 1 if all the source operand is 0; otherwise, the ZF flag is cleared. The CF, OF, SF, AF, and PF, flags are undefined.

Protected Mode Exceptions

#GP(0)	If a memory operand effective address is outside the CS, DS, ES, FS, or GS segment limit.
	If the DS, ES, FS, or GS register contains a null segment selector.
#SS(0)	If a memory operand effective address is outside the SS segment limit.
#PF(fault-code)	If a page fault occurs.
#AC(0)	If alignment checking is enabled and an unaligned memory reference is made while the current privilege level is 3.

Real Address Mode Exceptions

#GP   If a memory operand effective address is outside the CS, DS, ES, FS, or GS segment limit.

#SS   If a memory operand effective address is outside the SS segment limit.

Virtual 8086 Mode Exceptions

#GP(0)   If a memory operand effective address is outside the CS, DS, ES, FS, or GS segment limit.

#SS(0)   If a memory operand effective address is outside the SS segment limit.

#PF(fault-code)   If a page fault occurs.

#AC(0)   If alignment checking is enabled and an unaligned memory reference is made.

BSWAP—Byte Swap

Opcode	Instruction	Description
0F C8+*rd*	BSWAP *r32*	Reverses the byte order of a 32-bit register.

Description

Reverses the byte order of a 32-bit (destination) register: bits 0 through 7 are swapped with bits 24 through 31, and bits 8 through 15 are swapped with bits 16 through 23. This instruction is provided for converting little-endian values to big-endian format and vice versa.

To swap bytes in a word value (16-bit register), use the XCHG instruction. When the BSWAP instruction references a 16-bit register, the result is undefined.

Operation

TEMP ← DEST
DEST(7..0) ← TEMP(31..24)
DEST(15..8) ← TEMP(23..16)
DEST(23..16) ← TEMP(15..8)
DEST(31..24) ← TEMP(7..0)

Flags Affected

None.

Exceptions (All Operating Modes)

None.

Intel Architecture Compatibility Information

The BSWAP instruction is not supported on Intel Architecture processors earlier than the Intel486 processor family. For compatibility with this instruction, include functionally-equivalent code for execution on Intel processors earlier than the Intel486 processor family.

BT—Bit Test

Opcode	Instruction	Description
0F A3	BT r/m16,r16	Store selected bit in CF flag
0F A3	BT r/m32,r32	Store selected bit in CF flag
0F BA /4 ib	BT r/m16,imm8	Store selected bit in CF flag
0F BA /4 ib	BT r/m32,imm8	Store selected bit in CF flag

Description

Selects the bit in a bit string (specified with the first operand, called the bit base) at the bit-position designated by the bit offset operand (second operand) and stores the value of the bit in the CF flag. The bit base operand can be a register or a memory location; the bit offset operand can be a register or an immediate value. If the bit base operand specifies a register, the instruction takes the modulo 16 or 32 (depending on the register size) of the bit offset operand, allowing any bit position to be selected in a 16- or 32-bit register, respectively (see Figure 11-2). If the bit base operand specifies a memory location, it represents the address of the byte in memory that contains the bit base (bit 0 of the specified byte) of the bit string (see Figure 11-3). The offset operand then selects a bit position within the range -2^{31} to $2^{31} - 1$ for a register offset and 0 to 31 for an immediate offset.

Some assemblers support immediate bit offsets larger than 31 by using the immediate bit offset field in combination with the displacement field of the memory operand. In this case, the low-order 3 or 5 bits (3 for 16-bit operands, 5 for 32-bit operands) of the immediate bit offset are stored in the immediate bit offset field, and the high-order bits are shifted and combined with the byte displacement in the addressing mode by the assembler. The processor will ignore the high order bits if they are not zero.

When accessing a bit in memory, the processor may access 4 bytes starting from the memory address for a 32-bit operand size, using by the following relationship:

Effective Address + (4 * (BitOffset DIV 32))

Or, it may access 2 bytes starting from the memory address for a 16-bit operand, using this relationship:

Effective Address + (2 * (BitOffset DIV 16))

It may do so even when only a single byte needs to be accessed to reach the given bit. When using this bit addressing mechanism, software should avoid referencing areas of memory close to address space holes. In particular, it should avoid references to memory-mapped I/O registers. Instead, software should use the MOV instructions to load from or store to these addresses, and use the register form of these instructions to manipulate the data.

Operation

CF ← Bit(BitBase, BitOffset)

Flags Affected

The CF flag contains the value of the selected bit. The OF, SF, ZF, AF, and PF flags are undefined.

Protected Mode Exceptions

#GP(0)	If a memory operand effective address is outside the CS, DS, ES, FS, or GS segment limit.
	If the DS, ES, FS, or GS register contains a null segment selector.
#SS(0)	If a memory operand effective address is outside the SS segment limit.
#PF(fault-code)	If a page fault occurs.
#AC(0)	If alignment checking is enabled and an unaligned memory reference is made while the current privilege level is 3.

Real Address Mode Exceptions

#GP	If a memory operand effective address is outside the CS, DS, ES, FS, or GS segment limit.
#SS	If a memory operand effective address is outside the SS segment limit.

Virtual 8086 Mode Exceptions

#GP(0)	If a memory operand effective address is outside the CS, DS, ES, FS, or GS segment limit.
#SS(0)	If a memory operand effective address is outside the SS segment limit.
#PF(fault-code)	If a page fault occurs.
#AC(0)	If alignment checking is enabled and an unaligned memory reference is made.

BTC—Bit Test and Complement

Opcode	Instruction	Description
0F BB	BTC *r/m16,r16*	Store selected bit in CF flag and complement
0F BB	BTC *r/m32,r32*	Store selected bit in CF flag and complement
0F BA */7 ib*	BTC *r/m16,imm8*	Store selected bit in CF flag and complement
0F BA */7 ib*	BTC *r/m32,imm8*	Store selected bit in CF flag and complement

Description

Selects the bit in a bit string (specified with the first operand, called the bit base) at the bit-position designated by the bit offset operand (second operand), stores the value of the bit in the CF flag, and complements the selected bit in the bit string. The bit base operand can be a register or a memory location; the bit offset operand can be a register or an immediate value. If the bit base operand specifies a register, the instruction takes the modulo 16 or 32 (depending on the register size) of the bit offset operand, allowing any bit position to be selected in a 16- or 32-bit register, respectively (see Figure 11-2). If the bit base operand specifies a memory location, it represents the address of the byte in memory that contains the bit base (bit 0 of the specified byte) of the bit string (see Figure 11-3). The offset operand then selects a bit position within the range -2^{31} to $2^{31} - 1$ for a register offset and 0 to 31 for an immediate offset.

Some assemblers support immediate bit offsets larger than 31 by using the immediate bit offset field in combination with the displacement field of the memory operand. See Chapter 11, "BT—Bit Test" for more information on this addressing mechanism.

Operation

CF ← Bit(BitBase, BitOffset)
Bit(BitBase, BitOffset) ← NOT Bit(BitBase, BitOffset);

Flags Affected

The CF flag contains the value of the selected bit before it is complemented. The OF, SF, ZF, AF, and PF flags are undefined.

Protected Mode Exceptions

#GP(0)	If the destination operand points to a nonwritable segment.
	If a memory operand effective address is outside the CS, DS, ES, FS, or GS segment limit.
	If the DS, ES, FS, or GS register contains a null segment selector.
#SS(0)	If a memory operand effective address is outside the SS segment limit.
#PF(fault-code)	If a page fault occurs.

#AC(0)   If alignment checking is enabled and an unaligned memory reference is
                    made while the current privilege level is 3.

Real Address Mode Exceptions

#GP   If a memory operand effective address is outside the CS, DS, ES, FS, or
                    GS segment limit.

#SS   If a memory operand effective address is outside the SS segment limit.

Virtual 8086 Mode Exceptions

#GP(0)   If a memory operand effective address is outside the CS, DS, ES, FS, or
                    GS segment limit.

#SS(0)   If a memory operand effective address is outside the SS segment limit.

#PF(fault-code)   If a page fault occurs.

#AC(0)   If alignment checking is enabled and an unaligned memory reference is
                    made.

INSTRUCTION SET REFERENCE

BTR—Bit Test and Reset

Opcode	Instruction	Description
0F B3	BTR *r/m16,r16*	Store selected bit in CF flag and clear
0F B3	BTR *r/m32,r32*	Store selected bit in CF flag and clear
0F BA /6 *ib*	BTR *r/m16,imm8*	Store selected bit in CF flag and clear
0F BA /6 *ib*	BTR *r/m32,imm8*	Store selected bit in CF flag and clear

Description

Selects the bit in a bit string (specified with the first operand, called the bit base) at the bit-position designated by the bit offset operand (second operand), stores the value of the bit in the CF flag, and clears the selected bit in the bit string to 0. The bit base operand can be a register or a memory location; the bit offset operand can be a register or an immediate value. If the bit base operand specifies a register, the instruction takes the modulo 16 or 32 (depending on the register size) of the bit offset operand, allowing any bit position to be selected in a 16- or 32-bit register, respectively (see Figure 11-2). If the bit base operand specifies a memory location, it represents the address of the byte in memory that contains the bit base (bit 0 of the specified byte) of the bit string (see Figure 11-3). The offset operand then selects a bit position within the range -2^{31} to $2^{31} - 1$ for a register offset and 0 to 31 for an immediate offset.

Some assemblers support immediate bit offsets larger than 31 by using the immediate bit offset field in combination with the displacement field of the memory operand. See Chapter 11, "BT—Bit Test" for more information on this addressing mechanism.

Operation

CF ← Bit(BitBase, BitOffset)
Bit(BitBase, BitOffset) ← 0;

Flags Affected

The CF flag contains the value of the selected bit before it is cleared. The OF, SF, ZF, AF, and PF flags are undefined.

Protected Mode Exceptions

#GP(0)	If the destination operand points to a nonwritable segment.
	If a memory operand effective address is outside the CS, DS, ES, FS, or GS segment limit.
	If the DS, ES, FS, or GS register contains a null segment selector.
#SS(0)	If a memory operand effective address is outside the SS segment limit.
#PF(fault-code)	If a page fault occurs.

#AC(0)   If alignment checking is enabled and an unaligned memory reference is made while the current privilege level is 3.

Real Address Mode Exceptions

#GP   If a memory operand effective address is outside the CS, DS, ES, FS, or GS segment limit.

#SS   If a memory operand effective address is outside the SS segment limit.

Virtual 8086 Mode Exceptions

#GP(0)   If a memory operand effective address is outside the CS, DS, ES, FS, or GS segment limit.

#SS(0)   If a memory operand effective address is outside the SS segment limit.

#PF(fault-code)   If a page fault occurs.

#AC(0)   If alignment checking is enabled and an unaligned memory reference is made.

BTS—Bit Test and Set

Opcode	Instruction	Description
0F AB	BTS *r/m16,r16*	Store selected bit in CF flag and set
0F AB	BTS *r/m32,r32*	Store selected bit in CF flag and set
0F BA /5 *ib*	BTS *r/m16,imm8*	Store selected bit in CF flag and set
0F BA /5 *ib*	BTS *r/m32,imm8*	Store selected bit in CF flag and set

Description

Selects the bit in a bit string (specified with the first operand, called the bit base) at the bit-position designated by the bit offset operand (second operand), stores the value of the bit in the CF flag, and sets the selected bit in the bit string to 1. The bit base operand can be a register or a memory location; the bit offset operand can be a register or an immediate value. If the bit base operand specifies a register, the instruction takes the modulo 16 or 32 (depending on the register size) of the bit offset operand, allowing any bit position to be selected in a 16- or 32-bit register, respectively (see Figure 11-2). If the bit base operand specifies a memory location, it represents the address of the byte in memory that contains the bit base (bit 0 of the specified byte) of the bit string (see Figure 11-3). The offset operand then selects a bit position within the range -2^{31} to $2^{31} - 1$ for a register offset and 0 to 31 for an immediate offset.

Some assemblers support immediate bit offsets larger than 31 by using the immediate bit offset field in combination with the displacement field of the memory operand. See Chapter 11, "BT—Bit Test" for more information on this addressing mechanism.

Operation

CF ← Bit(BitBase, BitOffset)
Bit(BitBase, BitOffset) ← 1;

Flags Affected

The CF flag contains the value of the selected bit before it is set. The OF, SF, ZF, AF, and PF flags are undefined.

Protected Mode Exceptions

#GP(0)	If the destination operand points to a nonwritable segment.
	If a memory operand effective address is outside the CS, DS, ES, FS, or GS segment limit.
	If the DS, ES, FS, or GS register contains a null segment selector.
#SS(0)	If a memory operand effective address is outside the SS segment limit.
#PF(fault-code)	If a page fault occurs.

#AC(0)   If alignment checking is enabled and an unaligned memory reference is
                  made while the current privilege level is 3.

Real Address Mode Exceptions

#GP   If a memory operand effective address is outside the CS, DS, ES, FS, or
                 GS segment limit.

#SS   If a memory operand effective address is outside the SS segment limit.

Virtual 8086 Mode Exceptions

#GP   If a memory operand effective address is outside the CS, DS, ES, FS, or
                 GS segment limit.

#SS   If a memory operand effective address is outside the SS segment limit.

#PF(fault-code) If a page fault occurs.

#AC(0)   If alignment checking is enabled and an unaligned memory reference is
                 made.

CALL—Call Procedure

Opcode	Instruction	Description
E8 *cw*	CALL *rel16*	Call near, displacement relative to next instruction
E8 *cd*	CALL *rel32*	Call near, displacement relative to next instruction
FF /2	CALL *r/m16*	Call near, *r/m16* indirect
FF /2	CALL *r/m32*	Call near, *r/m32* indirect
9A *cd*	CALL *ptr16:16*	Call far, to full pointer given
9A *cp*	CALL *ptr16:32*	Call far, to full pointer given
FF /3	CALL *m16:16*	Call far, address at *r/m16*
FF /3	CALL *m16:32*	Call far, address at *r/m32*

Description

Saves procedure linking information on the procedure stack and jumps to the procedure (called procedure) specified with the destination (target) operand. The target operand specifies the address of the first instruction in the called procedure. This operand can be an immediate value, a general-purpose register, or a memory location.

This instruction can be used to execute four different types of calls:

- Near call—A call to a procedure within the current code segment (the segment currently pointed to by the CS register), sometimes referred to as an intrasegment call.

- Far call—A call to a procedure located in a different segment than the current code segment, sometimes referred to as an intersegment call.

- Inter-privilege-level far call—A far call to a procedure in a segment at a different privilege level than that of the currently executing program or procedure.

- Task switch—A call to a procedure located in a different task.

The latter two call types (inter-privilege-level call and task switch) can only be executed in protected mode. See Section 4.3., "Calling Procedures Using CALL and RET" for detailed information on near, far, and inter-privilege-level calls; see Chapter 6 in the *Pentium® Pro Family Developer's Manual, Volume 3* for information on task switching with the CALL instruction.

When executing a near call, the processor pushes the value of the EIP register (which contains the address of the instruction following the CALL instruction) onto the procedure stack (for use later as a return-instruction pointer. The processor then jumps to the address specified with the target operand for the called procedure. The target operand specifies either an absolute address in the code segment (that is an offset from the base of the code segment) or a relative offset (a signed offset relative to the current value of the instruction pointer in the EIP register, which points to the instruction following the call). An absolute address is specified directly in a register or indirectly in a memory location (*r/m16* or *r/m32* target-operand form). (When accessing an absolute address indirectly using the stack pointer (ESP) as a base register, the base value used is the value of the ESP before the instruction executes.) A relative offset (*rel16* or *rel32*) is generally specified as a label in assembly code, but at the machine code level, it is encoded as a signed, 16- or 32-bit immediate value, which is added to the instruction pointer.

When executing a near call, the operand-size attribute determines the size of the target operand (16 or 32 bits) for absolute addresses. Absolute addresses are loaded directly into the EIP register. When a relative offset is specified, it is added to the value of the EIP register. If the operand-size attribute is 16, the upper two bytes of the EIP register are cleared to 0s, resulting in a maximum instruction pointer size of 16 bits. The CS register is not changed on near calls.

When executing a far call, the processor pushes the current value of both the CS and EIP registers onto the procedure stack for use as a return-instruction pointer. The processor then performs a far jump to the code segment and address specified with the target operand for the called procedure. Here the target operand specifies an absolute far address either directly with a pointer (*ptr16:16* or *ptr16:32*) or indirectly with a memory location (*m16:16* or *m16:32*). With the pointer method, the segment and address of the called procedure is encoded in the instruction using a 4-byte (16-bit operand size) or 6-byte (32-bit operand size) far address immediate. With the indirect method, the target operand specifies a memory location that contains a 4-byte (16-bit operand size) or 6-byte (32-bit operand size) far address. The operand-size attribute determines the size of the offset (16 or 32 bits) in the far address. The far address is loaded directly into the CS and EIP registers. If the operand-size attribute is 16, the upper two bytes of the EIP register are cleared to 0s.

Any far call from a 32-bit code segment to a 16-bit code segment should be made from the first 64 Kbytes of the 32-bit code segment, because the operand-size attribute of the instruction is set to 16, allowing only a 16-bit return address offset to be saved. Also, the call should be made using a 16-bit call gate so that 16-bit values will be pushed on the stack.

When the processor is operating in protected mode, a far call can also be used to access a code segment at a different privilege level or to switch tasks. Here, the processor uses the segment selector part of the far address to access the segment descriptor for the segment being jumped to. Depending on the value of the type and access rights information in the segment selector, the CALL instructon can perform:

- A far call to the same privilege level (described in the previous paragraph).
- An far call to a different privilege level.
- A task switch.

When executing an inter-privilege-level far call, the code segment for the procedure being called is accessed through a call gate. The segment selector specified by the target operand identifies the call gate. In executing a call through a call gate where a change of privilege level occurs, the processor switches to the stack for the privilege level of the called procedure, pushes the current values of the CS and EIP registers and the SS and ESP values for the old stack onto the new stack, then performs a far jump to the new code segment. The new code segment is specified in the call gate descriptor; the new stack segment is specified in the TSS for the currently running task. The jump to the new code segment occurs after the stack switch. On the new stack, the processor pushes the segment selector and stack pointer for the calling procedure's stack, a set of parameters from the calling procedures stack, and the segment selector and instruction pointer for the calling procedure's code segment. (A value in the call gate descriptor determines how many parameters to copy to the new stack.)

Finally, the processor jumps to the address of the procedure being called within the new code segment. The procedure address is the offset specified by the target operand. Here again, the target operand can specify the far address of the call gate and procedure either directly with a pointer (*ptr16:16* or *ptr16:32*) or indirectly with a memory location (*m16:16* or *m16:32*).

Executing a task switch with the CALL instruction, is similar to executing a call through a call gate. Here the target operand specifies the segment selector of the task gate for the task being switched to and the address of the procedure being called in the task. The task gate in turn points to the TSS for the task, which contains the segment selectors for the task's code and stack segments. The CALL instruction can also specify the segment selector of the TSS directly. See Chapter 6, *Task Management*, in *Pentium® Pro Family Developer's Manual, Volume 3* the for detailed information on the mechanics of a task switch.

Operation

```
IF near call
    THEN IF near relative call
        IF the instruction pointer is not within code segment limit THEN #GP(0); FI;
        THEN IF OperandSize = 32
            THEN
                IF stack not large enough for a 4-byte return address THEN #SS(0); FI;
                Push(EIP);
                EIP ← EIP + DEST; (* DEST is rel32 *)
            ELSE (* OperandSize = 16 *)
                IF stack not large enough for a 2-byte return address THEN #SS(0); FI;
                Push(IP);
                EIP ← (EIP + DEST) AND 0000FFFFH; (* DEST is rel16 *)
        FI;
    FI;
    ELSE (* near absolute call *)
        IF the instruction pointer is not within code segment limit THEN #GP(0); FI;
        IF OperandSize = 32
            THEN
                IF stack not large enough for a 4-byte return address THEN #SS(0); FI;
                Push(EIP);
                EIP ← DEST; (* DEST is r/m32 *)
            ELSE (* OperandSize = 16 *)
                IF stack not large enough for a 2-byte return address THEN #SS(0); FI;
                Push(IP);
                EIP ← DEST AND 0000FFFFH; (* DEST is r/m16 *)
        FI;
    FI:
FI;
```

IF far call AND (PE = 0 OR (PE = 1 AND VM = 1)) (* real address or virtual 8086 mode *)
    THEN
        IF OperandSize = 32
            THEN
                IF stack not large enough for a 6-byte return address THEN #SS(0); FI;
                IF the instruction pointer is not within code segment limit THEN #GP(0); FI;
                Push(CS); (* padded with 16 high-order bits *)
                Push(EIP);
                CS ← DEST[47:32]; (* DEST is ptr16:32 or [m16:32] *)
                EIP ← DEST[31:0]; (* DEST is ptr16:32 or [m16:32] *)
            ELSE (* OperandSize = 16 *)
                IF stack not large enough for a 4-byte return address THEN #SS(0); FI;
                IF the instruction pointer is not within code segment limit THEN #GP(0); FI;
                Push(CS);
                Push(IP);
                CS ← DEST[31:16]; (* DEST is ptr16:16 or [m16:16] *)
                EIP ← DEST[15:0]; (* DEST is ptr16:16 or [m16:16] *)
                EIP ← EIP AND 0000FFFFH; (* clear upper 16 bits *)
        FI;
FI;

IF far call AND (PE = 1 AND VM = 0) (* Protected mode, not virtual 8086 mode *)
    THEN
        IF segment selector in target operand null THEN #GP(0); FI;
        IF segment selector index not within descriptor table limits
            THEN #GP(new code selector);
        FI;
        Read type and access rights of selected segment descriptor;
        IF segment type is not a conforming or nonconforming code segment, call gate,
            task gate, or TSS THEN #GP(segment selector); FI;
        Depending on type and access rights
            GO TO CONFORMING-CODE-SEGMENT;
            GO TO NONCONFORMING-CODE-SEGMENT;
            GO TO CALL-GATE;
            GO TO TASK-GATE;
            GO TO TASK-STATE-SEGMENT;
FI;

CONFORMING-CODE-SEGMENT:
    IF DPL > CPL THEN #GP(new code segment selector); FI;
    IF segment not present THEN #NP(new code segment selector); FI;
    IF OperandSize = 32
        THEN
            IF stack not large enough for a 6-byte return address THEN #SS(0); FI;
            IF the instruction pointer is not within code segment limit THEN #GP(0); FI;
            Push(CS); (* padded with 16 high-order bits *)
            Push(EIP);

```
            CS ← DEST(NewCodeSegmentSelector);
            (* segment descriptor information also loaded *)
            CS(RPL) ← CPL
            EIP ← DEST(offset);
        ELSE (* OperandSize = 16 *)
            IF stack not large enough for a 4-byte return address THEN #SS(0); FI;
            IF the instruction pointer is not within code segment limit THEN #GP(0); FI;
            Push(CS);
            Push(IP);
            CS ← DEST(NewCodeSegmentSelector);
            (* segment descriptor information also loaded *)
            CS(RPL) ← CPL
            EIP ← DEST(offset) AND 0000FFFFH; (* clear upper 16 bits *)
    FI;
END;


NONCONFORMING-CODE-SEGMENT:
    IF (RPL > CPL) OR (DPL ≠ CPL) THEN #GP(new code segment selector); FI;
    IF segment not present THEN #NP(new code segment selector); FI;
    IF stack not large enough for return address THEN #SS(0); FI;
    tempEIP ← DEST(offset)
    IF OperandSize=16
        THEN
            tempEIP ← tempEIP AND 0000FFFFH; (* clear upper 16 bits *)
    FI;
    IF tempEIP outside code segment limit THEN #GP(0); FI;
    IF OperandSize = 32
        THEN
            Push(CS); (* padded with 16 high-order bits *)
            Push(EIP);
            CS ← DEST(NewCodeSegmentSelector);
            (* segment descriptor information also loaded *)
            CS(RPL) ← CPL;
            EIP ← tempEIP;
        ELSE (* OperandSize = 16 *)
            Push(CS);
            Push(IP);
            CS ← DEST(NewCodeSegmentSelector);
            (* segment descriptor information also loaded *)
            CS(RPL) ← CPL;
            EIP ← tempEIP;
    FI;
END;
```

CALL-GATE:
    IF call gate DPL < CPL or RPL THEN #GP(call gate selector); FI;
    IF call gate not present THEN #NP(call gate selector); FI;
    IF call gate code-segment selector is null THEN #GP(0); FI;
    IF call gate code-segment selector index is outside descriptor table limits
        THEN #GP(code segment selector); FI;
    Read code segment descriptor;
    IF code-segment segment descriptor does not indicate a code segment
    OR code-segment segment descriptor DPL > CPL
        THEN #GP(code segment selector); FI;
    IF code segment not present THEN #NP(new code segment selector); FI;
    IF code segment is non-conforming AND DPL < CPL
        THEN go to MORE-PRIVILEGE;
        ELSE go to SAME-PRIVILEGE;
    FI;
END;

MORE-PRIVILEGE:
    IF current TSS is 32-bit TSS
        THEN
            TSSstackAddress ← new code segment (DPL ∗ 8) + 4
            IF (TSSstackAddress + 7) > TSS limit
                THEN #TS(current TSS selector); FI;
            newSS ← TSSstackAddress + 4;
            newESP ← stack address;
        ELSE (* TSS is 16-bit *)
            TSSstackAddress ← new code segment (DPL ∗ 4) + 2
            IF (TSSstackAddress + 4) > TSS limit
                THEN #TS(current TSS selector); FI;
            newESP ← TSSstackAddress;
            newSS ← TSSstackAddress + 2;
    FI;
    IF stack segment selector is null THEN #TS(stack segment selector); FI;
    IF stack segment selector index is not within its descriptor table limits
        THEN #TS(SS selector); FI
    Read code segment descriptor;
    IF stack segment selector's RPL ≠ DPL of code segment
        OR stack segment DPL ≠ DPL of code segment
        OR stack segment is not a writable data segment
            THEN #TS(SS selector); FI
    IF stack segment not present THEN #SS(SS selector); FI;
    IF CallGateSize = 32
        THEN
            IF stack does not have room for parameters plus 16 bytes
                THEN #SS(SS selector); FI;
            IF CallGate(InstructionPointer) not within code segment limit THEN #GP(0); FI;
            SS ← newSS;

```
                    (* segment descriptor information also loaded *)
                    ESP ← newESP;
                    CS:EIP ← CallGate(CS:InstructionPointer);
                    (* segment descriptor information also loaded *)
                    Push(oldSS:oldESP); (* from calling procedure *)
                    temp ← parameter count from call gate, masked to 5 bits;
                    Push(parameters from calling procedure's stack, temp)
                    Push(oldCS:oldEIP); (* return address to calling procedure *)
              ELSE (* CallGateSize = 16 *)
                    IF stack does not have room for parameters plus 8 bytes
                          THEN #SS(SS selector); FI;
                    IF (CallGate(InstructionPointer) AND FFFFH) not within code segment limit
                          THEN #GP(0); FI;
                    SS ← newSS;
                    (* segment descriptor information also loaded *)
                    ESP ← newESP;
                    CS:IP ← CallGate(CS:InstructionPointer);
                    (* segment descriptor information also loaded *)
                    Push(oldSS:oldESP); (* from calling procedure *)
                    temp ← parameter count from call gate, masked to 5 bits;
                    Push(parameters from calling procedure's stack, temp)
                    Push(oldCS:oldEIP); (* return address to calling procedure *)
        FI;
        CPL ← CodeSegment(DPL)
        CS(RPL) ← CPL
END;

SAME-PRIVILEGE:
    IF CallGateSize = 32
          THEN
                IF stack does not have room for 8 bytes
                      THEN #SS(0); FI;
                IF EIP not within code segment limit then #GP(0); FI;
                CS:EIP ← CallGate(CS:EIP) (* segment descriptor information also loaded *)
                Push(oldCS:oldEIP); (* return address to calling procedure *)
          ELSE (* CallGateSize = 16 *)
                IF stack does not have room for parameters plus 4 bytes
                      THEN #SS(0); FI;
                IF IP not within code segment limit THEN #GP(0); FI;
                CS:IP ← CallGate(CS:instruction pointer)
                (* segment descriptor information also loaded *)
                Push(oldCS:oldIP); (* return address to calling procedure *)
    FI;
    CS(RPL) ← CPL
END;
```

```
TASK-GATE:
    IF task gate DPL < CPL or RPL
        THEN #GP(task gate selector);
    FI;
    IF task gate not present
        THEN #NP(task gate selector);
    FI;
    Read the TSS segment selector in the task-gate descriptor;
    IF TSS segment selector local/global bit is set to local
        OR index not within GDT limits
            THEN #GP(TSS selector);
    FI;
    Access TSS descriptor in GDT;

    IF TSS descriptor specifies that the TSS is busy (low-order 5 bits set to 00001)
            THEN #GP(TSS selector);
    FI;
    IF TSS not present
        THEN #NP(TSS selector);
    FI;
    SWITCH-TASKS (with nesting) to TSS;
    IF EIP not within code segment limit
        THEN #GP(0);
    FI;
END;

TASK-STATE-SEGMENT:
    IF TSS DPL < CPL or RPL
    OR TSS descriptor indicates TSS not available
        THEN #GP(TSS selector);
    FI;
    IF TSS is not present
        THEN #NP(TSS selector);
    FI;
    SWITCH-TASKS (with nesting) to TSS
    IF EIP not within code segment limit
        THEN #GP(0);
    FI;
END;
```

Flags Affected

All flags are affected if a task switch occurs; no flags are affected if a task switch does not occur.

Protected Mode Exceptions

#GP(0)	If target offset in destination operand is beyond the new code segment limit.
	If the segment selector in the destination operand is null.
	If the code segment selector in the gate is null.
	If a memory operand effective address is outside the CS, DS, ES, FS, or GS segment limit.
	If the DS, ES, FS, or GS register is used to access memory and it contains a null segment selector.
#GP(selector)	If code segment or gate or TSS selector index is outside descriptor table limits.
	If the segment descriptor pointed to by the segment selector in the destination operand is not for a conforming-code segment, nonconforming-code segment, call gate, task gate, or task state segment.
	If the DPL for a nonconforming-code segment is not equal to the CPL or the RPL for the segment's segment selector is greater than the CPL.
	If the DPL for a conforming-code segment is greater than the CPL.
	If the DPL from a call-gate, task-gate, or TSS segment descriptor is less than the CPL or than the RPL of the call-gate, task-gate, or TSS's segment selector.
	If the segment descriptor for a segment selector from a call gate does not indicate it is a code segment.
	If the segment selector from a call gate is beyond the descriptor table limits.
	If the DPL for a code-segment obtained from a call gate is greater than the CPL.
	If the segment selector for a TSS has its local/global bit set for local.
	If a TSS segment descriptor specifies that the TSS is busy or not available.
#SS(0)	If pushing the return address, parameters, or stack segment pointer onto the stack exceeds the bounds of the stack segment, when no stack switch occurs.
	If a memory operand effective address is outside the SS segment limit.

#SS(selector)	If pushing the return address, parameters, or stack segment pointer onto the stack exceeds the bounds of the stack segment, when a stack switch occurs.
	If the SS register is being loaded as part of a stack switch and the segment pointed to is marked not present.
	If stack segment does not have room for the return address, parameters, or stack segment pointer, when stack switch occurs.
#NP(selector)	If a code segment, data segment, stack segment, call gate, task gate, or TSS is not present.
#TS(selector)	If the new stack segment selector and ESP are beyond the end of the TSS.
	If the new stack segment selector is null.
	If the RPL of the new stack segment selector in the TSS is not equal to the DPL of the code segment being accessed.
	If DPL of the stack segment descriptor for the new stack segment is not equal to the DPL of the code segment descriptor.
	If the new stack segment is not a writable data segment.
	If segment-selector index for stack segment is outside descriptor table limits.
#PF(fault-code)	If a page fault occurs.
#AC(0)	If an unaligned memory access occurs when the CPL is 3 and alignment checking is enabled.

Real Address Mode Exceptions

#GP	If a memory operand effective address is outside the CS, DS, ES, FS, or GS segment limit.
	If the target offset is beyond the code segment limit.

Virtual 8086 Mode Exceptions

#GP(0)	If a memory operand effective address is outside the CS, DS, ES, FS, or GS segment limit.
	If the target offset is beyond the code segment limit.
#PF(fault-code)	If a page fault occurs.
#AC(0)	If an unaligned memory access occurs when alignment checking is enabled.

CBW/CWDE—Convert Byte to Word/Convert Word to Doubleword

Opcode	Instruction	Description
98	CBW	AX ← sign-extend of AL
98	CWDE	EAX ← sign-extend of AX

Description

Double the size of the source operand by means of sign extension (see Figure 6-5). The CBW (convert byte to word) instruction copies the sign (bit 7) in the source operand into every bit in the AH register. The CWDE (convert word to doubleword) instruction copies the sign (bit 15) of the word in the AX register into the higher 16 bits of the EAX register.

The CBW and CWDE mnemonics reference the same opcode. The CBW instruction is intended for use when the operand-size attribute is 16 and the CWDE instruction for when the operand-size attribute is 32. Some assemblers may force the operand size to 16 when CBW is used and to 32 when CWDE is used. Others may treat these mnemonics as synonyms (CBW/CWDE) and use the current setting of the operand-size attribute to determine the size of values to be converted, regardless of the mnemonic used.

The CWDE instruction is different from the CWD (convert word to double) instruction. The CWD instruction uses the DX:AX register pair as a destination operand; whereas, the CWDE instruction uses the EAX register as a destination.

Operation

```
IF OperandSize = 16 (* instruction = CBW *)
    THEN AX ← SignExtend(AL);
    ELSE (* OperandSize = 32, instruction = CWDE *)
        EAX ← SignExtend(AX);
FI;
```

Flags Affected

None.

Exceptions (All Operating Modes)

None.

CDQ—Convert Double to Quad

See entry for CWD/CDQ — Convert Word to Double/Convert Double to Quad.

CLC—Clear Carry Flag

Opcode	Instruction	Description
F8	CLC	Clear CF flag

Description

Clears the CF flag in the EFLAGS register.

Operation

CF ← 0;

Flags Affected

The CF flag is cleared to 0. The OF, ZF, SF, AF, and PF flags are unaffected.

Exceptions (All Operating Modes)

None.

CLD—Clear Direction Flag

Opcode	Instruction	Description
FC	CLD	Clear DF flag

Description

Clears the DF flag in the EFLAGS register. When the DF flag is set to 0, string operations increment the index registers (ESI and/or EDI).

Operation

DF ← 0;

Flags Affected

The DF flag is cleared to 0. The CF, OF, ZF, SF, AF, and PF flags are unaffected.

Exceptions (All Operating Modes)

None.

intel

CLI—Clear Interrupt Flag

Opcode	Instruction	Description
FA	CLI	Clear interrupt flag; interrupts disabled when interrupt flag cleared

Description

Clears the IF flag in the EFLAGS register. No other flags are affected. Clearing the IF flag causes the processor to ignore maskable external interrupts. The IF flag and the CLI and STI instruction have no affect on the generation of exceptions and NMI interrupts.

The following decision table indicates the action of the CLI instruction (bottom of the table) depending on the processor's mode of operating and the CPL and IOPL of the currently running program or procedure (top of the table).

PE =	0	1	1	1	1
VM =	X	0	X	0	1
CPL	X	≤ IOPL	X	> IOPL	X
IOPL	X	X	= 3	X	< 3
IF ← 0	Y	Y	Y	N	N
#GP(0)	N	N	N	Y	Y

NOTES:

X Don't care

N Action in column 1 not taken

Y Action in column 1 taken

Operation

```
IF PE = 0 (* Executing in real-address mode *)
    THEN
        IF ← 0;
    ELSE
        IF VM = 0   (* Executing in protected mode *)
            THEN
                IF CPL ≤ IOPL
                    THEN
                        IF ← 0;
                    ELSE
                        #GP(0);
                FI;
        FI;
```

```
            ELSE  (* Executing in Virtual-8086 mode  *)
                IF IOPL = 3
                    THEN
                        IF ← 0
                    ELSE
                        #GP(0);
                FI;
        FI;
FI;
```

Flags Affected

The IF is cleared to 0 if the CPL is equal to or less than the IOPL; otherwise, the it is not affected. The other flags in the EFLAGS register are unaffected.

Protected Mode Exceptions

#GP(0)   If the CPL is greater (has less privilege) than the IOPL of the current program or procedure.

Real Address Mode Exceptions

None.

Virtual 8086 Mode Exceptions

#GP(0)   If the CPL is greater (has less privilege) than the IOPL of the current program or procedure.

CLTS—Clear Task-Switched Flag in CR0

Opcode	Instruction	Description
0F 06	CLTS	Clears TS flag in CR0

Description

Clears the task-switched (TS) flag in the CR0 register. This instruction is intended for use in operating-system procedures. It is a privileged instruction that can only be executed at a CPL of 0. It is allowed to be executed in real-address mode to allow initialization for protected mode.

The processor sets the TS flag every time a task switch occurs. The flag is used to synchronize the saving of FPU context in multitasking applications. See the description of the TS flag in Chapter 2, "Control Registers", of the *Pentium® Pro Family Developer's Manual, Volume 3* for more information about this flag.

Operation

CR0(TS) ← 0;

Flags Affected

The TS flag in CR0 register is cleared.

Protected Mode Exceptions

#GP(0)   If the CPL is greater than 0.

Real Address Mode Exceptions

None.

Virtual 8086 Mode Exceptions

#GP(0)   If the CPL is greater than 0.

CMC—Complement Carry Flag

Opcode	Instruction	Description
F5	CMC	Complement CF flag

Description

Complements the CF flag in the EFLAGS register.

Operation

CF ← NOT CF;

Flags Affected

The CF flag contains the complement of its original value. The OF, ZF, SF, AF, and PF flags are unaffected.

Exceptions (All Operating Modes)

None.

CMOV*cc*—Conditional Move

Opcode	Instruction	Description
0F 47 *cw/cd*	CMOVA *r16, r/m16*	Move if above (CF=0 and ZF=0)
0F 47 *cw/cd*	CMOVA *r32, r/m32*	Move if above (CF=0 and ZF=0)
0F 43 *cw/cd*	CMOVAE *r16, r/m16*	Move if above or equal (CF=0)
0F 43 *cw/cd*	CMOVAE *r32, r/m32*	Move if above or equal (CF=0)
0F 42 *cw/cd*	CMOVB *r16, r/m16*	Move if below (CF=1)
0F 42 *cw/cd*	CMOVB *r32, r/m32*	Move if below (CF=1)
0F 46 *cw/cd*	CMOVBE *r16, r/m16*	Move if below or equal (CF=1 or ZF=1)
0F 46 *cw/cd*	CMOVBE *r32, r/m32*	Move if below or equal (CF=1 or ZF=1)
0F 42 *cw/cd*	CMOVC *r16, r/m16*	Move if carry (CF=1)
0F 42 *cw/cd*	CMOVC *r32, r/m32*	Move if carry (CF=1)
0F 44 *cw/cd*	CMOVE *r16, r/m16*	Move if equal (ZF=1)
0F 44 *cw/cd*	CMOVE *r32, r/m32*	Move if equal (ZF=1)
0F 4F *cw/cd*	CMOVG *r16, r/m16*	Move if greater (ZF=0 and SF=OF)
0F 4F *cw/cd*	CMOVG *r32, r/m32*	Move if greater (ZF=0 and SF=OF)
0F 4D *cw/cd*	CMOVGE *r16, r/m16*	Move if greater or equal (SF=OF)
0F 4D *cw/cd*	CMOVGE *r32, r/m32*	Move if greater or equal (SF=OF)
0F 4C *cw/cd*	CMOVL *r16, r/m16*	Move if less (SF<>OF)
0F 4C *cw/cd*	CMOVL *r32, r/m32*	Move if less (SF<>OF)
0F 4E *cw/cd*	CMOVLE *r16, r/m16*	Move if less or equal (ZF=1 or SF<>OF)
0F 4E *cw/cd*	CMOVLE *r32, r/m32*	Move if less or equal (ZF=1 or SF<>OF)
0F 46 *cw/cd*	CMOVNA *r16, r/m16*	Move if not above (CF=1 or ZF=1)
0F 46 *cw/cd*	CMOVNA *r32, r/m32*	Move if not above (CF=1 or ZF=1)
0F 42 *cw/cd*	CMOVNAE *r16, r/m16*	Move if not above or equal (CF=1)
0F 42 *cw/cd*	CMOVNAE *r32, r/m32*	Move if not above or equal (CF=1)
0F 43 *cw/cd*	CMOVNB *r16, r/m16*	Move if not below (CF=0)
0F 43 *cw/cd*	CMOVNB *r32, r/m32*	Move if not below (CF=0)
0F 47 *cw/cd*	CMOVNBE *r16, r/m16*	Move if not below or equal (CF=0 and ZF=0)
0F 47 *cw/cd*	CMOVNBE *r32, r/m32*	Move if not below or equal (CF=0 and ZF=0)
0F 43 *cw/cd*	CMOVNC *r16, r/m16*	Move if not carry (CF=0)
0F 43 *cw/cd*	CMOVNC *r32, r/m32*	Move if not carry (CF=0)
0F 45 *cw/cd*	CMOVNE *r16, r/m16*	Move if not equal (ZF=0)
0F 45 *cw/cd*	CMOVNE *r32, r/m32*	Move if not equal (ZF=0)
0F 4E *cw/cd*	CMOVNG *r16, r/m16*	Move if not greater (ZF=1 or SF<>OF)
0F 4E *cw/cd*	CMOVNG *r32, r/m32*	Move if not greater (ZF=1 or SF<>OF)
0F 4C *cw/cd*	CMOVNGE *r16, r/m16*	Move if not greater or equal (SF<>OF)
0F 4C *cw/cd*	CMOVNGE *r32, r/m32*	Move if not greater or equal (SF<>OF)
0F 4D *cw/cd*	CMOVNL *r16, r/m16*	Move if not less (SF=OF)
0F 4D *cw/cd*	CMOVNL *r32, r/m32*	Move if not less (SF=OF)
0F 4F *cw/cd*	CMOVNLE *r16, r/m16*	Move if not less or equal (ZF=0 and SF=OF)
0F 4F *cw/cd*	CMOVNLE *r32, r/m32*	Move if not less or equal (ZF=0 and SF=OF)

Opcode	Instruction	Description
0F 41 *cw/cd*	CMOVNO *r16, r/m16*	Move if not overflow (OF=0)
0F 41 *cw/cd*	CMOVNO *r32, r/m32*	Move if not overflow (OF=0)
0F 4B *cw/cd*	CMOVNP *r16, r/m16*	Move if not parity (PF=0)
0F 4B *cw/cd*	CMOVNP *r32, r/m32*	Move if not parity (PF=0)
0F 49 *cw/cd*	CMOVNS *r16, r/m16*	Move if not sign (SF=0)
0F 49 *cw/cd*	CMOVNS *r32, r/m32*	Move if not sign (SF=0)
0F 45 *cw/cd*	CMOVNZ *r16, r/m16*	Move if not zero (ZF=0)
0F 45 *cw/cd*	CMOVNZ *r32, r/m32*	Move if not zero (ZF=0)
0F 40 *cw/cd*	CMOVO *r16, r/m16*	Move if overflow (OF=0)
0F 40 *cw/cd*	CMOVO *r32, r/m32*	Move if overflow (OF=0)
0F 4A *cw/cd*	CMOVP *r16, r/m16*	Move if parity (PF=1)
0F 4A *cw/cd*	CMOVP *r32, r/m32*	Move if parity (PF=1)
0F 4A *cw/cd*	CMOVPE *r16, r/m16*	Move if parity even (PF=1)
0F 4A *cw/cd*	CMOVPE *r32, r/m32*	Move if parity even (PF=1)
0F 4B *cw/cd*	CMOVPO *r16, r/m16*	Move if parity odd (PF=0)
0F 4B *cw/cd*	CMOVPO *r32, r/m32*	Move if parity odd (PF=0)
0F 48 *cw/cd*	CMOVS *r16, r/m16*	Move if sign (SF=1)
0F 48 *cw/cd*	CMOVS *r32, r/m32*	Move if sign (SF=1)
0F 44 *cw/cd*	CMOVZ *r16, r/m16*	Move if zero (ZF=1)
0F 44 *cw/cd*	CMOVZ *r32, r/m32*	Move if zero (ZF=1)

Description

The CMOV*cc* instructions check the state of one or more of the status flags in the EFLAGS register (CF, OF, PF, SF, and ZF) and perform a move operation if the flags are in a specified state (or condition). A condition code (*cc*) is associated with each instruction to indicate the condition being tested for. If the condition is not satisfied, a move is not performed and execution continues with the instruction following the CMOV*cc* instruction.

These instructions can move a 16- or 32-bit value from memory to a general-purpose register or from one general-purpose register to another. Conditional moves of 8-bit register operands are not supported.

The conditions for each CMOV*cc* mnemonic is given in the description column of the above table. The terms "less" and "greater" are used for comparisons of signed integers and the terms "above" and "below" are used for unsigned integers.

Because a particular state of the status flags can sometimes be interpreted in two ways, two mnemonics are defined for some opcodes. For example, the CMOVA (conditional move if above) instruction and the CMOVNBE (conditional move if not below or equal) instruction are alternate mnemonics for the opcode 0F 47H.

The CMOV*cc* instructions are new for the Pentium Pro processor family; however, they may not be supported by all the processors in the family. Software can determine if the CMOV*cc* instructions are supported by checking the processor's feature information with the CPUID instruction (see Chapter 11, "CPUID—CPU Identification").

Operation

temp ← DEST
IF condition TRUE
   THEN
        DEST ← SRC
   ELSE
        DEST ← temp
FI;

Flags Affected

None.

Protected Mode Exceptions

#GP(0)	If a memory operand effective address is outside the CS, DS, ES, FS, or GS segment limit.
	If the DS, ES, FS, or GS register contains a null segment selector.
#SS(0)	If a memory operand effective address is outside the SS segment limit.
#PF(fault-code)	If a page fault occurs.
#AC(0)	If alignment checking is enabled and an unaligned memory reference is made while the current privilege level is 3.

Real Address Mode Exceptions

#GP	If a memory operand effective address is outside the CS, DS, ES, FS, or GS segment limit.
#SS	If a memory operand effective address is outside the SS segment limit.

Virtual 8086 Mode Exceptions

#GP(0)	If a memory operand effective address is outside the CS, DS, ES, FS, or GS segment limit.
#SS(0)	If a memory operand effective address is outside the SS segment limit.
#PF(fault-code)	If a page fault occurs.
#AC(0)	If alignment checking is enabled and an unaligned memory reference is made.

CMP—Compare Two Operands

Opcode	Instruction	Description
3C *ib*	CMP AL, *imm8*	Compare *imm8* with AL
3D *iw*	CMP AX, *imm16*	Compare *imm16* with AX
3D *id*	CMP EAX, *imm32*	Compare *imm32* with EAX
80 /7 *ib*	CMP *r/m8, imm8*	Compare *imm8* with *r/m8*
81 /7 *iw*	CMP *r/m16, imm16*	Compare *imm16* with *r/m16*
81 /7 *id*	CMP *r/m32,imm32*	Compare *imm32* with *r/m32*
83 /7 *ib*	CMP *r/m16,imm8*	Compare *imm8* with *r/m16*
83 /7 *ib*	CMP *r/m32,imm8*	Compare *imm8* with *r/m32*
38 /r	CMP *r/m8,r8*	Compare *r8* with *r/m8*
39 /r	CMP *r/m16,r16*	Compare *r16* with *r/m16*
39 /r	CMP *r/m32,r32*	Compare *r32* with *r/m32*
3A /r	CMP *r8,r/m8*	Compare *r/m8* with *r8*
3B /r	CMP *r16,r/m16*	Compare *r/m16* with *r16*
3B /r	CMP *r32,r/m32*	Compare *r/m32* with *r32*

Description

Compares the first source operand with the second source operand and sets the status flags in the EFLAGS register according to the results. The comparison is performed by subtracting the second operand from the first operand and then setting the status flags in the same manner as the SUB instruction. When an immediate value is used as an operand, it is sign-extended to the length of the first operand.

The CMP instruction is typically used in conjunction with a conditional jump (J*cc*), condition move (CMOV*cc*), or SET*cc* instruction. The condition codes used by the J*cc*, CMOV*cc*, and SET*cc* instructions are based on the results of a CMP instruction. Appendix B, *EFLAGS Condition Codes*, shows the relationship of the status flags and the condition codes.

Operation

temp ← SRC1 − SignExtend(SRC2);
ModifyStatusFlags; (* Modify status flags in the same manner as the SUB instruction*)

Flags Affected

The CF, OF, SF, ZF, AF, and PF flags are set according to the result.

Protected Mode Exceptions

#GP(0)   If a memory operand effective address is outside the CS, DS, ES, FS, or GS segment limit.

                       If the DS, ES, FS, or GS register contains a null segment selector.

#SS(0)   If a memory operand effective address is outside the SS segment limit.

#PF(fault-code)   If a page fault occurs.

#AC(0)   If alignment checking is enabled and an unaligned memory reference is
                    made while the current privilege level is 3.

Real Address Mode Exceptions

#GP   If a memory operand effective address is outside the CS, DS, ES, FS, or
                    GS segment limit.

#SS   If a memory operand effective address is outside the SS segment limit.

Virtual 8086 Mode Exceptions

#GP(0)   If a memory operand effective address is outside the CS, DS, ES, FS, or
                    GS segment limit.

#SS(0)   If a memory operand effective address is outside the SS segment limit.

#PF(fault-code)   If a page fault occurs.

#AC(0)   If alignment checking is enabled and an unaligned memory reference is
                    made.

CMPS/CMPSB/CMPSW/CMPSD—Compare String Operands

Opcode	Instruction	Description
A6	CMPS DS:(E)SI, ES:(E)DI	Compares byte at address DS:(E)SI with byte at address ES:(E)DI and sets the status flags accordingly
A7	CMPS DS:SI, ES:DI	Compares byte at address DS:SI with byte at address ES:DI and sets the status flags accordingly
A7	CMPS DS:ESI, ES:EDI	Compares byte at address DS:ESI with byte at address ES:EDI and sets the status flags accordingly
A6	CMPSB	Compares byte at address DS:(E)SI with byte at address ES:(E)DI and sets the status flags accordingly
A7	CMPSW	Compares byte at address DS:SI with byte at address ES:DI and sets the status flags accordingly
A7	CMPSD	Compares byte at address DS:ESI with byte at address ES:EDI and sets the status flags accordingly

Description

Compares the byte, word, or double word specified with the first source operand with the byte, word, or double word specified with the second source operand and sets the status flags in the EFLAGS register according to the results. The first source operand specifies the memory location at the address DS:ESI and the second source operand specifies the memory location at address ES:EDI. (When the operand-size attribute is 16, the SI and DI register are used as the source-index and destination-index registers, respectively.) The DS segment may be overridden with a segment override prefix, but the ES segment cannot be overridden.

The CMPSB, CMPSW, and CMPSD mnemonics are synonyms of the byte, word, and double-word versions of the CMPS instructions. They are simpler to use, but provide no type or segment checking. (For the CMPS instruction, "DS:ESI" and "ES:EDI" must be explicitly specified in the instruction.)

After the comparison, the ESI and EDI registers are incremented or decremented automatically according to the setting of the DF flag in the EFLAGS register. (If the DF flag is 0, the ESI and EDI register are incremented; if the DF flag is 1, the ESI and EDI registers are decremented.) The registers are incremented or decremented by 1 for byte operations, by 2 for word operations, or by 4 for doubleword operations.

The CMPS, CMPSB, CMPSW, and CMPSD instructions can be preceded by the REP prefix for block comparisons of ECX bytes, words, or doublewords. More often, however, these instructions will be used in a LOOP construct that takes some action based on the setting of the status flags before the next comparison is made. See Chapter 11, "REP/REPE/REPZ/REPNE /REPNZ—Repeat String Operation Prefix" for a description of the REP prefix.

Operation

```
temp ←SRC1 – SRC2;
SetStatusFlags(temp);
IF (byte comparison)
    THEN IF DF = 0
        THEN (E)DI ← 1;
        ELSE (E)DI ← –1;
    FI;
    ELSE IF (word comparison)
        THEN IF DF = 0
            THEN DI ← 2;
            ELSE DI ← –2;
        FI;
        ELSE (* doubleword comparison *)
            THEN IF DF = 0
                THEN EDI ← 4;
                ELSE EDI ← –4;
            FI;
    FI;
FI;
```

Flags Affected

The CF, OF, SF, ZF, AF, and PF flags are set according to the temporary result of the comparison.

Protected Mode Exceptions

#GP(0)	If a memory operand effective address is outside the CS, DS, ES, FS, or GS segment limit.
	If the DS, ES, FS, or GS register contains a null segment selector.
#SS(0)	If a memory operand effective address is outside the SS segment limit.
#PF(fault-code)	If a page fault occurs.
#AC(0)	If alignment checking is enabled and an unaligned memory reference is made while the current privilege level is 3.

Real Address Mode Exceptions

#GP	If a memory operand effective address is outside the CS, DS, ES, FS, or GS segment limit.
#SS	If a memory operand effective address is outside the SS segment limit.

Virtual 8086 Mode Exceptions

#GP(0)   If a memory operand effective address is outside the CS, DS, ES, FS, or GS segment limit.

#SS(0)   If a memory operand effective address is outside the SS segment limit.

#PF(fault-code)   If a page fault occurs.

#AC(0)   If alignment checking is enabled and an unaligned memory reference is made.

CMPXCHG—Compare and Exchange

Opcode	Instruction	Description
0F B0/r	CMPXCHG r/m8,r8	Compare AL with r/m8. If equal, ZF is set and r8 is loaded into r/m8. Else, clear ZF and load r/m8 into AL.
0F B1/r	CMPXCHG r/m16,r16	Compare AX with r/m16. If equal, ZF is set and r16 is loaded into r/m16. Else, clear ZF and load r/m16 into AL
0F B1/r	CMPXCHG r/m32,r32	Compare EAX with r/m32. If equal, ZF is set and r32 is loaded into r/m32. Else, clear ZF and load r/m32 into AL

Description

Compares the value in the AL, AX, or EAX register (depending on the size of the operand) with the first operand (destination operand). If the two values are equal, the second operand (source operand) is loaded into the destination operand. Otherwise, the destination operand is loaded into the AL, AX, or EAX register.

This instruction can be used with a LOCK prefix to allow the instruction to be executed atomically. To simplify the interface to the processor's bus, the destination operand receives a write cycle without regard to the result of the comparison. The destination operand is written back if the comparison fails; otherwise, the source operand is written into the destination. (The processor never produces a locked read without also producing a locked write.)

Operation

```
(* accumulator = AL, AX, or EAX, depending on whether *)
(* a byte, word, or doubleword comparison is being performed*)
IF accumulator = DEST
    THEN
        ZF ← 1
        DEST ← SRC
    ELSE
        ZF ← 0
        accumulator ← DEST
FI;
```

Flags Affected

The ZF flag is set if the values in the destination operand and register AL, AX, or EAX are; otherwise it is cleared. The CF, PF, AF, SF, and OF flags are set according to the results of the comparison operation.

Protected Mode Exceptions

#GP(0)	If the destination is located in a nonwritable segment.
	If a memory operand effective address is outside the CS, DS, ES, FS, or GS segment limit.
	If the DS, ES, FS, or GS register contains a null segment selector.
#SS(0)	If a memory operand effective address is outside the SS segment limit.
#PF(fault-code)	If a page fault occurs.
#AC(0)	If alignment checking is enabled and an unaligned memory reference is made while the current privilege level is 3.

Real Address Mode Exceptions

#GP	If a memory operand effective address is outside the CS, DS, ES, FS, or GS segment limit.
#SS	If a memory operand effective address is outside the SS segment limit.

Virtual 8086 Mode Exceptions

#GP(0)	If a memory operand effective address is outside the CS, DS, ES, FS, or GS segment limit.
#SS(0)	If a memory operand effective address is outside the SS segment limit.
#PF(fault-code)	If a page fault occurs.
#AC(0)	If alignment checking is enabled and an unaligned memory reference is made.

Intel Architecture Compatibility

This instruction is not supported on Intel processors earlier than the Intel486 processors.

CMPXCHG8B—Compare and Exchange 8 Bytes

Opcode	Instruction	Description
0F C7 /1 m64	CMPXCHG8B *m64*	Compare EDX:EAX with *m64*. If equal, set ZF and load ECX:EBX into *m64*. Else, clear ZF and load *m64* into EDX:EAX.

Description

Compares the 64-bit value in EDX:EAX with the operand (destination operand). If the values are equal, the 64-bit value in ECX:EBX is stored in the destination operand. Otherwise, the value in the destination operand is loaded into EDX:EAX. The destination operand is an 8-byte memory location. For the EDX:EAX and ECX:EBX register pairs, EDX and ECX contain the high-order 32 bits and EAX and EBX contain the low-order 32 bits of a 64-bit value.

This instruction can be used with a LOCK prefix to allow the instruction to be executed atomically. To simplify the interface to the processor's bus, the destination operand receives a write cycle without regard to the result of the comparison. The destination operand is written back if the comparison fails; otherwise, the source operand is written into the destination. (The processor never produces a locked read without also producing a locked write.)

Operation

```
IF (EDX:EAX = DEST)
    ZF ← 1
    DEST ← ECX:EBX
ELSE
    ZF ← 0
    EDX:EAX ← DEST
```

Flags Affected

The ZF flag is set if the destination operand and EDX:EAX are equal; otherwise it is cleared. The CF, PF, AF, SF, and OF flags are unaffected.

Protected Mode Exceptions

#UD	If the destination operand is not a memory location.
#GP(0)	If the destination is located in a nonwritable segment.
	If a memory operand effective address is outside the CS, DS, ES, FS, or GS segment limit.
	If the DS, ES, FS, or GS register contains a null segment selector.
#SS(0)	If a memory operand effective address is outside the SS segment limit.
#PF(fault-code)	If a page fault occurs.

| #AC(0) | If alignment checking is enabled and an unaligned memory reference is made while the current privilege level is 3. |

Real Address Mode Exceptions

| #GP | If a memory operand effective address is outside the CS, DS, ES, FS, or GS segment limit. |
| #SS | If a memory operand effective address is outside the SS segment limit. |

Virtual 8086 Mode Exceptions

#GP(0)	If a memory operand effective address is outside the CS, DS, ES, FS, or GS segment limit.
#SS(0)	If a memory operand effective address is outside the SS segment limit.
#PF(fault-code)	If a page fault occurs.
#AC(0)	If alignment checking is enabled and an unaligned memory reference is made.

Intel Architecture Compatibility

This instruction is not supported on Intel processors earlier than the Pentium processors.

CPUID—CPU Identification

Opcode	Instruction	Description
0F A2	CPUID	EAX ← Processor identification information

Description

Provides processor identification information in registers EAX, EBX, ECX, and EDX. This information identifies Intel as the vendor, gives the family, model, and stepping of processor, feature information, and cache information. An input value loaded into the EAX register determines what information is returned, as shown in Table 11-7.

Table 11-7. Information Returned by CPUID Instruction

Initial EAX Value		Information Provided about the Processor
0	EAX	Maximum CPUID Input Value (2 for the Pentium® Pro Processor)
	EBX	"Genu"
	ECX	"inel"
	EDX	"ntel"
1	EAX	Version Information (Type, Family, Model, and Stepping ID)
	EBX	Reserved
	ECX	Reserved
	EDX	Feature Information
2	EAX	Cache Information
	EBX	Cache Information
	ECX	Cache Information
	EDX	Cache Information

The CPUID instruction can be executed at any privilege level to serialize instruction execution. Serializing instruction execution guarantees that any modifications to flags, registers, and memory for previous instructions are completed before the next instruction is fetched and executed (see "Serializing Instructions" in Chapter 7, *Multiple Processor Management*, of the *Pentium® Pro Family Developer's Manual, Volume 3*).

When the input value in register EAX is 0, the processor returns the highest value the CPUID instruction recognizes in the EAX register. For the Pentium Pro processor, the highest recognized value is 2. A vendor identification string is returned in the EBX, EDX, and ECX registers. For Intel processors, the vendor identification string is "GenuineIntel" as follows:

```
EBX ← 756e6547h (* "Genu", with G in the low nibble of BL *)
EDX ← 49656e69h (* "ineI", with i in the low nibble of DL *)
ECX ← 6c65746eh (* "ntel", with n in the low nibble of CL *)
```

When the input value is 1, the processor returns version information in the EAX register and feature information in the EDX register (see Figure 11-4).

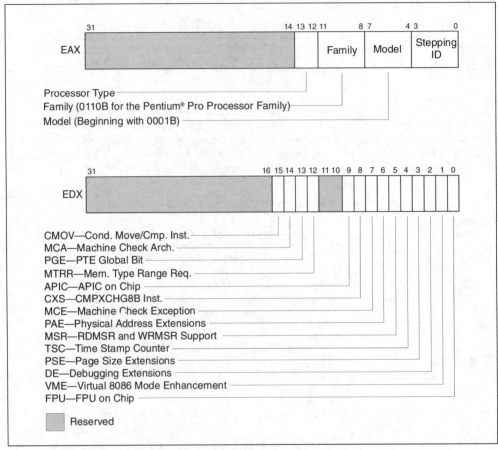

Figure 11-4. Version and Feature Information in Registers EAX and EDX

The version information consists of an Intel Architecture family identifier, a model identifier, a stepping ID, and a processor type. The model, family, and processor type for the first processor in the Intel Pentium Pro family is as follows:

- Model—0001B

- Family—0110B

- Processor Type—00B

See "Intel Application Note 485 — Intel Processor Identification With the CPUID Instruction" and the *"Intel Pentium® Pro Processor Specification Update"* for more information on identifying earlier Intel Architecture processors. The available processor types are given in Table 11-8. Intel releases information on stepping IDs as needed.

Table 11-8. Processor Type Field

Type	Encoding
Original OEM Processor	00B
Intel OverDrive® Processor	01B
Dual processor*	10B
Intel reserved.	11B

NOTE:

* Not applicable to Intel386 and Intel486 processors.

Table 11-9 shows the encoding of the feature flags in the EDX register. A feature flag set to 1 indicates the corresponding feature is supported. Software should identify Intel as the vendor to properly interpret the feature flags.

Table 11-9. Feature Flags Returned in EDX Register

Bit	Feature	Description
0	FPU—Floating Point Unit on Chip	Processor contains an FPU and executes the Intel387™ instruction set.
1	VME—Virtual 8086 Mode Enhancements	Processor supports the following virtual 8086 mode enhancements: • CR4.VME bit enables virtual 8086 mode extensions. • CR4.PVI bit enables protected-mode virtual interrupts. • Expansion of the TSS with the software indirection bitmap. • EFLAGS.VIF bit enables the virtual interrupt flag. • EFLAGS.VIP bit enables the virtual interrupt pending flag.
2	DE—Debugging Extensions	Processor supports I/O breakpoints, including the CR4.DE bit for enabling debug extensions and optional trapping of access to the DR4 and DR5 registers.
3	PSE—Page Size Extensions	Processor supports 4-Mbyte pages, including the CR4.PSE bit for enabling page size extensions, the modified bit in page directory entries (PDEs), page directory entries, and page table entries (PTEs).
4	TSC—Time Stamp Counter	Processor supports the RDTSC (read time stamp counter) instruction, including the CR4.TSD bit that, along with the CPL, controls whether the time stamp counter can be read.
5	MSR—Model Specific Registers	Processor supports the RDMSR (read model-specific register) and WRMSR (write model-specific register) instructions.
6	PAE—Physical Address Extension	Processor supports physical addresses greater than 32 bits, the extended page-table-entry format, an extra level in the page translation tables, and 2-MByte pages. The CR4.PAE bit enables this feature. The number of address bits is implementation specific. The Pentium® Pro processor supports 36 bits of addressing when the PAE bit is set.

Table 11-9. Feature Flags Returned in EDX Register (Contd.)

Bit	Feature	Description
7	MCE—Machine Check Exception	Processor supports the CR4.MCE bit, enabling machine check exceptions. However, this feature does not define the model-specific implementations of machine-check error logging, reporting, or processor shutdowns. Machine-check exception handlers might have to check the processor version to do model-specific processing of the exception or check for the presence of the standard machine-check feature.
8	CX8—CMPXCHG8B Instruction	Processor supports the CMPXCHG8B (compare and exchange 8 bytes) instruction.
9	APIC	Processor contains an on-chip Advanced Programmable Interrupt Controller (APIC) and it has been enabled and is available for use.
10,11	Reserved	
12	MTRR—Memory Type Range Registers	Processor supports machine-specific memory-type range registers (MTRRs). The MTRRs contains bit fields that indicate the processor's MTRR capabilities, including which memory types the processor supports, the number of variable MTRRs the processor supports, and whether the processor supports fixed MTRRs.
13	PGE—PTE Global Flag	Processor supports the CR4.PGE flag enabling the global bit in both PTDEs and PTEs. These bits are used to indicate translation lookaside buffer (TLB) entries that are common to different tasks and need not be flushed when control register CR3 is written.
14	MCA—Machine Check Architecture	Processor supports the MCG_CAP (machine check global capability) MSR. The MCG_CAP register indicates how many banks of error reporting MSRs the processor supports.
15	CMOV—Conditional Move and Compare Instructions	Processor supports the CMOVcc instruction and, if the FPU feature flag (bit 0) is also set, supports the FCMOVcc and FCOMI instructions.
16-31	Reserved	

When the input value is 2, the processor returns information about the processor's internal caches and TLBs in the EAX, EBX, ECX, and EDX registers. The encoding of these registers is as follows:

- The least-significant byte in register EAX (register AL) indicates the number of times the CPUID instruction must be executed with an input value of 2 to get a complete description of the processor's caches and TLBs. The Pentium Pro family of processors will return a 1.

- The most significant bit (bit 31) of each register indicates whether the register contains valid information (cleared to 0) or is reserved (set to 1).

- If a register contains valid information, the information is contained in 1 byte descriptors. Table 11-10 shows the encoding of these descriptors.

Table 11-10. Encoding of Cache and TLB Descriptors

Descriptor Value	Cache or TLB Description
00H	Null descriptor
01H	Instruction TLB: 4K-Byte Pages, 4-way set associative, 64 entries
02H	Instruction TLB: 4M-Byte Pages, 4-way set associative, 4 entries
03H	Data TLB: 4K-Byte Pages, 4-way set associative, 64 entries
04H	Data TLB: 4M-Byte Pages, 4-way set associative, 8 entries
06H	Instruction cache: 8K Bytes, 4-way set associative, 32 byte line size
0AH	Data cache: 8K Bytes, 2-way set associative, 32 byte line size
41H	Unified cache: 128K Bytes, 4-way set associative, 32 byte line size
42H	Unified cache: 256K Bytes, 4-way set associative, 32 byte line size
43H	Unified cache: 512K Bytes, 4-way set associative, 32 byte line size

The first member of the Pentium Pro processor family will return the following information about caches and TLBs when the CPUID instruction is executed with an input value of 2:

EAX	03 02 01 01H
EBX	0H
ECX	0H
EDX	06 04 0A 42H

These values are interpreted as follows:

- The least-significant byte (byte 0) of register EAX is set to 01H, indicating that the CPUID instruction needs to be executed only once with an input value of 2 to retrieve complete information about the processor's caches and TLBs.

- The most-significant bit of all four registers (EAX, EBX, ECX, and EDX) is set to 0, indicating that each register contains valid 1-byte descriptors.

- Bytes 1, 2, and 3 of register EAX indicate that the processor contains the following:

  — 01H—A 64-entry instruction TLB (4-way set associative) for mapping 4-KByte pages.

  — 02H—A 4-entry instruction TLB (4-way set associative) for mapping 4-MByte pages.

  — 03H—A 64-entry data TLB (4-way set associative) for mapping 4-KByte pages.

- The descriptors in registers EBX and ECX are valid, but contain null descriptors.

- Bytes 0, 1, 2, and 3 of register EDX indicate that the processor contains the following:

  — 42H—A 256-KByte unified cache (the L2 cache), 4-way set associative, with a 32-byte cache line size.

  — 0AH—An 8-KByte data cache (the L1 data cache), 2-way set associative, with a 32-byte cache line size.

  — 04H—An 8-entry data TLB (4-way set associative) for mapping 4M-byte pages.

— 06H—An 8-KByte instruction cache (the L1 instruction cache), 4-way set associative, with a 32-byte cache line size.

Operation

```
CASE (EAX) OF
    EAX = 0:
        EAX ← highest input value understood by CPUID; (* 2 for Pentium Pro processor *)
        EBX ← Vendor identification string;
        EDX ← Vendor identification string;
        ECX ← Vendor identification string;
    BREAK;
    EAX = 1:
        EAX[3:0] ← Stepping ID;
        EAX[7:4] ← Model;
        EAX[11:8] ← Family;
        EAX[13:12] ← Processor type;
        EAX[31:12] ← Reserved;
        EBX ← Reserved;
        ECX ← Reserved;
        EDX ← Feature flags;  (* See Figure 11-4 *)

    BREAK;
    EAX = 2:
        EAX ← Cache information;
        EBX ← Cache information;
        ECX ← Cache information;
        EDX ← Cache information;
    BREAK;
    DEFAULT: (* EAX > highest value recognized by CPUID *)
        EAX ← reserved, undefined;
        EBX ← reserved, undefined;
        ECX ← reserved, undefined;
        EDX ← reserved, undefined;
    BREAK;
ESAC;
```

Flags Affected

None.

Exceptions (All Operating Modes)

None.

Intel Architecture Compatibility

The CPUID instruction is not supported in early models of the Intel486 processor or in any Intel Architecture processor earlier than the Intel486 processor. The ID flag in the EFLAGS register can be used to determine if this instruction is supported. If a procedure is able to set or clear this flag, the CPUID is supported by the processor running the procedure.

CWD/CDQ—Convert Word to Doubleword/Convert Doubleword to Quadword

Opcode	Instruction	Description
99	CWD	DX:AX ← sign-extend of AX
99	CDQ	EDX:EAX ← sign-extend of EAX

Description

Doubles the size of the operand in register AX or EAX (depending on the operand size) by means of sign extension and stores the result in registers DX:AX or EDX:EAX, respectively. The CWD instruction copies the sign (bit 15) of the value in the AX register into every bit position in the DX register (see Figure 6-5). The CDQ instruction copies the sign (bit 31) of the value in the EAX register into every bit position in the EDX register.

The CWD instruction can be used to produce a doubleword dividend from a word before a word division, and the CDQ instruction can be used to produce a quadword dividend from a doubleword before doubleword division.

The CWD and CDQ mnemonics reference the same opcode. The CWD instruction is intended for use when the operand-size attribute is 16 and the CDQ instruction for when the operand-size attribute is 32. Some assemblers may force the operand size to 16 when CWD is used and to 32 when CDQ is used. Others may treat these mnemonics as synonyms (CWD/CDQ) and use the current setting of the operand-size attribute to determine the size of values to be converted, regardless of the mnemonic used.

Operation

```
IF OperandSize = 16 (* CWD instruction *)
    THEN DX ← SignExtend(AX);
    ELSE (* OperandSize = 32, CDQ instruction *)
        EDX ← SignExtend(EAX);
FI;
```

Flags Affected

None.

Exceptions (All Operating Modes)

None.

CWDE—Convert Word to Doubleword

See entry for CBW/CWDE—Convert Byte to Word/Convert Word to Doubleword.

DAA—Decimal Adjust AL after Addition

Opcode	Instruction	Description
27	DAA	Decimal adjust AL after addition

Description

Adjusts the sum of two packed BCD values to create a packed BCD result. The AL register is the implied source and destination operand. The DAA instruction is only useful when it follows an ADD instruction that adds (binary addition) two 2-digit, packed BCD values and stores a byte result in the AL register. The DAA instruction then adjusts the contents of the AL register to contain the correct 2-digit, packed BCD result. If a decimal carry is detected, the CF and AF flags are set accordingly.

Operation

```
IF (((AL AND 0FH) > 9) or AF = 1)
    THEN
        AL ← AL + 6;
        CF ← CF OR CarryFromLastAddition; (* CF OR carry from AL ← AL + 6 *)
        AF ← 1;
    ELSE
        AF ← 0;
FI;
IF ((AL AND F0H) > 90H) or CF = 1)
    THEN
        AL ← AL + 60H;
        CF ← 1;
    ELSE
        CF ← 0;
FI;
```

Example

```
ADD AL, BL      Before: AL=79H  BL=35H EFLAGS(OSZAPC)=XXXXXX
                After:  AL=AEH  BL=35H EFLAGS(OSZAPC)=110000
DAA             Before: AL=79H  BL=35H EFLAGS(OSZAPC)=110000
                After:  AL=AEH  BL=35H EFLAGS(OSZAPC)=X00111
```

Flags Affected

The CF and AF flags are set if the adjustment of the value results in a decimal carry in either digit of the result (see "Operation" above). The SF, ZF, and PF flags are set according to the result. The OF flag is undefined.

Exceptions (All Operating Modes)

None.

DAS—Decimal Adjust AL after Subtraction

Opcode	Instruction	Description
2F	DAS	Decimal adjust AL after subtraction

Description

Adjusts the result of the subtraction of two packed BCD values to create a packed BCD result. The AL register is the implied source and destination operand. The DAS instruction is only useful when it follows a SUB instruction that subtracts (binary subtraction) one 2-digit, packed BCD value from another and stores a byte result in the AL register. The DAS instruction then adjusts the contents of the AL register to contain the correct 2-digit, packed BCD result. If a decimal borrow is detected, the CF and AF flags are set accordingly.

Operation

```
IF (AL AND 0FH) > 9 OR AF = 1
    THEN
        AL ← AL – 6;
        CF ← CF OR BorrowFromLastSubtraction; (* CF OR borrow from AL ← AL – 6 *)
        AF ← 1;
    ELSE AF ← 0;
FI;
IF ((AL > 9FH) or CF = 1)
    THEN
        AL ← AL – 60H;
        CF ← 1;
    ELSE CF ← 0;
FI;
```

Example

```
SUB AL, BL      Before: AL=35H  BL=47H EFLAGS(OSZAPC)=XXXXXX
                After:  AL=EEH  BL=47H EFLAGS(0SZAPC)=010111
DAA             Before: AL=EEH  BL=47H EFLAGS(OSZAPC)=010111
                After:  AL=88H  BL=47H EFLAGS(0SZAPC)=X10111
```

Flags Affected

The CF and AF flags are set if the adjustment of the value results in a decimal borrow in either digit of the result (see "Operation" above). The SF, ZF, and PF flags are set according to the result. The OF flag is undefined.

Exceptions (All Operating Modes)

None.

DEC—Decrement by 1

Opcode	Instruction	Description
FE /1	DEC r/m8	Decrement r/m8 by 1
FF /1	DEC r/m16	Decrement r/m16 by 1
FF /1	DEC r/m32	Decrement r/m32 by 1
48+rw	DEC r16	Decrement r16 by 1
48+rd	DEC r32	Decrement r32 by 1

Description

Subtracts 1 from the operand, while preserving the state of the CF flag. The source operand can be a register or a memory location. This instruction allows a loop counter to be updated without disturbing the CF flag. (Use a SUB instruction with an immediate operand of 1 to perform a decrement operation that does updates the CF flag.)

Operation

DEST ← DEST – 1;

Flags Affected

The CF flag is not affected. The OF, SF, ZF, AF, and PF flags are set according to the result.

Protected Mode Exceptions

#GP(0)	If the destination is located in a nonwritable segment.
	If a memory operand effective address is outside the CS, DS, ES, FS, or GS segment limit.
	If the DS, ES, FS, or GS register contains a null segment selector.
#SS(0)	If a memory operand effective address is outside the SS segment limit.
#PF(fault-code)	If a page fault occurs.
#AC(0)	If alignment checking is enabled and an unaligned memory reference is made while the current privilege level is 3.

Real Address Mode Exceptions

#GP	If a memory operand effective address is outside the CS, DS, ES, FS, or GS segment limit.
#SS	If a memory operand effective address is outside the SS segment limit.

Virtual 8086 Mode Exceptions

#GP(0)	If a memory operand effective address is outside the CS, DS, ES, FS, or GS segment limit.
#SS(0)	If a memory operand effective address is outside the SS segment limit.
#PF(fault-code)	If a page fault occurs.
#AC(0)	If alignment checking is enabled and an unaligned memory reference is made.

DIV—Unsigned Divide

Opcode	Instruction	Description
F6 /6	DIV r/m8	Unsigned divide AX by r/m8; AL ← Quotient, AH ← Remainder
F7 /6	DIV r/m16	Unsigned divide DX:AX by r/m16; AX ← Quotient, DX ← Remainder
F7 /6	DIV r/m32	Unsigned divide EDX:EAX by r/m32 doubleword; EAX ← Quotient, EDX ← Remainder

Description

Divides (unsigned) the value in the AL, AX, or EAX register (dividend) by the source operand (divisor) and stores the result in the AX, DX:AX, or EDX:EAX registers. The source operand can be a general-purpose register or a memory location. The action of this instruction depends on the operand size, as shown in the following table:

Operand Size	Dividend	Divisor	Quotient	Remainder	Maximum Quotient
Word/byte	AX	r/m8	AL	AH	255
Doubleword/word	DX:AX	r/m16	AX	DX	65,535
Quadword/doubleword	EDX:EAX	r/m32	EAX	EDX	$2^{32} - 1$

Non-integral results are truncated (chopped) towards 0. The remainder is always less than the divisor in magnitude. Overflow is indicated with the #DE (divide error) exception rather than with the CF flag.

Operation

```
IF SRC = 0
    THEN #DE; (* divide error *)
FI;
IF OpernadSize = 8 (* word/byte operation *)
    THEN
        temp ← AX / SRC;
        IF temp > FFH
            THEN #DE; (* divide error *) ;
            ELSE
                AL ← temp;
                AH ← AX MOD SRC;
        FI;
    ELSE
        IF OpernadSize = 16 (* doubleword/word operation *)
            THEN
```

```
temp ← DX:AX / SRC;

IF temp > FFFFH
    THEN #DE; (* divide error *) ;
    ELSE
        AX ← temp;
        DX ← DX:AX MOD SRC;
FI;
ELSE (* quadword/doubleword operation *)
    temp ← EDX:EAX / SRC;
    IF temp > FFFFFFFFH
        THEN #DE; (* divide error *) ;
        ELSE
            EAX ← temp;
            EDX ← EDX:EAX MOD SRC;
    FI;
FI;
FI;
```

Flags Affected

The CF, OF, SF, ZF, AF, and PF flags are undefined.

Protected Mode Exceptions

#DE	If the source operand (divisor) is 0
	If the quotient is too large for the designated register.
#GP(0)	If a memory operand effective address is outside the CS, DS, ES, FS, or GS segment limit.
	If the DS, ES, FS, or GS register contains a null segment selector.
#SS(0)	If a memory operand effective address is outside the SS segment limit.
#PF(fault-code)	If a page fault occurs.
#AC(0)	If alignment checking is enabled and an unaligned memory reference is made while the current privilege level is 3.

Real Address Mode Exceptions

#DE	If the source operand (divisor) is 0.
	If the quotient is too large for the designated register.
#GP	If a memory operand effective address is outside the CS, DS, ES, FS, or GS segment limit.
	If the DS, ES, FS, or GS register contains a null segment selector.

Virtual 8086 Mode Exceptions

#DE	If the source operand (divisor) is 0.
	If the quotient is too large for the designated register.
#GP(0)	If a memory operand effective address is outside the CS, DS, ES, FS, or GS segment limit.
#SS	If a memory operand effective address is outside the SS segment limit.
#PF(fault-code)	If a page fault occurs.
#AC(0)	If alignment checking is enabled and an unaligned memory reference is made.

ENTER—Make Stack Frame for Procedure Parameters

Opcode	Instruction	Description
C8 iw 00	ENTER imm16,0	Create a stack frame for a procedure
C8 iw 01	ENTER imm16,1	Create a nested stack frame for a procedure
C8 iw ib	ENTER imm16,imm8	Create a nested stack frame for a procedure

Description

Creates a stack frame for a procedure. The first operand (size operand) specifies the size of the stack frame (that is, the number of bytes of dynamic storage allocated on the stack for the procedure). The second operand (nesting level operand) gives the lexical nesting level (0 to 31) of the procedure. The nesting level determines the number of stack frame pointers that are copied into the "display area" of the new stack frame from the preceding frame. Both of these operands are immediate values.

The stack-size attribute determines whether the BP (16 bits) or EBP (32 bits) register specifies the current frame pointer and whether SP (16 bits) or ESP (32 bits) specifies the stack pointer.

The ENTER and companion LEAVE instructions are provided to support block structured languages. They do not provide a jump or call to another procedure; they merely set up a new stack frame for an already called procedure. An ENTER instruction is commonly followed by a CALL, JMP, or Jcc instruction to transfer program control to the procedure being called.

If the nesting level is 0, the processor pushes the frame pointer from the EBP register onto the stack, copies the current stack pointer from the ESP register into the EBP register, and loads the ESP register with the current stack-pointer value minus the value in the size operand. For nesting levels of 1 or greater, the processor pushes additional frame pointers on the stack before adjusting the stack pointer. These additional frame pointers provide the called procedure with access points to other nested frames on the stack. See Section 4.5., "Procedure Calls for Block-Structured Languages" for more information about the actions of the ENTER instruction.

Operation

```
NestingLevel ← NestingLevel MOD 32
IF StackSize = 32
    THEN
        Push(EBP) ;
        FrameTemp ← ESP;
    ELSE (* StackSize = 16*)
        Push(BP);
        FrameTemp ← SP;
FI;
IF NestingLevel = 0
    THEN GOTO CONTINUE;
FI;
```

```
IF (NestingLevel > 0)
    FOR i ← 1 TO (NestingLevel – 1)
        DO
            IF OperandSize = 32
                THEN
                    IF StackSize = 32
                        EBP ← EBP – 4;
                        Push([EBP]); (* doubleword push *)
                    ELSE (* StackSize = 16*)
                        BP ← BP – 4;
                        Push([BP]); (* doubleword push *)
                    FI;
                ELSE (* OperandSize = 16 *)
                    IF StackSize = 32
                        THEN
                            EBP ← EBP – 2;
                            Push([EBP]); (* word push *)
                        ELSE (* StackSize = 16*)
                            BP ← BP – 2;
                            Push([BP]); (* word push *)
                    FI;
            FI;
        OD;
    IF OperandSize = 32
        THEN
            Push(FrameTemp); (* doubleword push *)
        ELSE (* OperandSize = 16 *)
            Push(FrameTemp); (* word push *)
    FI;
    GOTO CONTINUE;
FI;
CONTINUE:
IF StackSize = 32
    THEN
        EBP ← FrameTemp
        ESP ← EBP – Size;
    ELSE (* StackSize = 16*)
        BP ← FrameTemp
        SP ← BP – Size;
FI;
END;
```

Flags Affected

None.

Protected Mode Exceptions

#SS(0)   If the new value of the SP or ESP register is outside the stack segment limit.

#PF(fault-code)   If a page fault occurs.

Real Address Mode Exceptions

None.

Virtual 8086 Mode Exceptions

None.

F2XM1—Compute 2^x-1

Opcode	Instruction	Description
D9 F0	F2XM1	Replace ST(0) with $(2^{ST(0)} - 1)$

Description

Calculates the exponential value of 2 to the power of the source operand minus 1. The source operand is located in register ST(0) and the result is also stored in ST(0). The value of the source operand must lie in the range −1.0 to +1.0. If the source value is outside this range, the result is undefined.

The following table shows the results obtained when computing the exponential value of various classes of numbers, assuming that neither overflow nor underflow occurs.

ST(0) SRC	ST(0) DEST
-1.0 to –0	−0.5 to –0
–0	–0
+0	+0
+0 to +1.0	+0 to 1.0

Values other than 2 can be exponentiated using the following formula:

$$x^y = 2^{(y * \log_2 x)}$$

Operation

$ST(0) \leftarrow (2^{ST(0)} - 1);$

FPU Flags Affected

C1   Set to 0 if stack underflow occurred.

                    Indicates rounding direction if the inexact-result exception (#P) is generated: 0 = not roundup; 1 = roundup.

C0, C2, C3   Undefined.

Floating-Point Exceptions

#IS   Stack underflow occurred.

#IA   Source operand is an SNaN value or unsupported format.

#D   Result is a denormal value.

#U   Result is too small for destination format.

#P   Value cannot be represented exactly in destination format.

Protected Mode Exceptions

#NM   EM or TS in CR0 is set.

Real Address Mode Exceptions

#NM   EM or TS in CR0 is set.

Virtual 8086 Mode Exceptions

#NM   EM or TS in CR0 is set.

FABS—Absolute Value

Opcode	Instruction	Description
D9 E1	FABS	Replace ST with its absolute value.

Description

Clears the sign bit of ST(0) to create the absolute value of the operand. The following table shows the results obtained when creating the absolute value of various classes of numbers.

ST(0) SRC	ST(0) DEST
−∞	+∞
−F	+F
−0	+0
+0	+0
+F	+F
+∞	+∞
NaN	NaN

NOTE:
F Means finite-real number

Operation

$ST(0) \leftarrow |ST(0)|$

FPU Flags Affected

C1   Set to 0 if stack underflow occurred; otherwise, cleared to 0.
C0, C2, C3 Undefined.

Floating-Point Exceptions

#IS   Stack underflow occurred.

Protected Mode Exceptions

#NM   EM or TS in CR0 is set.

Real Address Mode Exceptions

#NM   EM or TS in CR0 is set.

Virtual 8086 Mode Exceptions

#NM   EM or TS in CR0 is set.

FADD/FADDP/FIADD—Add

Opcode	Instruction	Description
D8 /0	FADD *m32 real*	Add *m32real* to ST(0) and store result in ST(0)
DC /0	FADD *m64real*	Add *m64real* to ST(0) and store result in ST(0)
D8 C0+i	FADD ST(0), ST(i)	Add ST(0) to ST(i) and store result in ST(0)
DC C0+i	FADD ST(i), ST(0)	Add ST(i) to ST(0) and store result in ST(*i*)
DE C0+i	FADDP ST(i), ST(0)	Add ST(0) to ST(i), store result in ST(*i*), and pop the register stack
DE C1	FADDP	Add ST(0) to ST(1), store result in ST(1), and pop the register stack
DA /0	FIADD *m32int*	Add *m32int* to ST(0) and store result in ST(0)
DE /0	FIADD *m16int*	Add *m16int* to ST(0) and store result in ST(0)

Description

Adds the destination and source operands and stores the sum in the destination location. The destination operand is always an FPU register; the source operand can be a register or a memory location. Source operands in memory can be in single-real, double-real, word-integer, or short-integer formats.

The no-operand version of the instruction adds the contents of the ST(0) register to the ST(1) register. The one-operand version adds the contents of a memory location (either a real or an integer value) to the contents of the ST(0) register. The two-operand version, adds the contents of the ST(0) register to the ST(*i*) register or vice versa. The value in ST(0) can be doubled by coding:

```
FADD ST(0), ST(0);
```

The FADDP instructions perform the additional operation of popping the FPU register stack after storing the result. To pop the register stack, the processor marks the ST(0) register as empty and increments the stack pointer (TOP) by 1. (The no-operand version of the floating-point add instructions always results in the register stack being popped. In some assemblers, the mnemonic for this instruction is FADD rather than FADDP.)

The FIADD instructions convert an integer source operand to extended-real format before performing the addition.

The table on the following page shows the results obtained when adding various classes of numbers, assuming that neither overflow nor underflow occurs.

When the sum of two operands with opposite signs is 0, the result is +0, except for the round toward −∞ mode, in which case the result is −0. When the source operand is an integer 0, it is treated as a +0.

When both operand are infinities of the same sign, the result is ∞ of the expected sign. If both operands are infinities of opposite signs, an invalid-operation exception is generated.

		DEST						
		−∞	−F	−0	+0	+F	+∞	NaN
SRC	−∞	−∞	−∞	−∞	−∞	−∞	*	NaN
	−F or −I	−∞	−F	SRC	SRC	±F or ±0	+∞	NaN
	−0	−∞	DEST	−0	±0	DEST	+∞	NaN
	+0	−∞	DEST	±0	+0	DEST	+∞	NaN
	+F or +I	−∞	±F or ±0	SRC	SRC	+F	+∞	NaN
	+∞	*	+∞	+∞	+∞	+∞	+∞	NaN
	NaN	NaN	NaN	NaN	NaN	NaN	NaN	NaN

NOTES:

F Means finite-real number.

I Means integer.

* Indicates floating-point invalid-arithmetic-operand (#IA) exception.

Operation

```
IF instruction is FIADD
    THEN
        DEST ← DEST + ConvertExtendedReal(SRC);
    ELSE (* source operand is real number *)
        DEST ← DEST + SRC;
FI;
IF instruction = FADDP
    THEN
        PopRegisterStack;
FI;
```

FPU Flags Affected

C1	Set to 0 if stack underflow occurred.
	Indicates rounding direction if the inexact-result exception (#P) is generated: 0 = not roundup; 1 = roundup.
C0, C2, C3	Undefined.

Floating-Point Exceptions

#IS	Stack underflow occurred.
#IA	Operand is an SNaN value or unsupported format.
	Operands are infinities of unlike sign.
#D	Result is a denormal value.

#U	Result is too small for destination format.
#O	Result is too large for destination format.
#P	Value cannot be represented exactly in destination format.

Protected Mode Exceptions

#GP(0)	If a memory operand effective address is outside the CS, DS, ES, FS, or GS segment limit.
	If the DS, ES, FS, or GS register contains a null segment selector.
#SS(0)	If a memory operand effective address is outside the SS segment limit.
#NM	EM or TS in CR0 is set.
#PF(fault-code)	If a page fault occurs.
#AC(0)	If alignment checking is enabled and an unaligned memory reference is made while the current privilege level is 3.

Real Address Mode Exceptions

#GP	If a memory operand effective address is outside the CS, DS, ES, FS, or GS segment limit.
#SS	If a memory operand effective address is outside the SS segment limit.
#NM	EM or TS in CR0 is set.

Virtual 8086 Mode Exceptions

#GP(0)	If a memory operand effective address is outside the CS, DS, ES, FS, or GS segment limit.
#SS(0)	If a memory operand effective address is outside the SS segment limit.
#NM	EM or TS in CR0 is set.
#PF(fault-code)	If a page fault occurs.
#AC(0)	If alignment checking is enabled and an unaligned memory reference is made.

FBLD—Load Binary Coded Decimal

Opcode	Instruction	Description
DF /4	FBLD *m80 dec*	Convert BCD value to real and push onto the FPU stack.

Description

Converts the BCD source operand into extended-real format and pushes the value onto the FPU stack. The source operand is loaded without rounding errors. The sign of the source operand is preserved, including that of −0.

The packed BCD digits are assumed to be in the range 0 through 9; the instruction does not check for invalid digits (AH through FH). Attempting to load an invalid encoding produces an undefined result.

Operation

TOP ← TOP − 1;
ST(0) ← ExtendedReal(SRC);

FPU Flags Affected

C1	Set to 1 if stack overflow occurred; otherwise, cleared to 0.
C0, C2, C3	Undefined.

Floating-Point Exceptions

#IS	Stack overflow occurred.

Protected Mode Exceptions

#GP(0)	If a memory operand effective address is outside the CS, DS, ES, FS, or GS segment limit.
	If the DS, ES, FS, or GS register contains a null segment selector.
#SS(0)	If a memory operand effective address is outside the SS segment limit.
#NM	EM or TS in CR0 is set.
#PF(fault-code)	If a page fault occurs.
#AC(0)	If alignment checking is enabled and an unaligned memory reference is made while the current privilege level is 3.

Real Address Mode Exceptions

#GP	If a memory operand effective address is outside the CS, DS, ES, FS, or GS segment limit.
#SS	If a memory operand effective address is outside the SS segment limit.
#NM	EM or TS in CR0 is set.

Virtual 8086 Mode Exceptions

#GP(0)	If a memory operand effective address is outside the CS, DS, ES, FS, or GS segment limit.
#SS(0)	If a memory operand effective address is outside the SS segment limit.
#NM	EM or TS in CR0 is set.
#PF(fault-code)	If a page fault occurs.
#AC(0)	If alignment checking is enabled and an unaligned memory reference is made.

FBSTP—Store BCD Integer and Pop

Opcode	Instruction	Description
DF /6	FBSTP m80bcd	Store ST(0) in m80bcd and pop ST(0).

Description

Converts the value in the ST(0) register to an 18-digit packed BCD integer, stores the result in the destination operand, and pops the register stack. If the source value is a non-integral value, it is rounded to an integer value, according to rounding mode specified by the RC field of the FPU control word. To pop the register stack, the processor marks the ST(0) register as empty and increments the stack pointer (TOP) by 1.

The destination operand specifies the address where the first byte destination value is to be stored. The BCD value (including its sign bit) requires 10 bytes of space in memory.

The following table shows the results obtained when storing various classes of numbers in packed BCD format.

ST(0)	DEST
−∞	*
−F < −1	−D
−1 < −F < −0	**
−0	−0
+0	+0
+0 < +F < +1	**
+F > +1	+D
+∞	*
NaN	*

NOTES:

F Means finite-real number

D Means packed-BCD number

* Indicates floating-point invalid-operation (#IA) exception

** ±0 or ±1, depending on the rounding mode

If the source value is too large for the destination format and the invalid-operation exception is not masked, an invalid-operation exception is generated and no value is stored in the destination operand. If the invalid-operation exception is masked, the packed BCD indefinite value is stored in memory.

If the source value is a quiet NaN, an invalid-operation exception is generated. Quiet NaNs do not normally cause this exception to be generated.

Operation

DEST ← BCD(ST(0));
PopRegisterStack;

FPU Flags Affected

C1	Set to 0 if stack underflow occurred.
	Indicates rounding direction if the inexact exception (#P) is generated: 0 = not roundup; 1 = roundup.
C0, C2, C3	Undefined.

Floating-Point Exceptions

#IS	Stack underflow occurred.
#IA	Source operand is empty; contains a NaN, ±∞, or unsupported format; or contains value that exceeds 18 BCD digits in length.
#P	Value cannot be represented exactly in destination format.

Protected Mode Exceptions

#GP(0)	If a segment register is being loaded with a segment selector that points to a nonwritable segment.
	If a memory operand effective address is outside the CS, DS, ES, FS, or GS segment limit.
	If the DS, ES, FS, or GS register contains a null segment selector.
#SS(0)	If a memory operand effective address is outside the SS segment limit.
#NM	EM or TS in CR0 is set.
#PF(fault-code)	If a page fault occurs.
#AC(0)	If alignment checking is enabled and an unaligned memory reference is made while the current privilege level is 3.

Real Address Mode Exceptions

#GP	If a memory operand effective address is outside the CS, DS, ES, FS, or GS segment limit.
#SS	If a memory operand effective address is outside the SS segment limit.
#NM	EM or TS in CR0 is set.

Virtual 8086 Mode Exceptions

#GP(0)   If a memory operand effective address is outside the CS, DS, ES, FS, or
                   GS segment limit.

#SS(0)   If a memory operand effective address is outside the SS segment limit.

#NM   EM or TS in CR0 is set.

#PF(fault-code)   If a page fault occurs.

#AC(0)   If alignment checking is enabled and an unaligned memory reference is
                   made.

FCHS—Change Sign

Opcode	Instruction	Description
D9 E0	FCHS	Complements sign of ST(0)

Description

Complements the sign bit of ST(0). This operation changes a positive value into a negative value of equal magnitude or vice-versa. The following table shows the results obtained when creating the absolute value of various classes of numbers.

ST(0) SRC	ST(0) DEST
−∞	+∞
−F	+F
−0	+0
+0	−0
+F	−F
+∞	−∞
NaN	NaN

NOTE:
F Means finite-real number

Operation

SignBit(ST(0)) ← NOT (SignBit(ST(0)))

FPU Flags Affected

C1   Set to 0 if stack underflow occurred; otherwise, cleared to 0.

C0, C2, C3   Undefined.

Floating-Point Exceptions

#IS   Stack underflow occurred.

Protected Mode Exceptions

#NM   EM or TS in CR0 is set.

Real Address Mode Exceptions

#NM   EM or TS in CR0 is set.

Virtual 8086 Mode Exceptions

#NM   EM or TS in CR0 is set.

FCLEX/FNCLEX—Clear Exceptions

Opcode	Instruction	Description
9B DB E2	FCLEX	Clear floating-point exception flags after checking for pending unmasked floating-point exceptions.
DB E2	FNCLEX	Clear floating-point exception flags without checking for pending unmasked floating-point exceptions.

Description

Clears the floating-point exception flags (PE, UE, OE, ZE, DE, and IE), the exception summary status flag (ES), the stack fault flag (SF), and the busy flag (B) in the FPU status word. The FCLEX instruction checks for and handles any pending unmasked floating-point exceptions before clearing the exception flags; the FNCLEX instruction does not.

Operation

FPUStatusWord[0..7] ← 0;
FPUStatusWord[15] ← 0;

FPU Flags Affected

The PE, UE, OE, ZE, DE, IE, ES, SF, and B flags in the FPU status word are cleared. The C0, C1, C2, and C3 flags are undefined.

Floating-Point Exceptions

None.

Protected Mode Exceptions

#NM   EM or TS in CR0 is set.

Real Address Mode Exceptions

#NM   EM or TS in CR0 is set.

Virtual 8086 Mode Exceptions

#NM   EM or TS in CR0 is set.

FCMOV*cc*—Floating-Point Conditional Move

Opcode	Instruction	Description
DA C0+i	FCMOVB ST(0), ST(*i*)	Move if below (CF=1)
DA C8+i	FCMOVE ST(0), ST(*i*)	Move if equal (ZF=1)
DA D0+i	FCMOVBE ST(0), ST(*i*)	Move if below or equal (CF=1 or ZF=1)
DA D8+i	FCMOVU ST(0), ST(*i*)	Move if unordered (PF=1)
DB C0+i	FCMOVNB ST(0), ST(*i*)	Move if not below (CF=0)
DB C8+i	FCMOVNE ST(0), ST(*i*)	Move if not equal (ZF=0)
DB D0+i	FCMOVNBE ST(0), ST(*i*)	Move if not below or equal (CF=0 and ZF=0)
DB D8+i	FCMOVNU ST(0), ST(*i*)	Move if not unordered (PF=0)

Description

Tests the status flags in the EFLAGS register and moves the source operand (second operand) to the destination operand (first operand) if the given test condition is true. The conditions for each mnemonic are given in the Description column above and in Table 6-4. The source operand is always in the ST(*i*) register and the destination operand is always ST(0).

The FCMOV*cc* instructions are useful for optimizing small IF constructions. They also help eliminate branching overhead for IF operations and the possibility of branch mispredictions by the processor.

A processor in the Pentium Pro processor family may not support the FCMOV*cc* instructions. Software can check if the FCMOV*cc* instructions are supported by checking the processor's feature information with the CPUID instruction (see Chapter 11, "CPUID—CPU Identification"). If both the CMOV and FPU feature bits are set, the FCMOV*cc* instructions are supported.

Operation

```
IF condition TRUE
    ST(0) ← ST(i)
FI;
```

FPU Flags Affected

C1	Set to 0 if stack underflow occurred.
C0, C2, C3	Undefined.

Floating-Point Exceptions

#IS	Stack underflow occurred.

Integer Flags Affected

None.

intel®

Protected Mode Exceptions

#NM   EM or TS in CR0 is set.

Real Address Mode Exceptions

#NM   EM or TS in CR0 is set.

Virtual 8086 Mode Exceptions

#NM   EM or TS in CR0 is set.

FCOM/FCOMP/FCOMPP—Compare Real

Opcode	Instruction	Description
D8 /2	FCOM m32real	Compare ST(0) with m32real.
DC /2	FCOM m64real	Compare ST(0) with m64real.
D8 D0+i	FCOM ST(i)	Compare ST(0) with ST(i).
D8 D1	FCOM	Compare ST(0) with ST(1).
D8 /3	FCOMP m32real	Compare ST(0) with m32real and pop register stack.
DC /3	FCOMP m64real	Compare ST(0) with m64real and pop register stack.
D8 D8+i	FCOMP ST(i)	Compare ST(0) with ST(i) and pop register stack.
D8 D9	FCOMP	Compare ST(0) with ST(1) and pop register stack.
DE D9	FCOMPP	Compare ST(0) with ST(1) and pop register stack twice.

Description

Compares the contents of register ST(0) and source value and sets condition code flags C0, C2, and C3 in the FPU status word according to the results (see the table below). The source operand can be a data register or a memory location. If no source operand is given, the value in ST(0) is compared with the value in ST(1). The sign of zero is ignored, so that –0.0 = +0.0.

Condition	C3	C2	C0
ST(0) > SRC	0	0	0
ST(0) < SRC	0	0	1
ST(0) = SRC	1	0	0
Unordered*	1	1	1

NOTE:
* Flags not set if unmasked invalid-arithmetic-operand (#IA) exception is generated.

This instruction checks the class of the numbers being compared (see Chapter 11, "FXAM—Examine"). If either operand is a NaN or is in an unsupported format, an invalid-arithmetic-operand exception (#IA) is raised and, if the exception is masked, the condition flags are set to "unordered." If the invalid-arithmetic-operand exception is unmasked, the condition code flags are not set.

The FCOMP instruction pops the register stack following the comparison operation and the FCOMPP instruction pops the register stack twice following the comparison operation. To pop the register stack, the processor marks the ST(0) register as empty and increments the stack pointer (TOP) by 1.

The FCOM instructions perform the same operation as the FUCOM instructions. The only difference is how they handle QNaN operands. The FCOM instructions raise an invalid-arith-metic-operand exception (#IA) when either or both of the operands is a NaN value or is in an unsupported format. The FUCOM instructions perform the same operation as the FCOM instructions, except that they do not generate an invalid-arithmetic-operand exception for QNaNs.

Operation

```
CASE (relation of operands) OF
    ST > SRC:       C3, C2, C0 ← 000;
    ST < SRC:       C3, C2, C0 ← 001;
    ST = SRC:       C3, C2, C0 ← 100;
ESAC;
IF ST(0) or SRC = NaN or unsupported format
    THEN
        #IA
        IF FPUControlWord.IM = 1
            THEN
                C3, C2, C0 ← 111;
        FI;
FI;
IF instruction = FCOMP
    THEN
        PopRegisterStack;
FI;
IF instruction = FCOMPP
    THEN
        PopRegisterStack;
        PopRegisterStack;
FI;
```

FPU Flags Affected

C1	Set to 0 if stack underflow occurred; otherwise, cleared to 0.
C0, C2, C3	See table on previous page.

Floating-Point Exceptions

#IS	Stack underflow occurred.
#IA	One or both operands are NaN values or have unsupported formats.
	Register is marked empty.
#D	One or both operands are denormal values.

Protected Mode Exceptions

#GP(0)	If a memory operand effective address is outside the CS, DS, ES, FS, or GS segment limit.
	If the DS, ES, FS, or GS register contains a null segment selector.

#SS(0)   If a memory operand effective address is outside the SS segment limit.

#NM   EM or TS in CR0 is set.

#PF(fault-code)   If a page fault occurs.

#AC(0)   If alignment checking is enabled and an unaligned memory reference is
                    made while the current privilege level is 3.

Real Address Mode Exceptions

#GP   If a memory operand effective address is outside the CS, DS, ES, FS, or
                    GS segment limit.

#SS   If a memory operand effective address is outside the SS segment limit.

#NM   EM or TS in CR0 is set.

Virtual 8086 Mode Exceptions

#GP(0)   If a memory operand effective address is outside the CS, DS, ES, FS, or
                    GS segment limit.

#SS(0)   If a memory operand effective address is outside the SS segment limit.

#NM   EM or TS in CR0 is set.

#PF(fault-code)   If a page fault occurs.

#AC(0)   If alignment checking is enabled and an unaligned memory reference is
                    made.

FCOMI/FCOMIP/FUCOMI/FUCOMIP—Compare Real and Set EFLAGS

Opcode	Instruction	Description
DB F0+i	FCOMI ST, ST(*i*)	Compare ST(0) with ST(*i*) and set status flags accordingly
DF F0+i	FCOMIP ST, ST(*i*)	Compare ST(0) with ST(*i*), set status flags accordingly, and pop register stack
DB E8+i	FUCOMI ST, ST(*i*)	Compare ST(0) with ST(*i*), check for ordered values, and set status flags accordingly
DF E8+i	FUCOMIP ST, ST(*i*)	Compare ST(0) with ST(*i*), check for ordered values, set status flags accordingly, and pop register stack

Description

Compares the contents of register ST(0) and ST(*i*) and sets the status flags ZF, PF, and CF in the EFLAGS register according to the results (see the table below). The sign of zero is ignored for comparisons, so that $-0.0 = +0.0$.

Comparison Results	ZF	PF	CF
ST0 > ST(*i*)	0	0	0
ST0 < ST(*i*)	0	0	1
ST0 = ST(*i*)	1	0	0
Unordered*	1	1	1

NOTE:

* Flags not set if unmasked invalid-arithmetic-operand (#IA) exception is generated.

The FCOMI/FCOMIP instructions perform the same operation as the FUCOMI/FUCOMIP instructions. The only difference is how they handle QNaN operands. The FCOMI/FCOMIP instructions set the status flags to "unordered" and generate an invalid-arithmetic-operand exception (#IA) when either or both of the operands is a NaN value (SNaN or QNaN) or is in an unsupported format.

The FUCOMI/FUCOMIP instructions perform the same operation as the FCOMI/FCOMIP instructions, except that they do not generate an invalid-arithmetic-operand exception for QNaNs. See Chapter 11, "FXAM—Examine" for additional information on unordered comparisons.

If invalid-operation exception is unmasked, the status flags are not set if the invalid-arithmetic-operand exception is generated.

The FCOMIP and FUCOMIP instructions also pop the register stack following the comparison operation. To pop the register stack, the processor marks the ST(0) register as empty and increments the stack pointer (TOP) by 1.

Operation

```
CASE (relation of operands) OF
    ST(0) > ST(i):    ZF, PF, CF ← 000;
    ST(0) < ST(i):    ZF, PF, CF ← 001;
    ST(0) = ST(i):    ZF, PF, CF ← 100;
ESAC;
IF instruction is FCOMI or FCOMIP
    THEN
        IF ST(0) or ST(i) = NaN or unsupported format
            THEN
                #IA
                IF FPUControlWord.IM = 1
                    THEN
                        ZF, PF, CF ← 111;
                FI;
        FI;
FI;
IF instruction is FUCOMI or FUCOMIP
    THEN
        IF ST(0) or ST(i) = QNaN, but not SNaN or unsupported format
            THEN
                ZF, PF, CF ← 111;
            ELSE (* ST(0) or ST(i) is SNaN or unsupported format *)
                #IA;
                IF FPUControlWord.IM = 1
                    THEN
                        ZF, PF, CF ← 111;
                FI;
        FI;
FI;
IF instruction is FCOMIP or FUCOMIP
    THEN
        PopRegisterStack;
FI;
```

FPU Flags Affected

C1   Set to 0 if stack underflow occurred; otherwise, cleared to 0.

C0, C2, C3   Not affected.

Floating-Point Exceptions

#IS   Stack underflow occurred.

#IA   (FCOMI or FCOMIP instruction) One or both operands are NaN values or have unsupported formats.

                       (FUCOMI or FUCOMIP instruction) One or both operands are SNaN values (but not QNaNs) or have undefined formats. Detection of a QNaN value does not raise an invalid-operand exception.

Protected Mode Exceptions

#NM   EM or TS in CR0 is set.

Real Address Mode Exceptions

#NM   EM or TS in CR0 is set.

Virtual 8086 Mode Exceptions

#NM   EM or TS in CR0 is set.

FCOS—Cosine

Opcode	Instruction	Description
D9 FF	FCOS	Replace ST(0) with its cosine

Description

Calculates the cosine of the source operand in register ST(0) and stores the result in ST(0). The source operand must be given in radians and must be within the range -2^{63} to $+2^{63}$. The following table shows the results obtained when taking the cosine of various classes of numbers, assuming that neither overflow nor underflow occurs.

ST(0) SRC	ST(0) DEST
$-\infty$	*
$-F$	-1 to $+1$
-0	$+1$
$+0$	$+1$
$+F$	-1 to $+1$
$+\infty$	*
NaN	NaN

NOTES:

F Means finite-real number

* Indicates floating-point invalid-arithmetic-operand (#IA) exception.

If the source operand is outside the acceptable range, the C2 flag in the FPU status word is set, and the value in register ST(0) remains unchanged. The instruction does not raise an exception when the source operand is out of range. It is up to the program to check the C2 flag for out-of-range conditions. Source values outside the range -2^{63} to $+2^{63}$ can be reduced to the range of the instruction by subtracting an appropriate integer multiple of 2π or by using the FPREM instruction with a divisor of 2π. See Section 7.5.8., "Pi" for a discussion of the proper value to use for π in performing such reductions.

Operation

```
IF |ST(0)| < 2^63
THEN
    C2 ← 0;
    ST(0) ← cosine(ST(0));
ELSE (*source operand is out-of-range *)
    C2 ← 1;
FI;
```

FPU Flags Affected

C1	Set to 0 if stack underflow occurred.
	Indicates rounding direction if the inexact-result exception (#P) is generated: 0 = not roundup; 1 = roundup.
	Undefined if C2 is 1.
C2	Set to 1 if source operand is outside the range -2^{63} to $+2^{63}$; otherwise, cleared to 0.
C0, C3	Undefined.

Floating-Point Exceptions

#IS	Stack underflow occurred.
#IA	Source operand is an SNaN value, ∞, or unsupported format.
#D	Result is a denormal value.
#U	Result is too small for destination format.
#P	Value cannot be represented exactly in destination format.

Protected Mode Exceptions

#NM	EM or TS in CR0 is set.

Real Address Mode Exceptions

#NM	EM or TS in CR0 is set.

Virtual 8086 Mode Exceptions

#NM	EM or TS in CR0 is set.

FDECSTP—Decrement Stack-Top Pointer

Opcode	Instruction	Description
D9 F6	FDECSTP	Decrement TOP field in FPU status word.

Description

Subtracts one from the TOP field of the FPU status word (decrements the top-of-stack pointer). The contents of the FPU data registers and tag register are not affected.

Operation

IF TOP = 0
   THEN TOP ← 7;
   ELSE TOP ← TOP – 1;
FI;

FPU Flags Affected

The C1 flag is set to 0; otherwise, cleared to 0. The C0, C2, and C3 flags are undefined.

Floating-Point Exceptions

None.

Protected Mode Exceptions

#NM   EM or TS in CR0 is set.

Real Address Mode Exceptions

#NM   EM or TS in CR0 is set.

Virtual 8086 Mode Exceptions

#NM   EM or TS in CR0 is set.

FDIV/FDIVP/FIDIV—Divide

Opcode	Instruction	Description
D8 /6	FDIV m32real	Divide ST(0) by m32real and store result in ST(0)
DC /6	FDIV m64real	Divide ST(0) by m64real and store result in ST(0)
D8 F0+i	FDIV ST(0), ST(i)	Divide ST(0) by ST(i) and store result in ST(0)
DC F8+i	FDIV ST(i), ST(0)	Divide ST(i) by ST(0) and store result in ST(i)
DE F8+i	FDIVP ST(i), ST(0)	Divide ST(i) by ST(0), store result in ST(i), and pop the register stack
DE F9	FDIVP	Divide ST(1) by ST(0), store result in ST(1), and pop the register stack
DA /6	FIDIV m32int	Divide ST(0) by m32int and store result in ST(0)
DE /6	FIDIV m16int	Divide ST(0) by m64int and store result in ST(0)

Description

Divides the destination operand by the source operand and stores the result in the destination location. The destination operand (dividend) is always in an FPU register; the source operand (divisor) can be a register or a memory location. Source operands in memory can be in single-real, double-real, word-integer, or short-integer formats.

The no-operand version of the instruction divides the contents of the ST(1) register by the contents of the ST(0) register. The one-operand version divides the contents of the ST(0) register by the contents of a memory location (either a real or an integer value). The two-operand version, divides the contents of the ST(0) register by the contents of the ST(i) register or vice versa.

The FDIVP instructions perform the additional operation of popping the FPU register stack after storing the result. To pop the register stack, the processor marks the ST(0) register as empty and increments the stack pointer (TOP) by 1. The no-operand version of the floating-point divide instructions always results in the register stack being popped. In some assemblers, the mnemonic for this instruction is FDIV rather than FDIVP.

The FIDIV instructions convert an integer source operand to extended-real format before performing the division. When the source operand is an integer 0, it is treated as a +0.

If an unmasked divide by zero exception (#Z) is generated, no result is stored; if the exception is masked, an ∞ of the appropriate sign is stored in the destination operand.

The following table shows the results obtained when dividing various classes of numbers, assuming that neither overflow nor underflow occurs.

		DEST						
		−∞	−F	−0	+0	+F	+∞	NaN
SRC	−∞	*	+0	+0	−0	−0	*	NaN
	−F	+∞	+F	+0	−0	−F	−∞	NaN
	−I	+∞	+F	+0	−0	−F	−∞	NaN
	−0	+∞	**	*	*	**	−∞	NaN
	+0	−∞	**	*	*	**	+∞	NaN
	+I	−∞	−F	−0	+0	+F	+∞	NaN
	+F	−∞	−F	−0	+0	+F	+∞	NaN
	+∞	*	−0	−0	+0	+0	*	NaN
	NaN	NaN	NaN	NaN	NaN	NaN	NaN	NaN

NOTES:

F   Means finite-real number.

I   Means integer.

*   Indicates floating-point invalid-arithmetic-operand (#IA) exception.

** Indicates floating-point zero-divide (#Z) exception.

Operation

```
IF SRC = 0
    THEN
        #Z
    ELSE
        IF instruction is FIDIV
            THEN
                DEST ← DEST / ConvertExtendedReal(SRC);
            ELSE (* source operand is real number *)
                DEST ← DEST / SRC;
        FI;
FI;
IF instruction = FDIVP
    THEN
        PopRegisterStack
FI;
```

FPU Flags Affected

C1   Set to 0 if stack underflow occurred.

                Indicates rounding direction if the inexact-result exception (#P) is gener-
                ated: 0 = not roundup; 1 = roundup.

C0, C2, C3   Undefined.

Floating-Point Exceptions

#IS	Stack underflow occurred.
#IA	Operand is an SNaN value or unsupported format.
	$\pm\infty \,/\, \pm\infty$; $\pm 0 \,/\, \pm 0$
#D	Result is a denormal value.
#Z	DEST $/\, \pm 0$, where DEST is not equal to ± 0.
#U	Result is too small for destination format.
#O	Result is too large for destination format.
#P	Value cannot be represented exactly in destination format.

Protected Mode Exceptions

#GP(0)	If a memory operand effective address is outside the CS, DS, ES, FS, or GS segment limit.
	If the DS, ES, FS, or GS register contains a null segment selector.
#SS(0)	If a memory operand effective address is outside the SS segment limit.
#NM	EM or TS in CR0 is set.
#PF(fault-code)	If a page fault occurs.
#AC(0)	If alignment checking is enabled and an unaligned memory reference is made while the current privilege level is 3.

Real Address Mode Exceptions

#GP	If a memory operand effective address is outside the CS, DS, ES, FS, or GS segment limit.
#SS	If a memory operand effective address is outside the SS segment limit.
#NM	EM or TS in CR0 is set.

Virtual 8086 Mode Exceptions

#GP(0)	If a memory operand effective address is outside the CS, DS, ES, FS, or GS segment limit.
#SS(0)	If a memory operand effective address is outside the SS segment limit.
#NM	EM or TS in CR0 is set.
#PF(fault-code)	If a page fault occurs.
#AC(0)	If alignment checking is enabled and an unaligned memory reference is made.

FDIVR/FDIVRP/FIDIVR—Reverse Divide

Opcode	Instruction	Description
D8 /7	FDIVR m32real	Divide m32real by ST(0) and store result in ST(0)
DC /7	FDIVR m64real	Divide m64real by ST(0) and store result in ST(0)
D8 F8+i	FDIVR ST(0), ST(i)	Divide ST(i) by ST(0) and store result in ST(0)
DC F0+i	FDIVR ST(i), ST(0)	Divide ST(0) by ST(i) and store result in ST(i)
DE F0+i	FDIVRP ST(i), ST(0)	Divide ST(0) by ST(i), store result in ST(i), and pop the register stack
DE F1	FDIVRP	Divide ST(0) by ST(1), store result in ST(1), and pop the register stack
DA /7	FIDIVR m32int	Divide m32int by ST(0) and store result in ST(0)
DE /7	FIDIVR m16int	Divide m64int by ST(0) and store result in ST(0)

Description

Divides the source operand by the destination operand and stores the result in the destination location. The destination operand (divisor) is always in an FPU register; the source operand (dividend) can be a register or a memory location. Source operands in memory can be in single-real, double-real, word-integer, or short-integer formats.

These instructions perform the reverse operations of the FDIV, FDIVP, and FIDIV instructions. They are provided to support more efficient coding.

The no-operand version of the instruction divides the contents of the ST(0) register by the contents of the ST(1) register. The one-operand version divides the contents of a memory location (either a real or an integer value) by the contents of the ST(0) register. The two-operand version, divides the contents of the ST(i) register by the contents of the ST(0) register or vice versa.

The FDIVRP instructions perform the additional operation of popping the FPU register stack after storing the result. To pop the register stack, the processor marks the ST(0) register as empty and increments the stack pointer (TOP) by 1. The no-operand version of the floating-point divide instructions always results in the register stack being popped. In some assemblers, the mnemonic for this instruction is FDIVR rather than FDIVRP.

The FIDIVR instructions convert an integer source operand to extended-real format before performing the division.

If an unmasked divide by zero exception (#Z) is generated, no result is stored; if the exception is masked, an ∞ of the appropriate sign is stored in the destination operand.

The following table shows the results obtained when dividing various classes of numbers, assuming that neither overflow nor underflow occurs.

		DEST						
		−∞	−F	−0	+0	+F	+∞	NaN
	−∞	*	+∞	+∞	-•	−∞	*	NaN
SRC	−F	+0	+F	**	**	-F	−0	NaN
	−I	+0	+F	**	**	-F	−0	NaN
	−0	+0	+0	*	*	−0	−0	NaN
	+0	−0	−0	*	*	+0	+0	NaN
	+I	−0	-F	**	**	+F	+∞	NaN
	+F	−0	-F	**	**	+F	+∞	NaN
	+∞	*	−∞	−∞	+∞	+∞	*	NaN
	NaN	NaN	NaN	NaN	NaN	NaN	NaN	NaN

NOTES:

F Means finite-real number.

I Means integer.

* Indicates floating-point invalid-arithmetic-operand (#IA) exception.

** Indicates floating-point zero-divide (#Z) exception.

When the source operand is an integer 0, it is treated as a +0.

Operation

```
IF DEST = 0
    THEN
        #Z
    ELSE
        IF instruction is FIDIVR
            THEN
                DEST ← ConvertExtendedReal(SRC) / DEST;
            ELSE (* source operand is real number *)
                DEST ← SRC / DEST;
        FI;
FI;
IF instruction = FDIVRP
    THEN
        PopRegisterStack
FI;
```

FPU Flags Affected

C1   Set to 0 if stack underflow occurred.

                     Indicates rounding direction if the inexact-result exception (#P) is generated: 0 = not roundup; 1 = roundup.

C0, C2, C3   Undefined.

Floating-Point Exceptions

#IS   Stack underflow occurred.

#IA   Operand is an SNaN value or unsupported format.

                     $\pm\infty$ / $\pm\infty$; ± 0 / ± 0

#D   Result is a denormal value.

#Z   SRC / ± 0, where SRC is not equal to ± 0.

#U   Result is too small for destination format.

#O   Result is too large for destination format.

#P   Value cannot be represented exactly in destination format.

Protected Mode Exceptions

#GP(0)   If a memory operand effective address is outside the CS, DS, ES, FS, or GS segment limit.

                     If the DS, ES, FS, or GS register contains a null segment selector.

#SS(0)   If a memory operand effective address is outside the SS segment limit.

#NM   EM or TS in CR0 is set.

#PF(fault-code) If a page fault occurs.

#AC(0)   If alignment checking is enabled and an unaligned memory reference is made while the current privilege level is 3.

Real Address Mode Exceptions

#GP   If a memory operand effective address is outside the CS, DS, ES, FS, or GS segment limit.

#SS   If a memory operand effective address is outside the SS segment limit.

#NM   EM or TS in CR0 is set.

Virtual 8086 Mode Exceptions

#GP(0)	If a memory operand effective address is outside the CS, DS, ES, FS, or GS segment limit.
#SS(0)	If a memory operand effective address is outside the SS segment limit.
#NM	EM or TS in CR0 is set.
#PF(fault-code)	If a page fault occurs.
#AC(0)	If alignment checking is enabled and an unaligned memory reference is made.

FFREE—Free Floating-Point Register

Opcode	Instruction	Description
DD C0+i	FFREE ST(*i*)	Sets tag for ST(*i*) to empty

Description

Sets the tag in the FPU tag register associated with register ST(*i*) to empty (11B). The contents of ST(*i*) and the FPU stack-top pointer (TOP) are not affected.

Operation

TAG(i) ← 11B;

FPU Flags Affected

C0, C1, C2, C3 undefined.

Floating-Point Exceptions

None.

Protected Mode Exceptions

#NM   EM or TS in CR0 is set.

Real Address Mode Exceptions

#NM   EM or TS in CR0 is set.

Virtual 8086 Mode Exceptions

#NM   EM or TS in CR0 is set.

FICOM/FICOMP—Compare Integer

Opcode	Instruction	Description
DE /2	FICOM *m16int*	Compare ST(0) with *m16int*
DA /2	FICOM *m32int*	Compare ST(0) with *m32int*
DE /3	FICOMP *m16int*	Compare ST(0) with *m16int* and pop stack register
DA /3	FICOMP *m32int*	Compare ST(0) with *m32int* and pop stack register

Description

Compares the value in ST(0) with an integer source operand and sets the condition code flags C0, C2, and C3 in the FPU status word according to the results (see table below). The integer value is converted to extended-real format before the comparison is made.

Condition	C3	C2	C0
ST(0) > SRC	0	0	0
ST(0) < SRC	0	0	1
ST(0) = SRC	1	0	0
Unordered	1	1	1

These instructions perform an "unordered comparison." An unordered comparison also checks the class of the numbers being compared (see Chapter 11, "FXAM—Examine"). If either operand is a NaN or is in an undefined format, the condition flags are set to "unordered."

The sign of zero is ignored, so that −0.0 = +0.0.

The FICOMP instructions pop the register stack following the comparison. To pop the register stack, the processor marks the ST(0) register empty and increments the stack pointer (TOP) by 1.

Operation

```
CASE (relation of operands) OF
    ST(0) > SRC:     C3, C2, C0 ← 000;
    ST(0) < SRC:     C3, C2, C0 ← 001;
    ST(0) = SRC:     C3, C2, C0 ← 100;
    Unordered:       C3, C2, C0 ← 111;
ESAC;
IF instruction = FICOMP
    THEN
        PopRegisterStack;
FI;
```

FPU Flags Affected

C1   Set to 0 if stack underflow occurred; otherwise, set to 0.

C0, C2, C3   See table on previous page.

Floating-Point Exceptions

#IS   Stack underflow occurred.

#IA   One or both operands are NaN values or have unsupported formats.

#D   One or both operands are denormal values.

Protected Mode Exceptions

#GP(0)   If a memory operand effective address is outside the CS, DS, ES, FS, or GS segment limit.

                          If the DS, ES, FS, or GS register contains a null segment selector.

#SS(0)   If a memory operand effective address is outside the SS segment limit.

#NM   EM or TS in CR0 is set.

#PF(fault-code)   If a page fault occurs.

#AC(0)   If alignment checking is enabled and an unaligned memory reference is made while the current privilege level is 3.

Real Address Mode Exceptions

#GP   If a memory operand effective address is outside the CS, DS, ES, FS, or GS segment limit.

#SS   If a memory operand effective address is outside the SS segment limit.

#NM   EM or TS in CR0 is set.

Virtual 8086 Mode Exceptions

#GP(0)   If a memory operand effective address is outside the CS, DS, ES, FS, or GS segment limit.

#SS(0)   If a memory operand effective address is outside the SS segment limit.

#NM   EM or TS in CR0 is set.

#PF(fault-code)   If a page fault occurs.

#AC(0)   If alignment checking is enabled and an unaligned memory reference is made.

FILD—Load Integer

Opcode	Instruction	Description
DF /0	FILD *m16int*	Push *m16int* onto the FPU register stack.
DB /0	FILD *m32int*	Push *m32int* onto the FPU register stack.
DF /5	FILD *m64int*	Push *m64int* onto the FPU register stack.

Description

Converts the signed-integer source operand into extended-real format and pushes the value onto the FPU register stack. The source operand can be a word, short, or long integer value. It is loaded without rounding errors. The sign of the source operand is preserved.

Operation

TOP ← TOP − 1;
ST(0) ← ExtendedReal(SRC);

FPU Flags Affected

C1	Set to 1 if stack overflow occurred; cleared to 0 otherwise.
C0, C2, C3	Undefined.

Floating-Point Exceptions

#IS	Stack overflow occurred.

Protected Mode Exceptions

#GP(0)	If a memory operand effective address is outside the CS, DS, ES, FS, or GS segment limit.
	If the DS, ES, FS, or GS register contains a null segment selector.
#SS(0)	If a memory operand effective address is outside the SS segment limit.
#NM	EM or TS in CR0 is set.
#PF(fault-code)	If a page fault occurs.
#AC(0)	If alignment checking is enabled and an unaligned memory reference is made while the current privilege level is 3.

Real Address Mode Exceptions

#GP	If a memory operand effective address is outside the CS, DS, ES, FS, or GS segment limit.
#SS	If a memory operand effective address is outside the SS segment limit.
#NM	EM or TS in CR0 is set.

Virtual 8086 Mode Exceptions

#GP(0)	If a memory operand effective address is outside the CS, DS, ES, FS, or GS segment limit.
#SS(0)	If a memory operand effective address is outside the SS segment limit.
#NM	EM or TS in CR0 is set.
#PF(fault-code)	If a page fault occurs.
#AC(0)	If alignment checking is enabled and an unaligned memory reference is made.

FINCSTP—Increment Stack-Top Pointer

Opcode	Instruction	Description
D9 F7	FINCSTP	Increment the TOP field in the FPU status register

Description

Adds one to the TOP field of the FPU status word (increments the top-of-stack pointer). The contents of the FPU data registers and tag register are not affected. This operation is not equivalent to popping the stack, because the tag for the previous top-of-stack register is not marked empty.

Operation

```
IF TOP = 7
    THEN TOP ← 0;
    ELSE TOP ← TOP + 1;
FI;
```

FPU Flags Affected

The C1 flag is set to 0; otherwise, cleared to 0. The C0, C2, and C3 flags are undefined.

Floating-Point Exceptions

None.

Protected Mode Exceptions

#NM   EM or TS in CR0 is set.

Real Address Mode Exceptions

#NM   EM or TS in CR0 is set.

Virtual 8086 Mode Exceptions

#NM   EM or TS in CR0 is set.

FINIT/FNINIT—Initialize Floating-Point Unit

Opcode	Instruction	Description
9B DB E3	FINIT	Initialize FPU after checking for pending unmasked floating-point exceptions.
DB E3	FNINIT	Initialize FPU without checking for pending unmasked floating-point exceptions.

Description

Sets the FPU control, status, tag, instruction pointer, and data pointer registers to their default states. The FPU control word is set to 037FH (round to nearest, all exceptions masked, 64-bit precision). The status word is cleared (no exception flags set, TOP is set to 0). The data registers in the register stack are left unchanged, but they are all tagged as empty (11B). Both the instruction and data pointers are cleared.

The FINIT instruction checks for and handles any pending unmasked floating-point exceptions before performing the initialization; the FNINIT instruction does not.

Operation

FPUControlWord ← 037FH;
FPUStatusWord ← 0;
FPUTagWord ← FFFFH;
FPUDataPointer ← 0;
FPUInstructionPointer ← 0;
FPULastInstructionOpcode ← 0;

FPU Flags Affected

C0, C1, C2, C3 cleared to 0.

Floating-Point Exceptions

None.

Protected Mode Exceptions

#NM   EM or TS in CR0 is set.

Real Address Mode Exceptions

#NM   EM or TS in CR0 is set.

Virtual 8086 Mode Exceptions

#NM   EM or TS in CR0 is set.

FIST/FISTP—Store Integer

Opcode	Instruction	Description
DF /2	FIST *m16int*	Store ST(0) in *m16int*
DB /2	FIST *m32int*	Store ST(0) in *m32int*
DF /3	FISTP *m16int*	Store ST(0) in *m16int* and pop register stack
DB /3	FISTP *m32int*	Store ST(0) in *m32int* and pop register stack
DF /7	FISTP *m64int*	Store ST(0) in *m64int* and pop register stack

Description

The FIST instruction converts the value in the ST(0) register to a signed integer and stores the result in the destination operand. Values can be stored in word- or short-integer format. The destination operand specifies the address where the first byte of the destination value is to be stored.

The FISTP instruction performs the same operation as the FIST instruction and then pops the register stack. To pop the register stack, the processor marks the ST(0) register as empty and increments the stack pointer (TOP) by 1. The FISTP instruction can also stores values in long-integer format.

The following table shows the results obtained when storing various classes of numbers in integer format.

ST(0)	DEST
$-\infty$	*
$-F < -1$	$-I$
$-1 < -F < -0$	**
-0	0
$+0$	0
$+0 < +F < +1$	**
$+F > +1$	$+I$
$+\infty$	*
NaN	*

NOTES:

F Means finite-real number

I Means integer

* Indicates floating-point invalid-operation (#IA) exception

** ±0 or ±1, depending on the rounding mode

If the source value is a non-integral value, it is rounded to an integer value, according to the rounding mode specified by the RC field of the FPU control word.

If the value being stored is too large for the destination format, is an ∞, is a NaN, or is in an unsupported format and if the invalid-arithmetic-operand exception (#IA) is unmasked, an invalid-operation exception is generated and no value is stored in the destination operand. If the invalid-operation exception is masked, the integer indefinite value is stored in the destination operand.

Operation

```
DEST ← Integer(ST(0));
IF instruction = FISTP
    THEN
        PopRegisterStack;
FI;
```

FPU Flags Affected

C1	Set to 0 if stack underflow occurred.
	Indicates rounding direction of if the inexact exception (#P) is generated: 0 = not roundup; 1 = roundup.
	Cleared to 0 otherwise.
C0, C2, C3	Undefined.

Floating-Point Exceptions

#IS	Stack underflow occurred.
#IA	Source operand is too large for the destination format
	Source operand is a NaN value or unsupported format.
#P	Value cannot be represented exactly in destination format.

Protected Mode Exceptions

#GP(0)	If the destination is located in a nonwritable segment.
	If a memory operand effective address is outside the CS, DS, ES, FS, or GS segment limit.
	If the DS, ES, FS, or GS register is used to access memory and it contains a null segment selector.
#SS(0)	If a memory operand effective address is outside the SS segment limit.
#NM	EM or TS in CR0 is set.
#PF(fault-code)	If a page fault occurs.

#AC(0)   If alignment checking is enabled and an unaligned memory reference is made while the current privilege level is 3.

Real Address Mode Exceptions

#GP   If a memory operand effective address is outside the CS, DS, ES, FS, or GS segment limit.

#SS   If a memory operand effective address is outside the SS segment limit.

#NM   EM or TS in CR0 is set.

Virtual 8086 Mode Exceptions

#GP(0)   If a memory operand effective address is outside the CS, DS, ES, FS, or GS segment limit.

#SS(0)   If a memory operand effective address is outside the SS segment limit.

#NM   EM or TS in CR0 is set.

#PF(fault-code)   If a page fault occurs.

#AC(0)   If alignment checking is enabled and an unaligned memory reference is made.

FLD—Load Real

Opcode	Instruction	Description
D9 /0	FLD m32real	Push m32real onto the FPU register stack.
DD /0	FLD m64real	Push m64real onto the FPU register stack.
DB /5	FLD m80real	Push m80real onto the FPU register stack.
D9 C0+i	FLD ST(i)	Push ST(i) onto the FPU register stack.

Description

Pushes the source operand onto the FPU register stack. If the source operand is in single- or double-real format, it is automatically converted to the extended-real format before being pushed on the stack.

The FLD instruction can also push the value in a selected FPU register [ST(i)] onto the stack. Here, pushing register ST(0) duplicates the stack top.

Operation

```
IF SRC is ST(i)
    THEN
        temp ← ST(i)
TOP ← TOP – 1;
IF SRC is memory-operand
    THEN
        ST(0) ← ExtendedReal(SRC);
    ELSE (* SRC is ST(i) *)
        ST(0) ← temp;
```

FPU Flags Affected

C1	Set to 1 if stack overflow occurred; otherwise, cleared to 0.
C0, C2, C3	Undefined.

Floating-Point Exceptions

#IS	Stack overflow occurred.
#IA	Source operand is an SNaN value or unsupported format.
#D	Source operand is a denormal value. Does not occur if the source operand is in extended-real format.

Protected Mode Exceptions

#GP(0)	If destination is located in a nonwritable segment.
	If a memory operand effective address is outside the CS, DS, ES, FS, or GS segment limit.
	If the DS, ES, FS, or GS register is used to access memory and it contains a null segment selector.
#SS(0)	If a memory operand effective address is outside the SS segment limit.
#NM	EM or TS in CR0 is set.
#PF(fault-code)	If a page fault occurs.
#AC(0)	If alignment checking is enabled and an unaligned memory reference is made while the current privilege level is 3.

Real Address Mode Exceptions

#GP	If a memory operand effective address is outside the CS, DS, ES, FS, or GS segment limit.
#SS	If a memory operand effective address is outside the SS segment limit.
#NM	EM or TS in CR0 is set.

Virtual 8086 Mode Exceptions

#GP(0)	If a memory operand effective address is outside the CS, DS, ES, FS, or GS segment limit.
#SS(0)	If a memory operand effective address is outside the SS segment limit.
#NM	EM or TS in CR0 is set.
#PF(fault-code)	If a page fault occurs.
#AC(0)	If alignment checking is enabled and an unaligned memory reference is made.

FLD1/FLDL2T/FLDL2E/FLDPI/FLDLG2/FLDLN2/FLDZ—Load Constant

Opcode	Instruction	Description
D9 E8	FLD1	Push +1.0 onto the FPU register stack.
D9 E9	FLDL2T	Push $\log_2 10$ onto the FPU register stack.
D9 EA	FLDL2E	Push $\log_2 e$ onto the FPU register stack.
D9 EB	FLDPI	Push π onto the FPU register stack.
D9 EC	FLDLG2	Push $\log_{10} 2$ onto the FPU register stack.
D9 ED	FLDLN2	Push $\log_e 2$ onto the FPU register stack.
D9 EE	FLDZ	Push +0.0 onto the FPU register stack.

Description

Push one of seven commonly-used constants (in extended-real format) onto the FPU register stack. The constants that can be loaded with these instructions include +1.0, +0.0, $\log_2 10$, $\log_2 e$, π, $\log_{10} 2$, and $\log_e 2$. For each constant, an internal 66-bit constant is rounded (as specified by the RC field in the FPU control word) to external-real format. The inexact-result exception (#P) is not generated as a result of the rounding.

See Section 7.5.8., "Pi" for a description of the π constant.

Operation

TOP ← TOP – 1;
ST(0) ← CONSTANT;

FPU Flags Affected

C1	Set to 1 if stack overflow occurred; otherwise, cleared to 0.
C0, C2, C3	Undefined.

Floating-Point Exceptions

#IS	Stack overflow occurred.

Protected Mode Exceptions

#NM	EM or TS in CR0 is set.

Real Address Mode Exceptions

#NM	EM or TS in CR0 is set.

Virtual 8086 Mode Exceptions

#NM   EM or TS in CR0 is set.

Intel Architecture Compatibility Information

When the RC field is set to round-to-nearest, the FPU produces the same constants that is produced by the Intel 8087 and Intel287 math coprocessors.

FLDCW—Load Control Word

Opcode	Instruction	Description
D9 /5	FLDCW m2byte	Load FPU control word from *m2byte*.

Description

Loads the 16-bit source operand into the FPU control word. The source operand is a memory location. This instruction is typically used to establish or change the FPU's mode of operation.

If one or more exception flags are set in the FPU status word prior to loading a new FPU control word and the new control word unmasks one or more of those exceptions, a floating-point exception will be generated upon execution of the next floating-point instruction (except for the no-wait floating-point instructions, see Section 7.7.3., "Software Exception Handling"). To avoid raising exceptions when changing FPU operating modes, clear any pending exceptions (using the FCLEX or FNCLEX instruction) before loading the new control word.

Operation

FPUControlWord ← SRC;

FPU Flags Affected

C0, C1, C2, C3 undefined.

Floating-Point Exceptions

None; however, this operation might unmask a pending exception in the FPU status word. That exception is then generated upon execution of the next waiting floating-point instruction.

Protected Mode Exceptions

#GP(0)	If a memory operand effective address is outside the CS, DS, ES, FS, or GS segment limit.
	If the DS, ES, FS, or GS register is used to access memory and it contains a null segment selector.
#SS(0)	If a memory operand effective address is outside the SS segment limit.
#NM	EM or TS in CR0 is set.
#PF(fault-code)	If a page fault occurs.
#AC(0)	If alignment checking is enabled and an unaligned memory reference is made while the current privilege level is 3.

Real Address Mode Exceptions

#GP	If a memory operand effective address is outside the CS, DS, ES, FS, or GS segment limit.
#SS	If a memory operand effective address is outside the SS segment limit.
#NM	EM or TS in CR0 is set.

Virtual 8086 Mode Exceptions

#GP(0)	If a memory operand effective address is outside the CS, DS, ES, FS, or GS segment limit.
#SS(0)	If a memory operand effective address is outside the SS segment limit.
#NM	EM or TS in CR0 is set.
#PF(fault-code)	If a page fault occurs.
#AC(0)	If alignment checking is enabled and an unaligned memory reference is made.

FLDENV—Load FPU Environment

Opcode	Instruction	Description
D9 /4	FLDENV m14/28byte	Load FPU environment from m14byte or m28byte.

Description

Loads the complete FPU operating environment from memory into the FPU registers. The source operand specifies the first byte of the operating-environment data in memory. This data is typically written to the specified memory location by a FSTENV or FNSTENV instruction.

The FPU operating environment consists of the FPU control word, status word, tag word, instruction pointer, data pointer, and last opcode. Figures 7-13 through 7-14 show the layout in memory of the loaded environment, depending on the operating mode of the processor (protected or real) and the size of the current address attribute (16-bit or 32-bit). In virtual-8086 mode, the real mode layouts are used.

The FLDENV instruction should be executed in the same operating mode as the corresponding FSTENV/FNSTENV instruction.

If one or more unmasked exception flags are set in the new FPU status word, a floating-point exception will be generated upon execution of the next floating-point instruction (except for the no-wait floating-point instructions, see Section 7.7.3., "Software Exception Handling"). To avoid generating exceptions when loading a new environment, clear all the exception flags in the FPU status word that is being loaded.

Operation

```
FPUControlWord ← SRC(FPUControlWord);
FPUStatusWord ← SRC(FPUStatusWord);
FPUTagWord ← SRC(FPUTagWord);
FPUDataPointer ← SRC(FPUDataPointer);
FPUInstructionPointer ← SRC(FPUInstructionPointer);
FPULastInstructionOpcode ← SRC(FPULastInstructionOpcode);
```

FPU Flags Affected

The C0, C1, C2, C3 flags are loaded.

Floating-Point Exceptions

None; however, if an unmasked exception is loaded in the status word, it is generated upon execution of the next waiting floating-point instruction.

Protected Mode Exceptions

#GP(0)	If a memory operand effective address is outside the CS, DS, ES, FS, or GS segment limit.
	If the DS, ES, FS, or GS register is used to access memory and it contains a null segment selector.
#SS(0)	If a memory operand effective address is outside the SS segment limit.
#NM	EM or TS in CR0 is set.
#PF(fault-code)	If a page fault occurs.
#AC(0)	If alignment checking is enabled and an unaligned memory reference is made while the current privilege level is 3.

Real Address Mode Exceptions

#GP	If a memory operand effective address is outside the CS, DS, ES, FS, or GS segment limit.
#SS	If a memory operand effective address is outside the SS segment limit.
#NM	EM or TS in CR0 is set.

Virtual 8086 Mode Exceptions

#GP(0)	If a memory operand effective address is outside the CS, DS, ES, FS, or GS segment limit.
#SS(0)	If a memory operand effective address is outside the SS segment limit.
#NM	EM or TS in CR0 is set.
#PF(fault-code)	If a page fault occurs.
#AC(0)	If alignment checking is enabled and an unaligned memory reference is made.

FMUL/FMULP/FIMUL—Multiply

Opcode	Instruction	Description
D8 /1	FMUL *m32real*	Multiply ST(0) by *m32real* and store result in ST(0)
DC /1	FMUL *m64real*	Multiply ST(0) by *m64real* and store result in ST(0)
D8 C8+i	FMUL ST(0), ST(i)	Multiply ST(0) by ST(i) and store result in ST(0)
DC C8+i	FMUL ST(*i*), ST(0)	Multiply ST(*i*) by ST(0) and store result in ST(*i*)
DE C8+i	FMULP ST(*i*), ST(0)	Multiply ST(*i*) by ST(0), store result in ST(*i*), and pop the register stack
DE C9	FMULP	Multiply ST(0) by ST(1), store result in ST(0), and pop the register stack
DA /1	FIMUL *m32int*	Multiply *m32int* by ST(0) and store result in ST(0)
DE /1	FIMUL *m16int*	Multiply *m16int* by ST(0) and store result in ST(0)

Description

Multiplies the destination and source operands and stores the product in the destination location. The destination operand is always an FPU data register; the source operand can be a register or a memory location. Source operands in memory can be in single-real, double-real, word-integer, or short-integer formats.

The no-operand version of the instruction multiplies the contents of the ST(0) register by the contents of the ST(1) register. The one-operand version multiplies the contents of a memory location (either a real or an integer value) by the contents of the ST(0) register. The two-operand version, multiplies the contents of the ST(0) register by the contents of the ST(*i*) register or vice versa.

The FMULP instructions perform the additional operation of popping the FPU register stack after storing the product. To pop the register stack, the processor marks the ST(0) register as empty and increments the stack pointer (TOP) by 1. The no-operand version of the floating-point multiply instructions always results in the register stack being popped. In some assemblers, the mnemonic for this instruction is FMUL rather than FMULP.

The FIMUL instructions convert an integer source operand to extended-real format before performing the multiplication.

The sign of the result is always the exclusive-OR of the source signs, even if one or more of the values being multiplied is 0 or ∞. When the source operand is an integer 0, it is treated as a +0.

The following table shows the results obtained when multiplying various classes of numbers, assuming that neither overflow nor underflow occurs.

DEST

		−∞	−F	−0	+0	+F	+∞	NaN
	−∞	+∞	+∞	*	*	−∞	−∞	NaN
	−F	+∞	+F	+0	−0	−F	−∞	NaN
	−I	+∞	+F	+0	−0	−F	−∞	NaN
SRC	−0	*	+0	+0	−0	−0	*	NaN
	+0	*	−0	−0	+0	+0	*	NaN
	+I	−∞	−F	−0	+0	+F	+∞	NaN
	+F	−∞	−F	−0	+0	+F	+∞	NaN
	+∞	−∞	−∞	*	*	+∞	+∞	NaN
	NaN	NaN	NaN	NaN	NaN	NaN	NaN	NaN

NOTES:

F Means finite-real number

I Means Integer

* Indicates invalid-arithmetic-operand (#IA) exception.

Operation

```
IF instruction is FIMUL
    THEN
        DEST ← DEST * ConvertExtendedReal(SRC);
    ELSE (* source operand is real number *)
        DEST ← DEST * SRC;
FI;
IF instruction = FMULP
    THEN
        PopRegisterStack
FI;
```

FPU Flags Affected

C1   Set to 0 if stack underflow occurred.

                Indicates rounding direction if the inexact-result exception (#P) fault is
                generated: 0 = not roundup; 1 = roundup.

C0, C2, C3   Undefined.

Floating-Point Exceptions

#IS	Stack underflow occurred.
#IA	Operand is an SNaN value or unsupported format.
	One operand is ±0 and the other is ±∞.
#D	Source operand is a denormal value.
#U	Result is too small for destination format.
#O	Result is too large for destination format.
#P	Value cannot be represented exactly in destination format.

Protected Mode Exceptions

#GP(0)	If a memory operand effective address is outside the CS, DS, ES, FS, or GS segment limit.
	If the DS, ES, FS, or GS register is used to access memory and it contains a null segment selector.
#SS(0)	If a memory operand effective address is outside the SS segment limit.
#NM	EM or TS in CR0 is set.
#PF(fault-code)	If a page fault occurs.
#AC(0)	If alignment checking is enabled and an unaligned memory reference is made while the current privilege level is 3.

Real Address Mode Exceptions

#GP	If a memory operand effective address is outside the CS, DS, ES, FS, or GS segment limit.
#SS	If a memory operand effective address is outside the SS segment limit.
#NM	EM or TS in CR0 is set.

Virtual 8086 Mode Exceptions

#GP(0)	If a memory operand effective address is outside the CS, DS, ES, FS, or GS segment limit.
#SS(0)	If a memory operand effective address is outside the SS segment limit.
#NM	EM or TS in CR0 is set.
#PF(fault-code)	If a page fault occurs.
#AC(0)	If alignment checking is enabled and an unaligned memory reference is made.

FNOP—No Operation

Opcode	Instruction	Description
D9 D0	FNOP	No operation is performed.

Description

Performs no FPU operation. This instruction takes up space in the instruction stream but does not affect the FPU or machine context, except the EIP register.

FPU Flags Affected

C0, C1, C2, C3 undefined.

Floating-Point Exceptions

None.

Protected Mode Exceptions

#NM   EM or TS in CR0 is set.

Real Address Mode Exceptions

#NM   EM or TS in CR0 is set.

Virtual 8086 Mode Exceptions

#NM   EM or TS in CR0 is set.

FPATAN—Partial Arctangent

Opcode	Instruction	Description
D9 F3	FPATAN	Replace ST(1) with arctan(ST(1)/ST(0)) and pop the register stack

Description

Computes the arctangent of the source operand in register ST(1) divided by the source operand in register ST(0), stores the result in ST(1), and pops the FPU register stack. The result in register ST(0) has the same sign as the source operand ST(1) and a magnitude less than $+\pi$.

The following table shows the results obtained when computing the arctangent of various classes of numbers, assuming that underflow does not occur.

		ST(0)						
		$-\infty$	$-F$	-0	$+0$	$+F$	$+\infty$	NaN
	$-\infty$	$-3\pi/4$	$-\pi/2$	$-\pi/2$	$-\pi/2$	$-\pi/2$	$-\pi/4$	NaN
ST(1)	$-F$	$-\pi$	$-\pi$ to $-\pi/2$	$-\pi/2$	$-\pi/2$	$-\pi/2$ to -0	-0	NaN
	-0	$-\pi$	$-\pi$	$-\pi$	-0	-0	-0	NaN
	$+0$	$+\pi$	$+\pi$	$+\pi$	$+0$	$+0$	$+0$	NaN
	$+F$	$+\pi$	$+\pi$ to $+\pi/2$	$+\pi/2$	$+\pi/2$	$+\pi/2$ to $+0$	$+0$	NaN
	$+\infty$	$+3\pi/4$	$+\pi/2$	$+\pi/2$	$+\pi/2$	$+\pi/2$	$+\pi/4$	NaN
	NaN	NaN	NaN	NaN	NaN	NaN	NaN	NaN

NOTE:

F Means finite-real number

There is no restriction on the range of source operands that FPATAN can accept.

Operation

ST(1) ← arctan(ST(1) / ST(0));
PopRegisterStack;

FPU Flags Affected

C1	Set to 0 if stack underflow occurred.
	Indicates rounding direction if the inexact-result exception (#P) is generated: 0 = not roundup; 1 = roundup.
C0, C2, C3	Undefined.

Floating-Point Exceptions

#IS	Stack underflow occurred.
#IA	Source operand is an SNaN value or unsupported format.
#D	Source operand is a denormal value.
#U	Result is too small for destination format.
#P	Value cannot be represented exactly in destination format.

Protected Mode Exceptions

#NM   EM or TS in CR0 is set.

Real Address Mode Exceptions

#NM   EM or TS in CR0 is set.

Virtual 8086 Mode Exceptions

#NM   EM or TS in CR0 is set.

Intel Architecture Compatibility Information

The source operands for this instruction are restricted for the 80287 math coprocessor to the following range:

$$0 \leq |ST(1)| < |ST(0)| < +\infty$$

FPREM—Partial Remainder

Opcode	Instruction	Description
D9 F8	FPREM	Replace ST(0) with the remainder obtained on dividing ST(0) by ST(1)

Description

Computes the remainder obtained on dividing the value in the ST(0) register (the dividend) by the value in the ST(1) register (the divisor or *modulus*), and stores the result in ST(0). The remainder represents the following value:

Remainder = ST(0) − (N ∗ ST(1))

Here, N is an integer value that is obtained by truncating the real-number quotient of [ST(0) / ST(1)] toward zero. The sign of the remainder is the same as the sign of the dividend. The magnitude of the remainder is less than that of the modulus, unless a partial remainder was computed (as described below).

This instruction produces an exact result; the precision (inexact) exception does not occur and the rounding control has no effect. The following table shows the results obtained when computing the remainder of various classes of numbers, assuming that underflow does not occur.

		ST(1)						
		−∞	−F	−0	+0	+F	+∞	NaN
ST(0)	−∞	*	*	*	*	*	*	NaN
	−F	ST(0)	−F or −0	**	**	−F or −0	ST(0)	NaN
	−0	−0	−0	*	*	−0	−0	NaN
	+0	+0	+0	*	*	+0	+0	NaN
	+F	ST(0)	+F or +0	**	**	+F or +0	ST(0)	NaN
	+∞	*	*	*	*	*	*	NaN
	NaN	NaN	NaN	NaN	NaN	NaN	NaN	NaN

NOTES:

F Means finite-real number

* Indicates floating-point invalid-arithmetic-operand (#IA) exception.

** Indicates floating-point zero-divide (#Z) exception.

When the result is 0, its sign is the same as that of the dividend. When the modulus is ∞, the result is equal to the value in ST(0).

The FPREM instruction does not compute the remainder specified in IEEE Std 754. The IEEE specified remainder can be computed with the FPREM1 instruction. The FPREM instruction is provided for compatibility with the Intel 8087 and Intel287 math coprocessors.

The FPREM instruction gets its name "partial remainder" because of the way it computes the remainder. This instructions arrives at a remainder through iterative subtraction. It can, however, reduce the exponent of ST(0) by no more than 63 in one execution of the instruction. If the instruction succeeds in producing a remainder that is less than the modulus, the operation is complete and the C2 flag in the FPU status word is cleared. Otherwise, C2 is set, and the result in ST(0) is called the *partial remainder*. The exponent of the partial remainder will be less than the exponent of the original dividend by at least 32. Software can re-execute the instruction (using the partial remainder in ST(0) as the dividend) until C2 is cleared. (Note that while executing such a remainder-computation loop, a higher-priority interrupting routine that needs the FPU can force a context switch in-between the instructions in the loop.)

An important use of the FPREM instruction is to reduce the arguments of periodic functions. When reduction is complete, the instruction stores the three least-significant bits of the quotient in the C3, C1, and C0 flags of the FPU status word. This information is important in argument reduction for the tangent function (using a modulus of $\pi/4$), because it locates the original angle in the correct one of eight sectors of the unit circle.

Operation

```
D ← exponent(ST(0)) – exponent(ST(1));
IF D < 64
    THEN
        Q ← Integer(TruncateTowardZero(ST(0) / ST(1)));
        ST(0) ← ST(0) – (ST(1) * Q);
        C2 ← 0;
        C0, C3, C1 ← LeastSignificantBits(Q); (* Q2, Q1, Q0 *)
    ELSE
        C2 ← 1;
        N ← an implementation-dependent number between 32 and 63;
        QQ ← Integer(TruncateTowardZero((ST(0) / ST(1)) / 2^(D – N)));
        ST(0) ← ST(0) – (ST(1) * QQ * 2^(D – N));
FI;
```

FPU Flags Affected

C0	Set to bit 2 (Q2) of the quotient.
C1	Set to 0 if stack underflow occurred; otherwise, set to least significant bit of quotient (Q0).
C2	Set to 0 if reduction complete; set to 1 if incomplete.
C3	Set to bit 1 (Q1) of the quotient.

Floating-Point Exceptions

#IS	Stack underflow occurred.
#IA	Source operand is an SNaN value, modulus is 0, dividend is ∞, or unsupported format.

#D   Source operand is a denormal value.

#U   Result is too small for destination format.

Protected Mode Exceptions

#NM   EM or TS in CR0 is set.

Real Address Mode Exceptions

#NM   EM or TS in CR0 is set.

Virtual 8086 Mode Exceptions

#NM   EM or TS in CR0 is set.

FPREM1—Partial Remainder

Opcode	Instruction	Description
D9 F5	FPREM1	Replace ST(0) with the IEEE remainder obtained on dividing ST(0) by ST(1)

Description

Computes the IEEE remainder obtained on dividing the value in the ST(0) register (the dividend) by the value in the ST(1) register (the divisor or *modulus*), and stores the result in ST(0). The remainder represents the following value:

Remainder = ST(0) − (N * ST(1))

Here, N is an integer value that is obtained by rounding the real-number quotient of [ST(0) / ST(1)] toward the nearest integer value. The sign of the remainder is the same as the sign of the dividend. The magnitude of the remainder is less than half the magnitude of the modulus, unless a partial remainder was computed (as described below).

This instruction produces an exact result; the precision (inexact) exception does not occur and the rounding control has no effect. The following table shows the results obtained when computing the remainder of various classes of numbers, assuming that underflow does not occur.

		ST(1)						
		−∞	−F	−0	+0	+F	+∞	NaN
ST(0)	−∞	*	*	*	*	*	*	NaN
	−F	ST(0)	−F or −0	**	**	−F or −0	ST(0)	NaN
	−0	−0	−0	*	*	−0	−0	NaN
	+0	+0	+0	*	*	+0	+0	NaN
	+F	ST(0)	+F or +0	**	**	+F or +0	ST(0)	NaN
	+∞	*	*	*	*	*	*	NaN
	NaN	NaN	NaN	NaN	NaN	NaN	NaN	NaN

NOTES:

F Means finite-real number

* Indicates floating-point invalid-arithmetic-operand (#IA) exception.

** Indicates floating-point zero-divide (#Z) exception.

When the result is 0, its sign is the same as that of the dividend. When the modulus is ∞, the result is equal to the value in ST(0).

The FPREM1 instruction computes the remainder specified in IEEE Std 754. This instruction operates differently from the FPREM instruction in the way that it rounds the quotient of ST(0) divided by ST(1) to an integer (see the "Operation" below).

Like the FPREM instruction, the FPREM1 computes the remainder through iterative subtraction, but can reduce the exponent of ST(0) by no more than 63 in one execution of the instruction. If the instruction succeeds in producing a remainder that is less than one half the modulus, the operation is complete and the C2 flag in the FPU status word is cleared. Otherwise, C2 is set, and the result in ST(0) is called the *partial remainder*. The exponent of the partial remainder will be less than the exponent of the original dividend by at least 32. Software can re-execute the instruction (using the partial remainder in ST(0) as the dividend) until C2 is cleared. (Note that while executing such a remainder-computation loop, a higher-priority interrupting routine that needs the FPU can force a context switch in-between the instructions in the loop.)

An important use of the FPREM1 instruction is to reduce the arguments of periodic functions. When reduction is complete, the instruction stores the three least-significant bits of the quotient in the C3, C1, and C0 flags of the FPU status word. This information is important in argument reduction for the tangent function (using a modulus of $\pi/4$), because it locates the original angle in the correct one of eight sectors of the unit circle.

Operation

```
D ← exponent(ST(0)) – exponent(ST(1));
IF D < 64
    THEN
        Q ← Integer(RoundTowardNearestInteger(ST(0) / ST(1)));
        ST(0) ← ST(0) – (ST(1) * Q);
        C2 ← 0;
        C0, C3, C1 ← LeastSignificantBits(Q); (* Q2, Q1, Q0 *)
    ELSE
        C2 ← 1;
        N ← an implementation-dependent number between 32 and 63;
        QQ ← Integer(TruncateTowardZero((ST(0) / ST(1)) / 2^(D – N)));
        ST(0) ← ST(0) – (ST(1) * QQ * 2^(D – N));
FI;
```

FPU Flags Affected

C0   Set to bit 2 (Q2) of the quotient.

C1   Set to 0 if stack underflow occurred; otherwise, set to least significant bit of quotient (Q0).

C2   Set to 0 if reduction complete; set to 1 if incomplete.

C3   Set to bit 1 (Q1) of the quotient.

Floating-Point Exceptions

#IS   Stack underflow occurred.

#IA   Source operand is an SNaN value, modulus (divisor) is 0, dividend is ∞, or unsupported format.

#D   Source operand is a denormal value.

#U   Result is too small for destination format.

Protected Mode Exceptions

#NM   EM or TS in CR0 is set.

Real Address Mode Exceptions

#NM   EM or TS in CR0 is set.

Virtual 8086 Mode Exceptions

#NM   EM or TS in CR0 is set.

FPTAN—Partial Tangent

Opcode	Instruction	Clocks	Description
D9 F2	FPTAN	17-173	Replace ST(0) with its tangent and push 1 onto the FPU stack.

Description

Computes the tangent of the source operand in register ST(0), stores the result in ST(0), and pushes a 1.0 onto the FPU register stack. The source operand must be given in radians and must be less than $\pm 2^{63}$. The following table shows the unmasked results obtained when computing the partial tangent of various classes of numbers, assuming that underflow does not occur.

ST(0) SRC	ST(0) DEST
$-\infty$	*
$-F$	$-F$ to $+F$
-0	-0
$+0$	$+0$
$+F$	$-F$ to $+F$
$+\infty$	*
NaN	NaN

NOTES:

F Means finite-real number

* Indicates floating-point invalid-arithmetic-operand (#IA) exception.

If the source operand is outside the acceptable range, the C2 flag in the FPU status word is set, and the value in register ST(0) remains unchanged. The instruction does not raise an exception when the source operand is out of range. It is up to the program to check the C2 flag for out-of-range conditions. Source values outside the range -2^{63} to $+2^{63}$ can be reduced to the range of the instruction by subtracting an appropriate integer multiple of 2π or by using the FPREM instruction with a divisor of 2π. See Section 7.5.8., "Pi" for a discussion of the proper value to use for π in performing such reductions.

The value 1.0 is pushed onto the register stack after the tangent has been computed to maintain compatibility with the Intel 8087 and Intel287 math coprocessors. This operation also simplifies the calculation of other trigonometric functions. For instance, the cotangent (which is the reciprocal of the tangent) can be computed by executing a FDIVR instruction after the FPTAN instruction.

Operation

IF ST(0) < 2^{63}
THEN
    C2 ← 0;
    ST(0) ← tan(ST(0));
    TOP ← TOP − 1;
    ST(0) ← 1.0;
ELSE (*source operand is out-of-range *)
    C2 ← 1;
FI;

FPU Flags Affected

C1	Set to 0 if stack underflow occurred; set to 1 if stack overflow occurred.
	Indicates rounding direction if the inexact-result exception (#P) is generated: 0 = not roundup; 1 = roundup.
C2	Set to 1 if source operand is outside the range -2^{63} to $+2^{63}$; otherwise, cleared to 0.
C0, C3	Undefined.

Floating-Point Exceptions

#IS	Stack underflow occurred.
#IA	Source operand is an SNaN value, ∞, or unsupported format.
#D	Source operand is a denormal value.
#U	Result is too small for destination format.
#P	Value cannot be represented exactly in destination format.

Protected Mode Exceptions

#NM	EM or TS in CR0 is set.

Real Address Mode Exceptions

#NM	EM or TS in CR0 is set.

Virtual 8086 Mode Exceptions

#NM	EM or TS in CR0 is set.

FRNDINT—Round to Integer

Opcode	Instruction	Description
D9 FC	FRNDINT	Round ST(0) to an integer.

Description

Rounds the source value in the ST(0) register to the nearest integral value, depending on the current rounding mode (setting of the RC field of the FPU control word), and stores the result in ST(0).

If the source value is ∞, the value is not changed. If the source value is not an integral value, the floating-point inexact-result exception (#P) is generated.

Operation

ST(0) ← RoundToIntegralValue(ST(0));

FPU Flags Affected

C1	Set to 0 if stack underflow occurred.
	Indicates rounding direction if the inexact-result exception (#P) is generated: 0 = not roundup; 1 = roundup.
C0, C2, C3	Undefined.

Floating-Point Exceptions

#IS	Stack underflow occurred.
#IA	Source operand is an SNaN value or unsupported format.
#D	Source operand is a denormal value.
#P	Source operand is not an integral value.

Protected Mode Exceptions

#NM	EM or TS in CR0 is set.

Real Address Mode Exceptions

#NM	EM or TS in CR0 is set.

Virtual 8086 Mode Exceptions

#NM	EM or TS in CR0 is set.

FRSTOR—Restore FPU State

Opcode	Instruction	Description
DD /4	FRSTOR m94/108byte	Load FPU state from m94byte or m108byte.

Description

Loads the FPU state (operating environment and register stack) from the memory area specified with the source operand. This state data is typically written to the specified memory location by a previous FSAVE/FNSAVE instruction.

The FPU operating environment consists of the FPU control word, status word, tag word, instruction pointer, data pointer, and last opcode. Figures 7-13 through 7-14 show the layout in memory of the stored environment, depending on the operating mode of the processor (protected or real) and the size of the current address attribute (16-bit or 32-bit). In virtual-8086 mode, the real mode layouts are used. The contents of the FPU register stack are stored in the 80 bytes immediately follow the operating environment image.

The FRSTOR instruction should be executed in the same operating mode as the corresponding FSAVE/FNSAVE instruction.

If one or more unmasked exception bits are set in the new FPU status word, a floating-point exception will be generated. To avoid raising exceptions when loading a new operating environment, clear all the exception flags in the FPU status word that is being loaded.

Operation

FPUControlWord ← SRC(FPUControlWord);
FPUStatusWord ← SRC(FPUStatusWord);
FPUTagWord ← SRC(FPUTagWord);
FPUDataPointer ← SRC(FPUDataPointer);
FPUInstructionPointer ← SRC(FPUInstructionPointer);
FPULastInstructionOpcode ← SRC(FPULastInstructionOpcode);
ST(0) ← SRC(ST(0));
ST(1) ← SRC(ST(1));
ST(2) ← SRC(ST(2));
ST(3) ← SRC(ST(3));
ST(4) ← SRC(ST(4));
ST(5) ← SRC(ST(5));
ST(6) ← SRC(ST(6));
ST(7) ← SRC(ST(7));

FPU Flags Affected

The C0, C1, C2, C3 flags are loaded.

Floating-Point Exceptions

None; however, this operation might unmask an existing exception that has been detected but not generated, because it was masked. Here, the exception is generated at the completion of the instruction.

Protected Mode Exceptions

#GP(0)	If a memory operand effective address is outside the CS, DS, ES, FS, or GS segment limit.
	If the DS, ES, FS, or GS register is used to access memory and it contains a null segment selector.
#SS(0)	If a memory operand effective address is outside the SS segment limit.
#NM	EM or TS in CR0 is set.
#PF(fault-code)	If a page fault occurs.
#AC(0)	If alignment checking is enabled and an unaligned memory reference is made while the current privilege level is 3.

Real Address Mode Exceptions

#GP	If a memory operand effective address is outside the CS, DS, ES, FS, or GS segment limit.
#SS	If a memory operand effective address is outside the SS segment limit.
#NM	EM or TS in CR0 is set.

Virtual 8086 Mode Exceptions

#GP(0)	If a memory operand effective address is outside the CS, DS, ES, FS, or GS segment limit.
#SS(0)	If a memory operand effective address is outside the SS segment limit.
#NM	EM or TS in CR0 is set.
#PF(fault-code)	If a page fault occurs.
#AC(0)	If alignment checking is enabled and an unaligned memory reference is made.

FSAVE/FNSAVE—Store FPU State

Opcode	Instruction	Description
9B DD /6	FSAVE m94/108byte	Store FPU state to m94byte or m108byte after checking for pending unmasked floating-point exceptions. Then re-initialize the FPU.
DD /6	FNSAVE m94/108byte	Store FPU environment to m94byte or m108byte without checking for pending unmasked floating-point exceptions. Then re-initialize the FPU.

Description

Stores the current FPU state (operating environment and register stack) at the specified destination in memory, and then re-initializes the FPU. The FSAVE instruction checks for and handles pending unmasked floating-point exceptions before storing the FPU state; the FNSAVE instruction does not.

The FPU operating environment consists of the FPU control word, status word, tag word, instruction pointer, data pointer, and last opcode. Figures 7-13 through 7-14 show the layout in memory of the stored environment, depending on the operating mode of the processor (protected or real) and the size of the current address attribute (16-bit or 32-bit). In virtual-8086 mode, the real mode layouts are used. The contents of the FPU register stack are stored in the 80 bytes immediately follow the operating environment image.

The saved image reflects the state of the FPU after all floating-point instructions preceding the FSAVE/FNSAVE instruction in the instruction stream have been executed.

After the FPU state has been saved, the FPU is reset to the same default values it is set to with the FINIT/FNINIT instructions (see Chapter 11, "FINIT/FNINIT—Initialize Floating-Point Unit").

The FSAVE/FNSAVE instructions are typically used when the operating system needs to perform a context switch, an exception handler needs to use the FPU, or an application program needs to pass a "clean" FPU to a procedure.

Operation

```
(* Save FPU State and Registers *)
DEST(FPUControlWord) ← FPUControlWord;
DEST(FPUStatusWord) ← FPUStatusWord;
DEST(FPUTagWord) ← FPUTagWord;
DEST(FPUDataPointer) ← FPUDataPointer;
DEST(FPUInstructionPointer) ← FPUInstructionPointer;
DEST(FPULastInstructionOpcode) ← FPULastInstructionOpcode;
DEST(ST(0)) ← ST(0);
DEST(ST(1)) ← ST(1);
DEST(ST(2)) ← ST(2);
DEST(ST(3)) ← ST(3);
DEST(ST(4)) ← ST(4);
```

```
DEST(ST(5)) ← ST(5);
DEST(ST(6)) ← ST(6);
DEST(ST(7)) ← ST(7);
(* Initialize FPU *)
FPUControlWord ← 037FH;
FPUStatusWord ← 0;
FPUTagWord ← FFFFH;
FPUDataPointer ← 0;
FPUInstructionPointer ← 0;
FPULastInstructionOpcode ← 0;
```

FPU Flags Affected

The C0, C1, C2, and C3 flags are saved and then cleared.

Floating-Point Exceptions

None.

Protected Mode Exceptions

#GP(0)	If destination is located in a nonwritable segment.
	If a memory operand effective address is outside the CS, DS, ES, FS, or GS segment limit.
	If the DS, ES, FS, or GS register is used to access memory and it contains a null segment selector.
#SS(0)	If a memory operand effective address is outside the SS segment limit.
#NM	EM or TS in CR0 is set.
#PF(fault-code)	If a page fault occurs.
#AC(0)	If alignment checking is enabled and an unaligned memory reference is made while the current privilege level is 3.

Real Address Mode Exceptions

#GP	If a memory operand effective address is outside the CS, DS, ES, FS, or GS segment limit.
#SS	If a memory operand effective address is outside the SS segment limit.
#NM	EM or TS in CR0 is set.

Virtual 8086 Mode Exceptions

#GP(0)	If a memory operand effective address is outside the CS, DS, ES, FS, or GS segment limit.

#SS(0)	If a memory operand effective address is outside the SS segment limit.
#NM	EM or TS in CR0 is set.
#PF(fault-code)	If a page fault occurs.
#AC(0)	If alignment checking is enabled and an unaligned memory reference is made.

Intel Architecture Compatibility Information

For Intel math coprocessors and FPUs prior to the Intel Pentium processor, an FWAIT instruction should be executed before attempting to read from the memory image stored with a prior FSAVE/FNSAVE instruction. This FWAIT instruction helps insure that the storage operation has been completed.

FSCALE—Scale

Opcode	Instruction	Description
D9 FD	FSCALE	Scale ST(0) by ST(1).

Description

Multiplies the destination operand by 2 to the power of the source operand and stores the result in the destination operand. This instruction provides rapid multiplication or division by integral powers of 2. The destination operand is a real value that is located in register ST(0). The source operand is the nearest integer value that is smaller than the value in the ST(1) register (that is, the value in register ST(1) is truncate toward 0 to its nearest integer value to form the source operand). The actual scaling operation is performed by adding the source operand (integer value) to the exponent of the value in register ST(0). The following table shows the results obtained when scaling various classes of numbers, assuming that neither overflow nor underflow occurs.

		ST(1)		
		−N	0	+N
ST(0)	−∞	−∞	−∞	−∞
	−F	−F	−F	−F
	−0	−0	−0	−0
	+0	+0	+0	+0
	+F	+F	+F	+F
	+∞	+∞	+∞	+∞
	NaN	NaN	NaN	NaN

NOTES:

F Means finite-real number.

N Means integer.

In most cases, only the exponent is changed and the mantissa (significand) remains unchanged. However, when the value being scaled in ST(0) is a denormal value, the mantissa is also changed and the result may turn out to be a normalized number. Similarly, if overflow or underflow results from a scale operation, the resulting mantissa will differ from the source's mantissa.

The FSCALE instruction can also be used to reverse the action of the FXTRACT instruction, as shown in the following example:

```
FXTRACT;
FSCALE;
FSTP ST(1);
```

In this example, the FXTRACT instruction extracts the significand and exponent from the value in ST(0) and stores them in ST(0) and ST(1) respectively. The FSCALE then scales the significand in ST(0) by the exponent in ST(1), recreating the original value before the FXTRACT operation was performed. The FSTP ST(1) instruction returns the recreated value to the FPU register where it originally resided.

Operation

$ST(0) \leftarrow ST(0) * 2^{ST(1)}$;

FPU Flags Affected

C1	Set to 0 if stack underflow occurred.
	Indicates rounding direction if the inexact-result exception (#P) is generated: 0 = not roundup; 1 = roundup.
C0, C2, C3	Undefined.

Floating-Point Exceptions

#IS	Stack underflow occurred.
#IA	Source operand is an SNaN value or unsupported format.
#D	Source operand is a denormal value.
#U	Result is too small for destination format.
#O	Result is too large for destination format.
#P	Value cannot be represented exactly in destination format.

Protected Mode Exceptions

#NM	EM or TS in CR0 is set.

Real Address Mode Exceptions

#NM	EM or TS in CR0 is set.

Virtual 8086 Mode Exceptions

#NM	EM or TS in CR0 is set.

intel

FSIN—Sine

Opcode	Instruction	Description
D9 FE	FSIN	Replace ST(0) with its sine.

Description

Calculates the sine of the source operand in register ST(0) and stores the result in ST(0). The source operand must be given in radians and must be within the range -2^{63} to $+2^{63}$. The following table shows the results obtained when taking the sine of various classes of numbers, assuming that underflow does not occur.

SRC (ST(0))	DEST (ST(0))
$-\infty$	*
$-F$	-1 to $+1$
-0	-0
$+0$	$+0$
$+F$	-1 to $+1$
$+\infty$	*
NaN	NaN

NOTES:

F Means finite-real number

* Indicates floating-point invalid-arithmetic-operand (#IA) exception.

If the source operand is outside the acceptable range, the C2 flag in the FPU status word is set, and the value in register ST(0) remains unchanged. The instruction does not raise an exception when the source operand is out of range. It is up to the program to check the C2 flag for out-of-range conditions. Source values outside the range -2^{63} to $+2^{63}$ can be reduced to the range of the instruction by subtracting an appropriate integer multiple of 2π or by using the FPREM instruction with a divisor of 2π. See Section 7.5.8., "Pi" for a discussion of the proper value to use for π in performing such reductions.

Operation

```
IF ST(0) < 2^63
THEN
    C2 ← 0;
    ST(0) ← sin(ST(0));
ELSE (* source operand out of range *)
    C2 ← 1;
FI:
```

FPU Flags Affected

C1	Set to 0 if stack underflow occurred.
	Indicates rounding direction if the inexact-result exception (#P) is generated: 0 = not roundup; 1 = roundup.
C2	Set to 1 if source operand is outside the range -2^{63} to $+2^{63}$; otherwise, cleared to 0.
C0, C3	Undefined.

Floating-Point Exceptions

#IS	Stack underflow occurred.
#IA	Source operand is an SNaN value, ∞, or unsupported format.
#D	Source operand is a denormal value.
#P	Value cannot be represented exactly in destination format.

Protected Mode Exceptions

#NM	EM or TS in CR0 is set.

Real Address Mode Exceptions

#NM	EM or TS in CR0 is set.

Virtual 8086 Mode Exceptions

#NM	EM or TS in CR0 is set.

FSINCOS—Sine and Cosine

Opcode	Instruction	Description
D9 FB	FSINCOS	Compute the sine and cosine of ST(0); replace ST(0) with the sine, and push the cosine onto the register stack.

Description

Computes both the sine and the cosine of the source operand in register ST(0), stores the sine in ST(0), and pushes the cosine onto the top of the FPU register stack. (This instruction is faster than executing the FSIN and FCOS instructions in succession.)

The source operand must be given in radians and must be within the range -2^{63} to $+2^{63}$. The following table shows the results obtained when taking the sine and cosine of various classes of numbers, assuming that underflow does not occur.

SRC	DEST	
ST(0))	ST(0) Cosine	ST(1) Sine
$-\infty$	*	*
$-F$	-1 to $+1$	-1 to $+1$
-0	$+1$	-0
$+0$	$+1$	$+0$
$+F$	-1 to $+1$	-1 to $+1$
$+\infty$	*	*
NaN	NaN	NaN

NOTES:

F Means finite-real number

* Indicates floating-point invalid-arithmetic-operand (#IA) exception.

If the source operand is outside the acceptable range, the C2 flag in the FPU status word is set, and the value in register ST(0) remains unchanged. The instruction does not raise an exception when the source operand is out of range. It is up to the program to check the C2 flag for out-of-range conditions. Source values outside the range -2^{63} to $+2^{63}$ can be reduced to the range of the instruction by subtracting an appropriate integer multiple of 2π or by using the FPREM instruction with a divisor of 2π. See Section 7.5.8., "Pi" for a discussion of the proper value to use for π in performing such reductions.

Operation

IF ST(0) < 2^{63}
THEN
    C2 ← 0;
    TEMP ← cosine(ST(0));
    ST(0) ← sine(ST(0));

    TOP ← TOP − 1;
    ST(0) ← TEMP;
ELSE (* source operand out of range *)
    C2 ← 1;
FI:

FPU Flags Affected

C1	Set to 0 if stack underflow occurred; set to 1 of stack overflow occurs.
	Indicates rounding direction if the inexact-result exception (#P) is generated: 0 = not roundup; 1 = roundup.
C2	Set to 1 if source operand is outside the range -2^{63} to $+2^{63}$; otherwise, cleared to 0.
C0, C3	Undefined.

Floating-Point Exceptions

#IS	Stack underflow occurred.
#IA	Source operand is an SNaN value, ∞, or unsupported format.
#D	Source operand is a denormal value.
#U	Result is too small for destination format.
#P	Value cannot be represented exactly in destination format.

Protected Mode Exceptions

#NM	EM or TS in CR0 is set.

Real Address Mode Exceptions

#NM	EM or TS in CR0 is set.

Virtual 8086 Mode Exceptions

#NM	EM or TS in CR0 is set.

FSQRT—Square Root

Opcode	Instruction	Description
D9 FA	FSQRT	Calculates square root of ST(0) and stores the result in ST(0)

Description

Calculates the square root of the source value in the ST(0) register and stores the result in ST(0).

The following table shows the results obtained when taking the square root of various classes of numbers, assuming that neither overflow nor underflow occurs.

SRC (ST(0))	DEST (ST(0))
$-\infty$	*
$-F$	*
-0	-0
$+0$	$+0$
$+F$	$+F$
$+\infty$	$+\infty$
NaN	NaN

NOTES:

F Means finite-real number

* Indicates floating-point invalid-arithmetic-operand (#IA) exception.

Operation

ST(0) ← SquareRoot(ST(0));

FPU Flags Affected

C1	Set to 0 if stack underflow occurred.
	Indicates rounding direction if inexact-result exception (#P) is generated: 0 = not roundup; 1 = roundup.
C0, C2, C3	Undefined.

Floating-Point Exceptions

#IS	Stack underflow occurred.
#IA	Source operand is an SNaN value or unsupported format.
	Source operand is a negative value (except for –0).
#D	Source operand is a denormal value.
#P	Value cannot be represented exactly in destination format.

Protected Mode Exceptions

#NM	EM or TS in CR0 is set.

Real Address Mode Exceptions

#NM	EM or TS in CR0 is set.

Virtual 8086 Mode Exceptions

#NM	EM or TS in CR0 is set.

FST/FSTP—Store Real

Opcode	Instruction	Description
D9 /2	FST *m32real*	Copy ST(0) to *m32real*
DD /2	FST *m64real*	Copy ST(0) to *m64real*
DD D0+i	FST ST(*i*)	Copy ST(0) to ST(i)
D9 /3	FSTP *m32real*	Copy ST(0) to *m32real* and pop register stack
DD /3	FSTP *m64real*	Copy ST(0) to *m64real* and pop register stack
DB /7	FSTP *m80real*	Copy ST(0) to *m80real* and pop register stack
DD D8+i	FSTP ST(*i*)	Copy ST(0) to ST(*i*) and pop register stack

Description

The FST instruction copies the value in the ST(0) register to the destination operand, which can be a memory location or another register in the FPU registers stack. When storing the value in memory, the value is converted to single- or double-real format.

The FSTP instruction performs the same operation as the FST instruction and then pops the register stack. To pop the register stack, the processor marks the ST(0) register as empty and increments the stack pointer (TOP) by 1. The FSTP instruction can also stores values in memory in extended-real format.

If the destination operand is a memory location, the operand specifies the address where the first byte of the destination value is to be stored. If the destination operand is a register, the operand specifies a register in the register stack relative to the top of the stack.

If the destination size is single- or double-real, the significand of the value being stored is rounded to the width of the destination (according to rounding mode specified by the RC field of the FPU control word), and the exponent is converted to the width and bias of the destination format. If the value being stored is too large for the destination format, a numeric overflow exception (#O) is generated and, if the exception is unmasked, no value is stored in the destination operand. If the value being stored is a denormal value, the denormal exception (#D) is not generated. This condition is simply signaled as a numeric underflow exception (#U) condition.

If the value being stored is ±0, ±∞, or a NaN, the least-significant bits of the significand and the exponent are truncated to fit the destination format. This operation preserves the value's identity as a 0, ∞, or NaN.

If the destination operand is a non-empty register, the invalid-operation exception is not generated.

Operation

DEST ← ST(0);
IF instruction = FSTP
   THEN
      PopRegisterStack;
FI;

FPU Flags Affected

C1	Set to 0 if stack underflow occurred.
	Indicates rounding direction of if the floating-point inexact exception (#P) is generated: 0 = not roundup; 1 = roundup.
C0, C2, C3	Undefined.

Floating-Point Exceptions

#IS	Stack underflow occurred.
#IA	Source operand is an SNaN value or unsupported format.
#U	Result is too small for the destination format.
#O	Result is too large for the destination format.
#P	Value cannot be represented exactly in destination format.

Protected Mode Exceptions

#GP(0)	If the destination is located in a nonwritable segment.
	If a memory operand effective address is outside the CS, DS, ES, FS, or GS segment limit.
	If the DS, ES, FS, or GS register is used to access memory and it contains a null segment selector.
#SS(0)	If a memory operand effective address is outside the SS segment limit.
#NM	EM or TS in CR0 is set.
#PF(fault-code)	If a page fault occurs.
#AC(0)	If alignment checking is enabled and an unaligned memory reference is made while the current privilege level is 3.

Real Address Mode Exceptions

#GP	If a memory operand effective address is outside the CS, DS, ES, FS, or GS segment limit.
#SS	If a memory operand effective address is outside the SS segment limit.
#NM	EM or TS in CR0 is set.

Virtual 8086 Mode Exceptions

#GP(0)   If a memory operand effective address is outside the CS, DS, ES, FS, or GS segment limit.

#SS(0)   If a memory operand effective address is outside the SS segment limit.

#NM   EM or TS in CR0 is set.

#PF(fault-code) If a page fault occurs.

#AC(0)   If alignment checking is enabled and an unaligned memory reference is made.

FSTCW/FNSTCW—Store Control Word

Opcode	Instruction	Description
9B D9 /7	FSTCW m2byte	Store FPU control word to m2byte after checking for pending unmasked floating-point exceptions.
D9 /7	FNSTCW m2byte	Store FPU control word to m2byte without checking for pending unmasked floating-point exceptions.

Description

Stores the current value of the FPU control word at the specified destination in memory. The FSTCW instruction checks for and handles pending unmasked floating-point exceptions before storing the control word; the FNSTCW instruction does not.

Operation

DEST ← FPUControlWord;

FPU Flags Affected

The C0, C1, C2, and C3 flags are undefined.

Floating-Point Exceptions

None.

Protected Mode Exceptions

#GP(0)	If the destination is located in a nonwritable segment.
	If a memory operand effective address is outside the CS, DS, ES, FS, or GS segment limit.
	If the DS, ES, FS, or GS register is used to access memory and it contains a null segment selector.
#SS(0)	If a memory operand effective address is outside the SS segment limit.
#NM	EM or TS in CR0 is set.
#PF(fault-code)	If a page fault occurs.
#AC(0)	If alignment checking is enabled and an unaligned memory reference is made while the current privilege level is 3.

Real Address Mode Exceptions

#GP	If a memory operand effective address is outside the CS, DS, ES, FS, or GS segment limit.
#SS	If a memory operand effective address is outside the SS segment limit.
#NM	EM or TS in CR0 is set.

Virtual 8086 Mode Exceptions

#GP(0)	If a memory operand effective address is outside the CS, DS, ES, FS, or GS segment limit.
#SS(0)	If a memory operand effective address is outside the SS segment limit.
#NM	EM or TS in CR0 is set.
#PF(fault-code)	If a page fault occurs.
#AC(0)	If alignment checking is enabled and an unaligned memory reference is made.

FSTENV/FNSTENV—Store FPU Environment

Opcode	Instruction	Description
9B D9 /6	FSTENV m14/28byte	Store FPU environment to m14byte or m28byte after checking for pending unmasked floating-point exceptions. Then mask all floating-point exceptions.
D9 /6	FNSTENV m14/28byte	Store FPU environment to m14byte or m28byte without checking for pending unmasked floating-point exceptions. Then mask all floating-point exceptions.

Description

Saves the current FPU operating environment at the memory location specified with the destination operand, and then masks all floating-point exceptions. The FPU operating environment consists of the FPU control word, status word, tag word, instruction pointer, data pointer, and last opcode. Figures 7-13 through 7-14 show the layout in memory of the stored environment, depending on the operating mode of the processor (protected or real) and the size of the current address attribute (16-bit or 32-bit). (In virtual-8086 mode, the real mode layouts are used.)

The FSTENV instruction checks for and handles any pending unmasked floating-point exceptions before storing the FPU environment; the FNSTENV instruction does not.The saved image reflects the state of the FPU after all floating-point instructions preceding the FSTENV/FNSTENV instruction in the instruction stream have been executed.

These instructions are often used by exception handlers because they provide access to the FPU instruction and data pointers. The environment is typically saved in the procedure stack. Masking all exceptions after saving the environment prevents floating-point exceptions from interrupting the exception handler.

Operation

DEST(FPUControlWord) ← FPUControlWord;
DEST(FPUStatusWord) ← FPUStatusWord;
DEST(FPUTagWord) ← FPUTagWord;
DEST(FPUDataPointer) ← FPUDataPointer;
DEST(FPUInstructionPointer) ← FPUInstructionPointer;
DEST(FPULastInstructionOpcode) ← FPULastInstructionOpcode;

FPU Flags Affected

The C0, C1, C2, and C3 are undefined.

Floating-Point Exceptions

None.

Protected Mode Exceptions

#GP(0)	If the destination is located in a nonwritable segment.
	If a memory operand effective address is outside the CS, DS, ES, FS, or GS segment limit.
	If the DS, ES, FS, or GS register is used to access memory and it contains a null segment selector.
#SS(0)	If a memory operand effective address is outside the SS segment limit.
#NM	EM or TS in CR0 is set.
#PF(fault-code)	If a page fault occurs.
#AC(0)	If alignment checking is enabled and an unaligned memory reference is made while the current privilege level is 3.

Real Address Mode Exceptions

#GP	If a memory operand effective address is outside the CS, DS, ES, FS, or GS segment limit.
#SS	If a memory operand effective address is outside the SS segment limit.
#NM	EM or TS in CR0 is set.

Virtual 8086 Mode Exceptions

#GP(0)	If a memory operand effective address is outside the CS, DS, ES, FS, or GS segment limit.
#SS(0)	If a memory operand effective address is outside the SS segment limit.
#NM	EM or TS in CR0 is set.
#PF(fault-code)	If a page fault occurs.
#AC(0)	If alignment checking is enabled and an unaligned memory reference is made.

FSTSW/FNSTSW—Store Status Word

Opcode	Instruction	Description
9B DD /7	FSTSW *m2byte*	Store FPU status word at *m2byte* after checking for pending unmasked floating-point exceptions.
9B DF E0	FSTSW AX	Store FPU status word in AX register after checking for pending unmasked floating-point exceptions.
DD /7	FNSTSW *m2byte*	Store FPU status word at *m2byte* without checking for pending unmasked floating-point exceptions.
DF E0	FNSTSW AX	Store FPU status word in AX register without checking for pending unmasked floating-point exceptions.

Description

Stores the current value of the FPU status word in the destination location. The destination operand can be either a two-byte memory location or the AX register. The FSTSW instruction checks for and handles pending unmasked floating-point exceptions before storing the status word; the FNSTSW instruction does not.

The FNSTSW AX form of the instruction is used primarily in conditional branching (for instance, after an FPU comparison instruction or an FPREM, FPREM1, or FXAM instruction), where the direction of the branch depends on the state of the FPU condition code flags. (See Section 7.3.3., "Branching and Conditional Moves on FPU Condition Codes".) This instruction can also be used to invoke exception handlers (by examining the exception flags) in environments that do not use interrupts. When the FNSTSW AX instruction is executed, the AX register is updated before the processor executes any further instructions. The status stored in the AX register is thus guaranteed to be from the completion of the prior FPU instruction.

Operation

DEST ← FPUStatusWord;

FPU Flags Affected

The C0, C1, C2, and C3 are undefined.

Floating-Point Exceptions

None.

Protected Mode Exceptions

#GP(0)   If the destination is located in a nonwritable segment.

If a memory operand effective address is outside the CS, DS, ES, FS, or GS segment limit.

If the DS, ES, FS, or GS register is used to access memory and it contains a null segment selector.

#SS(0)   If a memory operand effective address is outside the SS segment limit.

#NM   EM or TS in CR0 is set.

#PF(fault-code)   If a page fault occurs.

#AC(0)   If alignment checking is enabled and an unaligned memory reference is made while the current privilege level is 3.

Real Address Mode Exceptions

#GP   If a memory operand effective address is outside the CS, DS, ES, FS, or GS segment limit.

#SS   If a memory operand effective address is outside the SS segment limit.

#NM   EM or TS in CR0 is set.

Virtual 8086 Mode Exceptions

#GP(0)   If a memory operand effective address is outside the CS, DS, ES, FS, or GS segment limit.

#SS(0)   If a memory operand effective address is outside the SS segment limit.

#NM   EM or TS in CR0 is set.

#PF(fault-code)   If a page fault occurs.

#AC(0)   If alignment checking is enabled and an unaligned memory reference is made.

FSUB/FSUBP/FISUB—Subtract

Opcode	Instruction	Description
D8 /4	FSUB *m32real*	Subtract *m32real* from ST(0) and store result in ST(0)
DC /4	FSUB *m64real*	Subtract *m64real* from ST(0) and store result in ST(0)
D8 E0+i	FSUB ST(0), ST(*i*)	Subtract ST(*i*) from ST(0) and store result in ST(0)
DC E8+i	FSUB ST(*i*), ST(0)	Subtract ST(0) from ST(*i*) and store result in ST(*i*)
DE E8+i	FSUBP ST(*i*), ST(0)	Subtract ST(0) from ST(*i*), store result in ST(*i*), and pop register stack
DE E9	FSUBP	Subtract ST(0) from ST(1), store result in ST(1), and pop register stack
DA /4	FISUB *m32int*	Subtract *m32int* from ST(0) and store result in ST(0)
DE /4	FISUB *m16int*	Subtract *m16int* from ST(0) and store result in ST(0)

Description

Subtracts the source operand from the destination operand and stores the difference in the destination location. The destination operand is always an FPU data register; the source operand can be a register or a memory location. Source operands in memory can be in single-real, double-real, word-integer, or short-integer formats.

The no-operand version of the instruction subtracts the contents of the ST(0) register from the ST(1) register and stores the result in ST(1). The one-operand version subtracts the contents of a memory location (either a real or an integer value) from the contents of the ST(0) register and stores the result in ST(0). The two-operand version, subtracts the contents of the ST(0) register from the ST(*i*) register or vice versa.

The FSUBP instructions perform the additional operation of popping the FPU register stack following the subtraction. To pop the register stack, the processor marks the ST(0) register as empty and increments the stack pointer (TOP) by 1. The no-operand version of the floating-point subtract instructions always results in the register stack being popped. In some assemblers, the mnemonic for this instruction is FSUB rather than FSUBP.

The FISUB instructions convert an integer source operand to extended-real format before performing the subtraction.

The following table shows the results obtained when subtracting various classes of numbers from one another, assuming that neither overflow nor underflow occurs. Here, the SRC value is subtracted from the DEST value (DEST − SRC = result).

When the difference between two operands of like sign is 0, the result is +0, except for the round toward −∞ mode, in which case the result is −0. This instruction also guarantees that +0 − (−0) = +0, and that −0 − (+0) = −0. When the source operand is an integer 0, it is treated as a +0.

When one operand is ∞, the result is ∞ of the expected sign. If both operands are ∞ of the same sign, an invalid-operation exception is generated.

	SRC						
	−∞	−F or −I	−0	+0	+F or +I	+∞	NaN
−∞	*	−∞	−∞	−∞	−∞	−∞	NaN
−F	+∞	±F or ±0	DEST	DEST	−F	−∞	NaN
−0	+∞	−SRC	±0	−0	−SRC	−∞	NaN
+0	+∞	−SRC	+0	±0	−SRC	−∞	NaN
+F	+∞	+F	DEST	DEST	±F or ±0	−∞	NaN
+∞	+∞	+∞	+∞	+∞	+∞	*	NaN
NaN	NaN	NaN	NaN	NaN	NaN	NaN	NaN

(Left header label: **DEST**)

NOTES:

F Means finite-real number

I Means integer.

* Indicates floating-point invalid-arithmetic-operand (#IA) exception.

Operation

```
IF instruction is FISUB
    THEN
        DEST ← DEST − ConvertExtendedReal(SRC);
    ELSE (* source operand is real number *)
        DEST ← DEST − SRC;
FI;
IF instruction = FSUBP
    THEN
        PopRegisterStack
FI;
```

FPU Flags Affected

C1	Set to 0 if stack underflow occurred.
	Indicates rounding direction if the inexact-result exception (#P) fault is generated: 0 = not roundup; 1 = roundup.
C0, C2, C3	Undefined.

Floating-Point Exceptions

#IS	Stack underflow occurred.
#IA	Operand is an SNaN value or unsupported format.
	Operands are infinities of like sign.
#D	Source operand is a denormal value.

#U	Result is too small for destination format.
#O	Result is too large for destination format.
#P	Value cannot be represented exactly in destination format.

Protected Mode Exceptions

#GP(0)	If a memory operand effective address is outside the CS, DS, ES, FS, or GS segment limit.
	If the DS, ES, FS, or GS register is used to access memory and it contains a null segment selector.
#SS(0)	If a memory operand effective address is outside the SS segment limit.
#NM	EM or TS in CR0 is set.
#PF(fault-code)	If a page fault occurs.
#AC(0)	If alignment checking is enabled and an unaligned memory reference is made while the current privilege level is 3.

Real Address Mode Exceptions

#GP	If a memory operand effective address is outside the CS, DS, ES, FS, or GS segment limit.
#SS	If a memory operand effective address is outside the SS segment limit.
#NM	EM or TS in CR0 is set.

Virtual 8086 Mode Exceptions

#GP(0)	If a memory operand effective address is outside the CS, DS, ES, FS, or GS segment limit.
#SS(0)	If a memory operand effective address is outside the SS segment limit.
#NM	EM or TS in CR0 is set.
#PF(fault-code)	If a page fault occurs.
#AC(0)	If alignment checking is enabled and an unaligned memory reference is made.

FSUBR/FSUBRP/FISUBR—Reverse Subtract

Opcode	Instruction	Description
D8 /5	FSUBR m32real	Subtract ST(0) from m32real and store result in ST(0)
DC /5	FSUBR m64real	Subtract ST(0) from m64real and store result in ST(0)
D8 E8+i	FSUBR ST(0), ST(i)	Subtract ST(0) from ST(i) and store result in ST(0)
DC E0+i	FSUBR ST(i), ST(0)	Subtract ST(i) from ST(0) and store result in ST(i)
DE E0+i	FSUBRP ST(i), ST(0)	Subtract ST(0) from ST(i), store result in ST(i), and pop register stack
DE E1	FSUBRP	Subtract ST(1) from ST(0), store result in ST(1), and pop register stack
DA /5	FISUBR m32int	Subtract ST(0) from m32int and store result in ST(0)
DE /5	FISUBR m16int	Subtract ST(0) from m16int and store result in ST(0)

Description

Subtracts the destination operand from the source operand and stores the difference in the destination location. The destination operand is always an FPU register; the source operand can be a register or a memory location. Source operands in memory can be in single-real, double-real, word-integer, or short-integer formats.

These instructions perform the reverse operations of the FSUB, FSUBP, and FISUB instructions. They are provided to support more efficient coding.

The no-operand version of the instruction subtracts the contents of the ST(1) register from the ST(0) register and stores the result in ST(1). The one-operand version subtracts the contents of the ST(0) register from the contents of a memory location (either a real or an integer value) and stores the result in ST(0). The two-operand version, subtracts the contents of the ST(i) register from the ST(0) register or vice versa.

The FSUBRP instructions perform the additional operation of popping the FPU register stack following the subtraction. To pop the register stack, the processor marks the ST(0) register as empty and increments the stack pointer (TOP) by 1. The no-operand version of the floating-point reverse subtract instructions always results in the register stack being popped. In some assemblers, the mnemonic for this instruction is FSUBR rather than FSUBRP.

The FISUBR instructions convert an integer source operand to extended-real format before performing the subtraction.

The following table shows the results obtained when subtracting various classes of numbers from one another, assuming that neither overflow nor underflow occurs. Here, the DEST value is subtracted from the SRC value (SRC − DEST = result).

When the difference between two operands of like sign is 0, the result is +0, except for the round toward −∞ mode, in which case the result is −0. This instruction also guarantees that +0 − (−0) = +0, and that −0 − (+0) = −0. When the source operand is an integer 0, it is treated as a +0.

When one operand is ∞, the result is ∞ of the expected sign. If both operands are ∞ of the same sign, an invalid-operation exception is generated.

	SRC						
		−∞	−F	−0	+0	+F	+∞	NaN
DEST	−∞	*	+∞	+∞	+∞	+∞	+∞	NaN
	−F or −I	−∞	±F or ±0	−DEST	−DEST	+F	+∞	NaN
	−0	−∞	SRC	±0	+0	SRC	+∞	NaN
	+0	−∞	SRC	−0	±0	SRC	+∞	NaN
	+F or +I	−∞	−F	−DEST	−DEST	±F or ±0	+∞	NaN
	+∞	−∞	−∞	−∞	−∞	−∞	*	NaN
	NaN	NaN	NaN	NaN	NaN	NaN	NaN	NaN

NOTES:

F Means finite-real number

I Means integer

* Indicates floating-point invalid-arithmetic-operand (#IA) exception.

Operation

```
IF instruction is FISUBR
    THEN
        DEST ← ConvertExtendedReal(SRC) – DEST;
    ELSE (* source operand is real number *)
        DEST ← SRC – DEST;
FI;
IF instruction = FSUBRP
    THEN
        PopRegisterStack
FI;
```

FPU Flags Affected

C1   Set to 0 if stack underflow occurred.

                Indicates rounding direction if the inexact-result exception (#P) fault is generated: 0 = not roundup; 1 = roundup.

C0, C2, C3   Undefined.

Floating-Point Exceptions

#IS   Stack underflow occurred.

#IA   Operand is an SNaN value or unsupported format.

                Operands are infinities of like sign.

#D   Source operand is a denormal value.

#U	Result is too small for destination format.
#O	Result is too large for destination format.
#P	Value cannot be represented exactly in destination format.

Protected Mode Exceptions

#GP(0)	If a memory operand effective address is outside the CS, DS, ES, FS, or GS segment limit.
	If the DS, ES, FS, or GS register is used to access memory and it contains a null segment selector.
#SS(0)	If a memory operand effective address is outside the SS segment limit.
#NM	EM or TS in CR0 is set.
#PF(fault-code)	If a page fault occurs.
#AC(0)	If alignment checking is enabled and an unaligned memory reference is made while the current privilege level is 3.

Real Address Mode Exceptions

#GP	If a memory operand effective address is outside the CS, DS, ES, FS, or GS segment limit.
#SS	If a memory operand effective address is outside the SS segment limit.
#NM	EM or TS in CR0 is set.

Virtual 8086 Mode Exceptions

#GP(0)	If a memory operand effective address is outside the CS, DS, ES, FS, or GS segment limit.
#SS(0)	If a memory operand effective address is outside the SS segment limit.
#NM	EM or TS in CR0 is set.
#PF(fault-code)	If a page fault occurs.
#AC(0)	If alignment checking is enabled and an unaligned memory reference is made.

FTST—TEST

Opcode	Instruction	Description
D9 E4	FTST	Compare ST(0) with 0.0.

Description

Compares the value in the ST(0) register with 0.0 and sets the condition code flags C0, C2, and C3 in the FPU status word according to the results (see table below).

Condition	C3	C2	C0
ST(0) > 0.0	0	0	0
ST(0) < 0.0)	0	0	1
ST(0) = 0.0	1	0	0
Unordered	1	1	1

This instruction performs an "unordered comparison." An unordered comparison also checks the class of the numbers being compared (see Chapter 11, "FXAM—Examine"). If the value in register ST(0) is a NaN or is in an undefined format, the condition flags are set to "unordered.")

The sign of zero is ignored, so that –0.0 = +0.0.

Operation

```
CASE (relation of operands) OF
    Not comparable:  C3, C2, C0 ← 111;
    ST(0) > 0.0:     C3, C2, C0 ← 000;
    ST(0) < 0.0:     C3, C2, C0 ← 001;
    ST(0) = 0.0:     C3, C2, C0 ← 100;
ESAC;
```

FPU Flags Affected

C1   Set to 0 if stack underflow occurred; otherwise, cleared to 0.

C0, C2, C3   See above table.

Floating-Point Exceptions

#IS   Stack underflow occurred.

#IA   One or both operands are NaN values or have unsupported formats.

#D   One or both operands are denormal values.

Protected Mode Exceptions

#NM   EM or TS in CR0 is set.

Real Address Mode Exceptions

#NM   EM or TS in CR0 is set.

Virtual 8086 Mode Exceptions

#NM   EM or TS in CR0 is set.

FUCOM/FUCOMP/FUCOMPP—Unordered Compare Real

Opcode	Instruction	Description
DD E0+i	FUCOM ST(i)	Compare ST(0) with ST(i)
DD E1	FUCOM	Compare ST(0) with ST(1)
DD E8+i	FUCOMP ST(i)	Compare ST(0) with ST(i) and pop register stack
DD E9	FUCOMP	Compare ST(0) with ST(1) and pop register stack
DA E9	FUCOMPP	Compare ST(0) with ST(1) and pop register stack twice

Description

Performs an unordered comparison of the contents of register ST(0) and ST(i) and sets condition code flags C0, C2, and C3 in the FPU status word according to the results (see the table below). If no operand is specified, the contents of registers ST(0) and ST(1) are compared. The sign of zero is ignored, so that $-0.0 = +0.0$.

Comparison Results	C3	C2	C0
ST0 > ST(i)	0	0	0
ST0 < ST(i)	0	0	1
ST0 = ST(i)	1	0	0
Unordered	1	1	1

NOTE:

* Flags not set if unmasked invalid-arithmetic-operand (#IA) exception is generated.

An unordered comparison checks the class of the numbers being compared (see Chapter 11, "FXAM—Examine"). The FUCOM instructions perform the same operation as the FCOM instructions. The only difference is that the FUCOM instruction raises the invalid-arithmetic-operand exception (#IA) only when either or both operands is an SNaN or is in an unsupported format; QNaNs cause the condition code flags to be set to unordered, but do not cause an exception to be generated. The FCOM instruction raises an invalid-operation exception when either or both of the operands is a NaN value of any kind or is in an unsupported format.

As with the FCOM instructions, if the operation results in an invalid-arithmetic-operand exception being raised, the condition code flags are set only if the exception is masked.

The FUCOMP instructions pop the register stack following the comparison operation and the FUCOMPP instructions pops the register stack twice following the comparison operation. To pop the register stack, the processor marks the ST(0) register as empty and increments the stack pointer (TOP) by 1.

Operation

```
CASE (relation of operands) OF
    ST > SRC:        C3, C2, C0 ← 000;
    ST < SRC:        C3, C2, C0 ← 001;
    ST = SRC:        C3, C2, C0 ← 100;
ESAC;
IF ST(0) or SRC = QNaN, but not SNaN or unsupported format
    THEN
        C3, C2, C0 ← 111;
    ELSE (* ST(0) or SRC is SNaN or unsupported format *)
        #IA;
        IF FPUControlWord.IM = 1
            THEN
                C3, C2, C0 ← 111;
        FI;
FI;
IF instruction = FUCOMP
    THEN
        PopRegisterStack;
FI;
IF instruction = FUCOMPP
    THEN
        PopRegisterStack;
        PopRegisterStack;
FI;
```

FPU Flags Affected

C1   Set to 0 if stack underflow occurred.

C0, C2, C3   See table on previous page.

Floating-Point Exceptions

#IS   Stack underflow occurred.

#IA   One or both operands are SNaN values or have unsupported formats. Detection of a QNaN value in and of itself does not raise an invalid-operand exception.

#D   One or both operands are denormal values.

Protected Mode Exceptions

#NM   EM or TS in CR0 is set.

Real Address Mode Exceptions

#NM   EM or TS in CR0 is set.

Virtual 8086 Mode Exceptions

#NM   EM or TS in CR0 is set.

FWAIT—Wait

See entry for WAIT.

FXAM—Examine

Opcode	Instruction	Description
D9 E5	FXAM	Classify value or number in ST(0)

Description

Examines the contents of the ST(0) register and sets the condition code flags C0, C2, and C3 in the FPU status word to indicate the class of value or number in the register (see the table below).

Class	C3	C2	C0
Unsupported	0	0	0
NaN	0	0	1
Normal finite number	0	1	0
Infinity	0	1	1
Zero	1	0	0
Empty	1	0	1
Denormal number	1	1	0

The C1 flag is set to the sign of the value in ST(0), regardless of whether the register is empty or full.

Operation

```
C1 ← sign bit of ST; (* 0 for positive, 1 for negative *)
CASE (class of value or number in ST(0)) OF
     Unsupported:C3, C2, C0 ← 000;
     NaN:        C3, C2, C0 ← 001;
     Normal:     C3, C2, C0 ← 010;
     Infinity:   C3, C2, C0 ← 011;
     Zero:       C3, C2, C0 ← 100;
     Empty:      C3, C2, C0 ← 101;
     Denormal:   C3, C2, C0 ← 110;
ESAC;
```

FPU Flags Affected

C1   Sign of value in ST(0).

C0, C2, C3   See table above.

Floating-Point Exceptions

None.

Protected Mode Exceptions

#NM   EM or TS in CR0 is set.

Real Address Mode Exceptions

#NM   EM or TS in CR0 is set.

Virtual 8086 Mode Exceptions

#NM   EM or TS in CR0 is set.

FXCH—Exchange Register Contents

Opcode	Instruction	Description
D9 C8+i	FXCH ST(i)	Exchange the contents of ST(0) and ST(*i*)
D9 C9	FXCH	Exchange the contents of ST(0) and ST(1)

Description

Exchanges the contents of registers ST(0) and ST(*i*). If no source operand is specified, the contents of ST(0) and ST(1) are exchanged.

This instruction provides a simple means of moving values in the FPU register stack to the top of the stack [ST(0)], so that they can be operated on by those floating-point instructions that can only operate on values in ST(0). For example, the following instruction sequence takes the square root of the third register from the top of the register stack:

```
FXCH ST(3);
FSQRT;
FXCH ST(3);
```

Operation

```
IF number-of-operands is 1
    THEN
        temp ← ST(0);
        ST(0) ← SRC;
        SRC ← temp;
    ELSE
        temp ← ST(0);
        ST(0) ← ST(1);
        ST(1) ← temp;
```

FPU Flags Affected

C1   Set to 0 if stack underflow occurred; otherwise, cleared to 0.

C0, C2, C3   Undefined.

Floating-Point Exceptions

#IS   Stack underflow occurred.

Protected Mode Exceptions

#NM   EM or TS in CR0 is set.

Real Address Mode Exceptions

#NM   EM or TS in CR0 is set.

Virtual 8086 Mode Exceptions

#NM   EM or TS in CR0 is set.

FXTRACT—Extract Exponent and Significand

Opcode	Instruction	Description
D9 F4	FXTRACT	Separate value in ST(0) into exponent and significand, store exponent in ST(0), and push the significand onto the register stack.

Description

Separates the source value in the ST(0) register into its exponent and significand, stores the exponent in ST(0), and pushes the significand onto the register stack. Following this operation, the new top-of-stack register ST(0) contains the value of the original significand expressed as a real number. The sign and significand of this value are the same as those found in the source operand, and the exponent is 3FFFH (biased value for a true exponent of zero). The ST(1) register contains the value of the original operand's true (unbiased) exponent expressed as a real number. (The operation performed by this instruction is a superset of the IEEE-recommended $logb(x)$ function.)

This instruction and the F2XM1 instruction are useful for performing power and range scaling operations. The FXTRACT instruction is also useful for converting numbers in extended-real format to decimal representations (e.g., for printing or displaying).

If the floating-point zero-divide exception (#Z) is masked and the source operand is zero, an exponent value of $-\infty$ is stored in register ST(1) and 0 with the sign of the source operand is stored in register ST(0).

Operation

TEMP ← Significand(ST(0));
ST(0) ← Exponent(ST(0));
TOP← TOP − 1;
ST(0) ← TEMP;

FPU Flags Affected

C1   Set to 0 if stack underflow occurred; set to 1 if stack overflow occurred.

C0, C2, C3   Undefined.

Floating-Point Exceptions

#IS   Stack underflow occurred.

                Stack overflow occurred.

#IA   Source operand is an SNaN value or unsupported format.

#Z   ST(0) operand is ±0.

#D   Source operand is a denormal value.

Protected Mode Exceptions

#NM   EM or TS in CR0 is set.

Real Address Mode Exceptions

#NM   EM or TS in CR0 is set.

Virtual 8086 Mode Exceptions

#NM   EM or TS in CR0 is set.

FYL2X—Compute y × log₂x

Opcode	Instruction	Description
D9 F1	FYL2X	Replace ST(1) with (ST(1) ∗ log₂ST(0)) and pop the register stack

Description

Calculates $(ST(1) * \log_2 (ST(0)))$, stores the result in resister ST(1), and pops the FPU register stack. The source operand in ST(0) must be a non-zero positive number.

The following table shows the results obtained when taking the log of various classes of numbers, assuming that neither overflow nor underflow occurs.

		ST(0)						
		$-\infty$	$-F$	$+0$	$+0$	$+F$	$+\infty$	NaN
	$-\infty$	*	*	$+\infty$	$+\infty$	$+\infty$	$-\infty$	NaN
ST(1)	$-F$	*	*	**	**	$\pm F$	$-\infty$	NaN
	-0	*	*	*	*	$+0$	*	NaN
	$+0$	*	*	*	*	$+0$	*	NaN
	$+F$	*	*	**	**	$\pm F$	$+\infty$	NaN
	$+\infty$	*	*	$-\infty$	$-\infty$	$-\infty$	$+\infty$	NaN
	NaN	NaN	NaN	NaN	NaN	NaN	NaN	NaN

NOTES:

F Means finite-real number

* Indicates floating-point invalid-operation (#IA) exception.

** Indicates floating-point zero-divide (#Z) exception.

If the divide-by-zero exception is masked and register ST(0) contains ±0, the instruction returns ∞ with a sign that is the opposite of the sign of the source operand in register ST(1).

The FYL2X instruction is designed with a built-in multiplication to optimize the calculation of logarithms with an arbitrary positive base (b):

$\log_b x = (\log_2 b)^{-1} * \log_2 x$

Operation

ST(1) ← ST(1) ∗ log₂ST(0);
PopRegisterStack;

FPU Flags Affected

C1	Set to 0 if stack underflow occurred.
	Indicates rounding direction if the inexact-result exception (#P) is generated: 0 = not roundup; 1 = roundup.
C0, C2, C3	Undefined.

Floating-Point Exceptions

#IS	Stack underflow occurred.
#IA	Either operand is an SNaN or unsupported format.
	Source operand in register ST(0) is a negative finite value (not −0).
#Z	Source operand in register ST(0) is ±0.
#D	Source operand is a denormal value.
#U	Result is too small for destination format.
#O	Result is too large for destination format.
#P	Value cannot be represented exactly in destination format.

Protected Mode Exceptions

#NM	EM or TS in CR0 is set.

Real Address Mode Exceptions

#NM	EM or TS in CR0 is set.

Virtual 8086 Mode Exceptions

#NM	EM or TS in CR0 is set.

FYL2XP1—Compute y $*$ log$_2$(x +1)

Opcode	Instruction	Description
D9 F9	FYL2XP1	Replace ST(1) with ST(1) $*$ log$_2$(ST(0) + 1.0) and pop the register stack

Description

Calculates the log epsilon (ST(1) $*$ log$_2$(ST(0) + 1.0)), stores the result in register ST(1), and pops the FPU register stack. The source operand in ST(0) must be in the range:

$$-(1 - \sqrt{2}/2)\ )\ \text{to}\ (1 - \sqrt{2}/2)$$

The source operand in ST(1) can range from −∞ to +∞. If either of the source operands is outside its acceptable range, the result is undefined and no exception is generated.

The following table shows the results obtained when taking the log epsilon of various classes of numbers, assuming that underflow does not occur.

		ST(0)					
	−∞	−(1 − ($\sqrt{2}/2$)) to −0	−0	+0	+0 to +(1 − ($\sqrt{2}/2$))	+∞	NaN
ST(1) −∞	*	+∞	*	*	−∞	−∞	NaN
−F	*	+F	+0	−0	−F	−∞	NaN
−0	*	+0	+0	−0	−0	*	NaN
+0	*	−0	−0	+0	+0	*	NaN
+F	*	−F	−0	+0	+F	+∞	NaN
+∞	*	−∞	*	*	+∞	+∞	NaN
NaN	NaN	NaN	NaN	NaN	NaN	NaN	NaN

NOTES:

F   Means finite-real number
*   Indicates floating-point invalid-operation (#IA) exception.

This instruction provides optimal accuracy for values of epsilon [the value in register ST(0)] that are close to 0. When the epsilon value (ε) is small, more significant digits can be retained by using the FYL2XP1 instruction than by using (ε+1) as an argument to the FYL2X instruction. The (ε+1) expression is commonly found in compound interest and annuity calculations. The result can be simply converted into a value in another logarithm base by including a scale factor in the ST(1) source operand. The following equation is used to calculate the scale factor for a particular logarithm base, where n is the logarithm base desired for the result of the FYL2XP1 instruction:

$$\text{scale factor} = \log_n 2$$

HLT—Halt

Opcode	Instruction	Description
F4	HLT	Halt

Description

Stops instruction execution and places the processor in a HALT state. An enabled interrupt, NMI, or a reset will resume execution. If an interrupt (including NMI) is used to resume execution after a HLT instruction, the saved instruction pointer (CS:EIP) points to the instruction following the HLT instruction.

The HLT instruction is a privileged instruction. When the processor is running in protected or virtual 8086 mode, the privilege level of a program or procedure must to 0 to execute the HLT instruction.

Operation

Enter Halt state;

Flags Affected

None.

Protected Mode Exceptions

#GP(0)   If the current privilege level is not 0.

Real Address Mode Exceptions

None.

Virtual 8086 Mode Exceptions

#GP(0)   If the current privilege level is not 0.

IDIV—Signed Divide

Opcode	Instruction	Description
F6 /7	IDIV r/m8	Signed divide AX (where AH must contain sign-extension of AL) by r/m byte. (Results: AL=Quotient, AH=Remainder)
F7 /7	IDIV r/m16	Signed divide DX:AX (where DX must contain sign-extension of AX) by r/m word. (Results: AX=Quotient, DX=Remainder)
F7 /7	IDIV r/m32	Signed divide EDX:EAX (where EDX must contain sign-extension of EAX) by r/m doubleword. (Results: EAX=Quotient, EDX=Remainder)

Description

Divides (signed) the value in the AL, AX, or EAX register by the source operand and stores the result in the AX, DX:AX, or EDX:EAX registers. The source operand can be a general-purpose register or a memory location. The action of this instruction depends on the operand size, as shown in the following table:

Operand Size	Dividend	Divisor	Quotient	Remainder	Quotient Range
Word/byte	AX	r/m8	AL	AH	−128 to +127
Doubleword/word	DX:AX	r/m16	AX	DX	−32,768 to +32,767
Quadword/doubleword	EDX:EAX	r/m32	EAX	EDX	-2^{31} to $2^{32} - 1$

Non-integral results are truncated (chopped) towards 0. The sign of the remainder is always the same as the sign of the dividend. The absolute value of the remainder is always less than the absolute value of the divisor. Overflow is indicated with the #DE (divide error) exception rather than with the OF flag.

Operation

```
IF SRC = 0
    THEN #DE; (* divide error *)
FI;
IF OpernadSize = 8 (* word/byte operation *)
    THEN
        temp ← AX / SRC; (* signed division *)
        IF (temp > 7FH) OR (temp < 80H)
        (* if a positive result is greater than 7FH or a negative result is less than 80H *)
            THEN #DE; (* divide error *) ;
            ELSE
```

```
                    AL ← temp;
                    AH ← AX SignedModulus SRC;
          FI;
     ELSE
          IF OpernadSize = 16 (* doubleword/word operation *)
                    THEN
                         temp ← DX:AX / SRC; (* signed division *)
                         IF (temp > 7FFFH) OR (temp < 8000H)
                         (* if a positive result is greater than 7FFFH *)
                         (* or a negative result is less than 8000H *)
                              THEN #DE; (* divide error *) ;
                              ELSE
                                   AX ← temp;
                                   DX ← DX:AX SignedModulus SRC;
                         FI;
                    ELSE (* quadword/doubleword operation *)
                         temp ← EDX:EAX / SRC; (* signed division *)
                         IF (temp > 7FFFFFFFH) OR (temp < 80000000H)
                         (* if a positive result is greater than 7FFFFFFFH *)
                         (* or a negative result is less than 80000000H *)
                              THEN #DE; (* divide error *) ;
                              ELSE
                                   EAX ← temp;
                                   EDX ← EDXE:AX SignedModulus SRC;
                         FI;
          FI;
     FI;
FI;
```

Flags Affected

The CF, OF, SF, ZF, AF, and PF flags are undefined.

Protected Mode Exceptions

#DE	If the source operand (divisor) is 0.
	The signed result (quotient) is too large for the destination.
#GP(0)	If a memory operand effective address is outside the CS, DS, ES, FS, or GS segment limit.
	If the DS, ES, FS, or GS register is used to access memory and it contains a null segment selector.
#SS(0)	If a memory operand effective address is outside the SS segment limit.
#PF(fault-code)	If a page fault occurs.
#AC(0)	If alignment checking is enabled and an unaligned memory reference is made while the current privilege level is 3.

Real Address Mode Exceptions

#DE	If the source operand (divisor) is 0.
	The signed result (quotient) is too large for the destination.
#GP	If a memory operand effective address is outside the CS, DS, ES, FS, or GS segment limit.
#SS	If a memory operand effective address is outside the SS segment limit.

Virtual 8086 Mode Exceptions

#DE	If the source operand (divisor) is 0.
	The signed result (quotient) is too large for the destination.
#GP(0)	If a memory operand effective address is outside the CS, DS, ES, FS, or GS segment limit.
#SS(0)	If a memory operand effective address is outside the SS segment limit.
#PF(fault-code)	If a page fault occurs.
#AC(0)	If alignment checking is enabled and an unaligned memory reference is made.

IMUL—Signed Multiply

Opcode	Instruction	Description
F6 /5	IMUL r/m8	AX← AL * r/m byte
F7 /5	IMUL r/m16	DX:AX ← AX * r/m word
F7 /5	IMUL r/m32	EDX:EAX ← EAX * r/m doubleword
0F AF /r	IMUL r16,r/m16	word register ← word register * r/m word
0F AF /r	IMUL r32,r/m32	doubleword register ← doubleword register * r/m doubleword
6B /r ib	IMUL r16,r/m16,imm8	word register ← r/m16 * sign-extended immediate byte
6B /r ib	IMUL r32,r/m32,imm8	doubleword register ← r/m32 * sign-extended immediate byte
6B /r ib	IMUL r16,imm8	word register ← word register * sign-extended immediate byte
6B /r ib	IMUL r32,imm8	doubleword register ← doubleword register * sign-extended immediate byte
69 /r iw	IMUL r16,r/m16,imm16	word register ← r/m16 * immediate word
69 /r id	IMUL r32,r/m32,imm32	doubleword register ← r/m32 * immediate doubleword
69 /r iw	IMUL r16,imm16	word register ← r/m16 * immediate word
69 /r id	IMUL r32,imm32	doubleword register ← r/m32 * immediate doubleword

Description

Performs a signed multiplication of two operands. This instruction has three forms, depending on the number of operands.

- **One-operand form.** This form is identical to that used by the MUL instruction. Here, the source operand (in a general-purpose register or memory location) is multiplied by the value in the AL, AX, or EAX register (depending on the operand size) and the product is stored in the AX, DX:AX, or EDX:EAX registers, respectively.

- **Two-operand form.** With this form the destination operand (the first operand) is multiplied by the source operand (second operand). The destination operand is a general-purpose register and the source operand is an immediate value, a general-purpose register, or a memory location. The product is then stored in the destination operand location.

- **Three-operand form.** This form requires a destination operand (the first operand) and two source operands (the second and the third operands). Here, the first source operand (which can be a general-purpose register or a memory location) is multiplied by the second source operand (an immediate value). The product is then stored in the destination operand (a general-purpose register).

When an immediate value is used as an operand, it is sign-extended to the length of the destination operand format.

The CF and OF flags are set when significant bits are carried into the upper half of the result. The CF and OF flags are cleared when the result fits exactly in the lower half of the result.

The three forms of the IMUL instruction are similar in that the length of the product is calculated to twice the length of the operands. With the one-operand form, the product is stored exactly in the destination. With the two- and three- operand forms, however, result is truncated to the length of the destination before it is stored in the destination register. Because of this truncation, the CF or OF flag should be tested to ensure that no significant bits are lost.

The two- and three-operand forms may also be used with unsigned operands because the lower half of the product is the same regardless if the operands are signed or unsigned. The CF and OF flags, however, cannot be used to determine if the upper half of the result is non-zero.

Operation

```
IF (NumberOfOperands = 1)
    THEN IF (OperandSize = 8)
        THEN
            AX ← AL * SRC  (* signed multiplication *)
            IF ((AH = 00H) OR (AH = FFH))
                THEN CF = 0; OF = 0;
                ELSE CF = 1; OF = 1;
            FI;
        ELSE IF OperandSize = 16
            THEN
                DX:AX ← AX * SRC  (* signed multiplication *)
                IF ((DX = 0000H) OR (DX = FFFFH))
                    THEN CF = 0; OF = 0;
                    ELSE CF = 1; OF = 1;
                FI;
            ELSE (* OperandSize = 32 *)
                EDX:EAX ← EAX * SRC  (* signed multiplication *)
                IF ((EDX = 00000000H) OR (EDX = FFFFFFFFH))
                    THEN CF = 0; OF = 0;
                    ELSE CF = 1; OF = 1;
                FI;
    FI;
    ELSE IF (NumberOfOperands = 2)
        THEN
            temp ← DEST * SRC   (* signed multiplication; temp is double DEST size*)
            DEST ← DEST * SRC  (* signed multiplication *)
            IF temp ≠ DEST
                THEN CF = 1; OF = 1;
                ELSE CF = 0; OF = 0;
            FI;

        ELSE (* NumberOfOperands = 3 *)
            DEST ← SRC1 * SRC2   (* signed multiplication *)
            temp ← SRC1 * SRC2    (* signed multiplication; temp is double SRC1 size *)
```

```
            IF temp ≠ DEST
                THEN CF = 1; OF = 1;
                ELSE CF = 0; OF = 0;
            FI;
    FI;
FI;
```

Flags Affected

For the one operand form of the instruction, the CF and OF flags are set when significant bits are carried into the upper half of the result and cleared when the result fits exactly in the lower half of the result. For the two- and three-operand forms of the instruction, the CF and OF flags are set when the result must be truncated to fit in the destination operand size and cleared when the result fits exactly in the destination operand size. The SF, ZF, AF, and PF flags are undefined.

Protected Mode Exceptions

#GP(0)	If a memory operand effective address is outside the CS, DS, ES, FS, or GS segment limit.
	If the DS, ES, FS, or GS register is used to access memory and it contains a null segment selector.
#SS(0)	If a memory operand effective address is outside the SS segment limit.
#PF(fault-code)	If a page fault occurs.
#AC(0)	If alignment checking is enabled and an unaligned memory reference is made while the current privilege level is 3.

Real Address Mode Exceptions

#GP	If a memory operand effective address is outside the CS, DS, ES, FS, or GS segment limit.
#SS	If a memory operand effective address is outside the SS segment limit.

Virtual 8086 Mode Exceptions

#GP(0)	If a memory operand effective address is outside the CS, DS, ES, FS, or GS segment limit.
#SS(0)	If a memory operand effective address is outside the SS segment limit.
#PF(fault-code)	If a page fault occurs.
#AC(0)	If alignment checking is enabled and an unaligned memory reference is made.

IN—Input from Port

Opcode	Instruction	Description
E4 *ib*	IN AL,*imm8*	Input byte from *imm8* I/O port address into AL
E5 *ib*	IN AX,*imm8*	Input byte from *imm8* I/O port address into AX
E5 *ib*	IN EAX,*imm8*	Input byte from *imm8* I/O port address into EAX
EC	IN AL,DX	Input byte from I/O port in DX into AL
ED	IN AX,DX	Input word from I/O port in DX into AX
ED	IN EAX,DX	Input doubleword from I/O port in DX into EAX

Description

Copies the value from the I/O port specified with the second operand (source operand) to the destination operand (first operand). The source operand can be a byte-immediate or the DX register; the destination operand can be register AL, AX, or EAX, depending on the size of the port being accessed (8, 16, or 32 bits, respectively). Using the DX register as a source operand allows I/O port addresses from 0 to 65,535 to be accessed; using a byte immediate allows I/O port addresses 0 to 255 to be accessed.

When accessing an 8-bit I/O port, the opcode determines the port size; when accessing a 16- and 32-bit I/O port, the operand-size attribute determines the port size.

At the machine code level, I/O instructions are shorter when accessing 8-bit I/O ports. Here, the upper eight bits of the port address will be 0.

This instruction is only useful for accessing I/O ports located in the processor's I/O address space. See Chapter 8, *Input/Output*, for more information on accessing I/O ports in the I/O address space.

Operation

```
IF ((PE = 1) AND ((VM = 1) OR (CPL > IOPL)))
    THEN (* Protected mode or virtual-8086 mode with CPL > IOPL *)
        IF (Any I/O Permission Bit for I/O port being accessed = 1)
            THEN #GP(0);
        FI;
    ELSE ( * Real-address mode or protected mode with CPL ≤ IOPL *)
    (* or virtual-8086 mode with all I/O permission bits for I/O port cleared *)
        DEST ← SRC; (* Reads from I/O port *)
FI;
```

Flags Affected

None.

Protected Mode Exceptions

#GP(0)   If the CPL is greater than (has less privilege) the I/O privilege level (IOPL) and any of the corresponding I/O permission bits in TSS for the I/O port being accessed is 1.

Real Address Mode Exceptions

None.

Virtual 8086 Mode Exceptions

#GP(0)   If any of the I/O permission bits in the TSS for the I/O port being accessed is 1.

INC—Increment by 1

Opcode	Instruction	Description
FE /0	INC r/m8	Increment r/m byte by 1
FF /0	INC r/m16	Increment r/m word by 1
FF /0	INC r/m32	Increment r/m doubleword by 1
40+ rw	INC r16	Increment word register by 1
40+ rd	INC r32	Increment doubleword register by 1

Description

Adds 1 to the operand, while preserving the state of the CF flag. The source operand can be a register or a memory location. This instruction allows a loop counter to be updated without disturbing the CF flag. (Use a ADD instruction with an immediate operand of 1 to perform a increment operation that does updates the CF flag.)

Operation

DEST ← DEST − 1;

Flags Affected

The CF flag is not affected. The OF, SF, ZF, AF, and PF flags are set according to the result.

Protected Mode Exceptions

#GP(0)	If the operand is located in a nonwritable segment.
	If a memory operand effective address is outside the CS, DS, ES, FS, or GS segment limit.
	If the DS, ES, FS, or GS register is used to access memory and it contains a null segment selector.
#SS(0)	If a memory operand effective address is outside the SS segment limit.
#PF(fault-code)	If a page fault occurs.
#AC(0)	If alignment checking is enabled and an unaligned memory reference is made while the current privilege level is 3.

Real Address Mode Exceptions

#GP	If a memory operand effective address is outside the CS, DS, ES, FS, or GS segment limit.
#SS	If a memory operand effective address is outside the SS segment limit.

Virtual 8086 Mode Exceptions

#GP(0)   If a memory operand effective address is outside the CS, DS, ES, FS, or GS segment limit.

#SS(0)   If a memory operand effective address is outside the SS segment limit.

#PF(fault-code)   If a page fault occurs.

#AC(0)   If alignment checking is enabled and an unaligned memory reference is made.

INS/INSB/INSW/INSD—Input from Port to String

Opcode	Instruction	Description
6C	INS ES:(E)DI, DX	Input byte from port DX into ES:(E)DI
6D	INS ES:DI, DX	Input word from port DX into ES:DI
6D	INS ES:EDI, DX	Input doubleword from port DX into ES:EDI
6C	INSB	Input byte from port DX into ES:(E)DI
6D	INSW	Input word from port DX into ES:DI
6D	INSD	Input doubleword from port DX into ES:EDI

Description

Copies the data from the I/O port specified with the second operand (source operand) to the destination operand (first operand). The source operand must be the DX register, allowing I/O port addresses from 0 to 65,535 to be accessed. When accessing an 8-bit I/O port, the opcode determines the port size; when accessing a 16- and 32-bit I/O port, the operand-size attribute determines the port size.

The destination operand is a memory location at the address ES:EDI. (When the operand-size attribute is 16, the DI register is used as the destination-index register.) The ES segment cannot be overridden with a segment override prefix.

The INSB, INSW, and INSD mnemonics are synonyms of the byte, word, and doubleword versions of the INS instructions. (For the INS instruction, "ES:EDI" must be explicitly specified in the instruction.)

After the byte, word, or doubleword is transfer from the I/O port to the memory location, the EDI register is incremented or decremented automatically according to the setting of the DF flag in the EFLAGS register. (If the DF flag is 0, the EDI register is incremented; if the DF flag is 1, the EDI register is decremented.) The EDI register is incremented or decremented by 1 for byte operations, by 2 for word operations, or by 4 for doubleword operations.

The INS, INSB, INSW, and INSD instructions can be preceded by the REP prefix for block input of ECX bytes, words, or doublewords. See Chapter 11, "REP/REPE/REPZ/REPNE /REPNZ—Repeat String Operation Prefix" for a description of the REP prefix.

This instruction is only useful for accessing I/O ports located in the processor's I/O address space. See Chapter 8, *Input/Output*, for more information on accessing I/O ports in the I/O address space.

Operation

```
IF ((PE = 1) AND ((VM = 1) OR (CPL > IOPL)))
    THEN (* Protected mode or virtual-8086 mode with CPL > IOPL *)
        IF (Any I/O Permission Bit for I/O port being accessed = 1)
            THEN #GP(0);
        FI;
    ELSE ( * I/O operation is allowed *)
        DEST ← SRC; (* Reads from I/O port *)
        IF (byte transfer)
            THEN IF DF = 0
                THEN (E)DI ← 1;
                ELSE (E)DI ← −1;
            FI;
            ELSE IF (word transfer)
                THEN IF DF = 0
                    THEN DI ← 2;
                    ELSE DI ← −2;
                FI;
                ELSE (* doubleword transfer *)
                    THEN IF DF = 0
                        THEN EDI ← 4;
                        ELSE EDI ← −4;
                    FI;
            FI;
    FI;
FI;
```

Flags Affected

None.

Protected Mode Exceptions

#GP(0)   If the CPL is greater than (has less privilege) the I/O privilege level (IOPL) and any of the corresponding I/O permission bits in TSS for the I/O port being accessed is 1.

                         If the destination is located in a nonwritable segment.

                         If an illegal memory operand effective address in the ES segments is given.

#PF(fault-code)   If a page fault occurs.

#AC(0)   If alignment checking is enabled and an unaligned memory reference is made while the current privilege level is 3.

Real Address Mode Exceptions

#GP	If a memory operand effective address is outside the CS, DS, ES, FS, or GS segment limit.
#SS	If a memory operand effective address is outside the SS segment limit.

Virtual 8086 Mode Exceptions

#GP(0)	If any of the I/O permission bits in the TSS for the I/O port being accessed is 1.
#PF(fault-code)	If a page fault occurs.
#AC(0)	If alignment checking is enabled and an unaligned memory reference is made.

INT*n*/INTO/INT3—Call to Interrupt Procedure

Opcode		Instruction	Description
CC		INT3	Interrupt 3—trap to debugger
CD	*ib*	INT *imm8*	Interrupt vector numbered by immediate byte
CE		INTO	Interrupt 4—if overflow flag is 1

Description

The INT*n* instruction generates a call to the interrupt or exception handler specified with the destination operand (see Section 4.4., "Interrupts and Exceptions"). The destination operand specifies an interrupt vector from 0 to 255, encoded as an 8-bit unsigned intermediate value. The first 32 interrupt vectors are reserved by Intel for system use. Some of these interrupts are used for internally generated exceptions.

The INT*n* instruction is the general mnemonic for executing a software-generated call to an interrupt handler. The INTO instruction is a special mnemonic for calling overflow exception (#OF), interrupt vector 4. The overflow interrupt checks the OF flag in the EFLAGS register and calls the overflow interrupt handler if the OF flag is set to 1.

The INT3 instruction is a special mnemonic for calling the debug exception handler. The action of the INT3 instruction (opcode CC) is slightly different from the operation of the INT 3 instruction (opcode CC03), as follows:

* Interrupt redirection does not happen when in VME mode; the interrupt is handled by a protected-mode handler.

* The virtual-8086 mode IOPL checks do not occur. The interrupt is taken without faulting at any IOPL level.

The action of the INT*n* instruction (including the INTO and INT3 instructions) is similar to that of a far call made with the CALL instruction. The primary difference is that with the INT*n* instruction, the EFLAGS register is pushed onto the stack before the return address. (The return address is a far address consisting of the current values of the CS and EIP registers.) Returns from interrupt procedures are handled with the IRET instruction, which pops the EFLAGS information and return address from the stack.

The interrupt vector specifies an interrupt descriptor in the interrupt descriptor table (IDT); that is, it provides index into the IDT. The selected interrupt descriptor in turn contains a pointer to an interrupt or exception handler procedure. In protected mode, the IDT contains an array of 8-byte descriptors, each of which points to an interrupt gate, trap gate, or task gate. In real-address mode, the IDT is an array of 4-byte far pointers (2-byte code segment selector and a 2-byte instruction pointer), each of which point directly to procedure in the selected segment.

The following decision table indicates which action in the lower portion of the table is taken given the conditions in the upper portion of the table. Each Y in the lower section of the decision table represents a procedure defined in the "Operation" section for this instruction (except #GP).

PE	0	1	1	1	1	1	1	1
VM	–	–	–	–	–	0	1	1
IOPL	–	–	–	–	–	–	<3	=3
DPL/CPL RELATIONSHIP	–	DPL< CPL	–	DPL> CPL	DPL= CPL or C	DPL< CPL & NC	–	–
INTERRUPT TYPE	–	S/W	–	–	–	–	–	–
GATE TYPE	–	–	Task	Trap or Interrupt	Trap or Interrupt	Trap or Interrupt	Trap or Interrupt	Trap or Interrupt
REAL-ADDRESS-MODE	Y							
PROTECTED-MODE		Y	Y	Y	Y	Y	Y	Y
TRAP-OR-INTERRUPT-GATE				Y	Y	Y	Y	Y
INTER-PRIVILEGE-LEVEL-INTERRUPT						Y		
INTRA-PRIVILEGE-LEVEL-INTERRUPT					Y			
INTERRUPT-FROM-VIRTUAL-8086-MODE								Y
TASK-GATE			Y					
#GP		Y		Y			Y	

NOTES:

– Don't Care

Y Yes, Action Taken

BlankAction Not Taken

When the processor is executing in virtual-8086 mode, the IOPL determines the action of the INTn instruction. If the IOPL is less than 3, the processor generates a general protection exception (#GP); if the IOPL is 3, the processor executes a protected mode interrupt to privilege level 0. The interrupt gate's DPL must be set to three and the target CPL of the interrupt handler procedure must be 0 to execute the protected mode interrupt to privilege level 0.

The interrupt descriptor table register (IDTR) specifies the base linear address and limit of the IDT. The initial base address value of the IDTR after the processor is powered up or reset is 0.

Operation

The following operational description applies not only to the INTn and INTO instructions, but also to external interrupts and exceptions.

IF PE=0
   THEN
      GOTO REAL-ADDRESS-MODE;
   ELSE (* PE=1 *)
      IF (VM=1 AND IOPL < 3 AND INT*n*)
        THEN
          #GP(0);
        ELSE (* protected mode or virtual-8086 mode interrupt *)
          GOTO PROTECTED-MODE;
      FI;
FI;

REAL-ADDRESS-MODE:
   IF ((DEST $*$ 4) + 3) is not within IDT limit THEN #GP; FI;
   IF stack not large enough for a 6-byte return information THEN #SS; FI;
   Push (EFLAGS[15:0]);
   IF ← 0; (* Clear interrupt flag *)
   TF ← 0; (* Clear trap flag *)
   AC ← 0; (*Clear AC flag*)
   Push(CS);
   Push(IP);
   (* No error codes are pushed *)
   CS ← IDT(Descriptor (vector $*$ 4), selector));
   EIP ← IDT(Descriptor (vector $*$ 4), offset)); (* 16 bit offset AND 0000FFFFH *)
END;

PROTECTED-MODE:
   IF ((DEST $*$ 8) + 7) is not within IDT limits
      OR selected IDT descriptor is not an interrupt-, trap-, or task-gate type
        THEN #GP((DEST $*$ 8) + 2 + EXT);
        (* EXT is bit 0 in error code *)
   FI;
   IF software interrupt (* generated by INT*n*, INT3, or INTO *)
      THEN
        IF gate descriptor DPL < CPL
          THEN #GP((vector number $*$ 8) + 2);
          (* PE=1, DPL<CPL, software interrupt *)
        FI;
   FI;
   IF gate not present THEN #NP((vector number $*$ 8) + 2 + EXT); FI;
   IF task gate (* specified in the selected interrupt table descriptor *)
      THEN GOTO TASK-GATE;
      ELSE GOTO TRAP-OR-INTERRUPT-GATE; (* PE=1, trap/interrupt gate *)
   FI;
END;

TASK-GATE: (* PE=1, task gate *)
    Read segment selector in task gate (IDT descriptor);
        IF local/global bit is set to local
            OR index not within GDT limits
                THEN #GP(TSS selector);
        FI;
        Access TSS descriptor in GDT;
        IF TSS descriptor specifies that the TSS is busy (low-order 5 bits set to 00001)
            THEN #GP(TSS selector);
        FI;
        IF TSS not present
            THEN #NP(TSS selector);
        FI;
    SWITCH-TASKS (with nesting) to TSS;
    IF interrupt caused by fault with error code
        THEN
            IF stack limit does not allow push of two bytes
                THEN #SS(0);
            FI;
            Push(error code);
    FI;
    IF EIP not within code segment limit
        THEN #GP(0);
    FI;
END;
TRAP-OR-INTERRUPT-GATE
    Read segment selector for trap or interrupt gate (IDT descriptor);
    IF segment selector for code segment is null
        THEN #GP(0H + EXT); (* null selector with EXT flag set *)
    FI;
    IF segment selector is not within its descriptor table limits
        THEN #GP(selector + EXT);
    FI;
    Read trap or interrupt handler descriptor;
    IF descriptor does not indicate a code segment
        OR code segment descriptor DPL > CPL
            THEN #GP(selector + EXT);
    FI;
    IF trap or interrupt gate segment is not present,
        THEN #NP(selector + EXT);
    FI;
    IF code segment is non-conforming AND DPL < CPL
        THEN IF VM=0
            THEN
                GOTO INTER-PRIVILEGE-LEVEL-INTERRUPT;
                (* PE=1, interrupt or trap gate, nonconforming *)
                (* code segment, DPL<CPL, VM=0 *)

```
            ELSE (* VM=1 *)
                IF code segment DPL ≠ 0 THEN #GP(new code segment selector); FI;
                GOTO INTERRUPT-FROM-VIRTUAL-8086-MODE;
                (* PE=1, interrupt or trap gate, DPL<CPL, VM=1 *)
        FI;
        ELSE (* PE=1, interrupt or trap gate, DPL ≥ CPL *)
            IF VM=1 THEN #GP(new code segment selector); FI;
            IF code segment is conforming OR code segment DPL = CPL
                THEN
                    GOTO INTRA-PRIVILEGE-LEVEL-INTERRUPT;
                ELSE
                    #GP(CodeSegmentSelector + EXT);
                    (* PE=1, interrupt or trap gate, nonconforming *)
                    (* code segment, DPL>CPL *)
            FI;
    FI;
END;


INTER-PREVILEGE-LEVEL-INTERRUPT
    (* PE=1, interrupt or trap gate, non-conforming code segment, DPL<CPL *)
    (* Check segment selector and descriptor for stack of new privilege level in current TSS *)
    IF current TSS is 32-bit TSS
        THEN
                TSSstackAddress ← new code segment (DPL * 8) + 4
                IF (TSSstackAddress + 7) > TSS limit
                    THEN #TS(current TSS selector); FI;
                NewSS ← TSSstackAddress + 4;
                NewESP ← stack address;
        ELSE (* TSS is 16-bit *)
                TSSstackAddress ← new code segment (DPL * 4) + 2
                IF (TSSstackAddress + 4) > TSS limit
                    THEN #TS(current TSS selector); FI;
                NewESP ← TSSstackAddress;
                NewSS ← TSSstackAddress + 2;
    FI;
    IF segment selector is null THEN #TS(EXT); FI;
    IF segment selector index is not within its descriptor table limits
        OR segment selector's RPL ≠ DPL of code segment,
            THEN #TS(SS selector + EXT);
    FI;
Read segment descriptor for stack segment in GDT or LDT;
    IF stack segment DPL ≠ DPL of code segment,
        OR stack segment does not indicate writable data segment,
            THEN #TS(SS selector + EXT);
    FI;
    IF stack segment not present THEN #SS(SS selector+EXT); FI;
    IF 32-bit gate
```

```
            THEN
                    IF new stack does not have room for 24 bytes (error code pushed)
                            OR 20 bytes (no error code pushed)
                                    THEN #SS(segment selector + EXT);
                    FI;
            ELSE (* 16-bit gate *)
                    IF new stack does not have room for 12 bytes (error code pushed)
                            OR 10 bytes (no error code pushed);
                                    THEN #SS(segment selector + EXT);
                    FI;
    FI;
    IF instruction pointer is not within code segment limits THEN #GP(0); FI;
    SS:ESP ← TSS(SS:ESP) (* segment descriptor information also loaded *)
    IF 32-bit gate
            THEN
                    CS:EIP ← Gate(CS:EIP); (* segment descriptor information also loaded *)
            ELSE (* 16-bit gate *)
                    CS:IP ← Gate(CS:IP); (* segment descriptor information also loaded *)
    FI;
    IF 32-bit gate
            THEN
                    Push(far pointer to old stack); (* old SS and ESP, 3 words padded to 4 *);
                    Push(EFLAGS);
                    Push(far pointer to return instruction); (* old CS and EIP, 3 words padded to 4*);
                    Push(ErrorCode); (* if needed, 4 bytes *)
            ELSE(* 16-bit gate *)
                    Push(far pointer to old stack); (* old SS and SP, 2 words *);
                    Push(EFLAGS);
                    Push(far pointer to return instruction); (* old CS and IP, 2 words *);
                    Push(ErrorCode); (* if needed, 2 bytes *)
    FI;
    CPL ← CodeSegmentDescriptor(DPL);
    CS(RPL) ← CPL;
    IF interrupt gate
            THEN IF ← 0 (* interrupt flag to 0 (disabled) *); FI;
    TF ← 0;
    VM ← 0;
    RF ← 0;
    NT ← 0;
    END;


INTERRUPT-FROM-VIRTUAL-8086-MODE:
    (* Check segment selector and descriptor for privilege level 0 stack in current TSS *)
    IF current TSS is 32-bit TSS
            THEN
                    TSSstackAddress ← new code segment (DPL * 8) + 4
                    IF (TSSstackAddress + 7) > TSS limit
```

```
                    THEN #TS(current TSS selector); FI;
                NewSS ← TSSstackAddress + 4;
                NewESP ← stack address;
            ELSE (* TSS is 16-bit *)
                TSSstackAddress ← new code segment (DPL * 4) + 2
                IF (TSSstackAddress + 4) > TSS limit
                    THEN #TS(current TSS selector); FI;
                NewESP ← TSSstackAddress;
                NewSS ← TSSstackAddress + 2;
    FI;
        IF segment selector is null THEN #TS(EXT); FI;
        IF segment selector index is not within its descriptor table limits
            OR segment selector's RPL ≠ DPL of code segment,
                THEN #TS(SS selector + EXT);
        FI;
Access segment descriptor for stack segment in GDT or LDT;
IF stack segment DPL ≠ DPL of code segment,
    OR stack segment does not indicate writable data segment,
        THEN #TS(SS selector + EXT);
FI;
IF stack segment not present THEN #SS(SS selector+EXT); FI;
IF 32-bit gate
    THEN
        IF new stack does not have room for 40 bytes (error code pushed)
            OR 36 bytes (no error code pushed);
                THEN #SS(segment selector + EXT);
        FI;
    ELSE (* 16-bit gate *)
        IF new stack does not have room for 20 bytes (error code pushed)
            OR 18 bytes (no error code pushed);
                THEN #SS(segment selector + EXT);
        FI;
FI;
IF instruction pointer is not within code segment limits THEN #GP(0); FI;
tempEFLAGS ← EFLAGS;
VM ← 0;
TF ← 0;
RF ← 0;
IF service through interrupt gate THEN IF ← 0; FI;
TempSS ← SS;
TempESP ← ESP;
SS:ESP ← TSS(SS0:ESP0); (* Change to level 0 stack segment *)
(* Following pushes are 16 bits for 16-bit gate and 32 bits for 32-bit gates *)
(* Segment selector pushes in 32-bit mode are padded to two words *)
Push(GS);
Push(FS);
Push(DS);
```

```
        Push(ES);
        Push(TempSS);
        Push(TempESP);
        Push(TempEFlags);
        Push(CS);
        Push(EIP);
        GS ← 0; (*segment registers nullified, invalid in protected mode *)
        FS ← 0;
        DS ← 0;
        ES ← 0;
        CS ← Gate(CS);
        IF OperandSize=32
            THEN
                    EIP ← Gate(instruction pointer);
            ELSE (* OperandSize is 16 *)
                    EIP ← Gate(instruction pointer) AND 0000FFFFH;
        FI;
        (* Starts execution of new routine in Protected Mode *)
END;


INTRA-PRIVILEGE-LEVEL-INTERRUPT:
    (* PE=1, DPL = CPL or conforming segment *)
    IF 32-bit gate
        THEN
                IF current stack does not have room for 16 bytes (error code pushed)
                    OR 12 bytes (no error code pushed); THEN #SS(0);
                FI;
        ELSE (* 16-bit gate *)
                IF current stack does not have room for 8 bytes (error code pushed)
                    OR 6 bytes (no error code pushed); THEN #SS(0);
                FI;
    IF instruction pointer not within code segment limit THEN #GP(0); FI;
    IF 32-bit gate
        THEN
                Push (EFLAGS);
                Push (far pointer to return instruction); (* 3 words padded to 4 *)
                CS:EIP ← Gate(CS:EIP); (* segment descriptor information also loaded *)
                Push (ErrorCode); (* if any *)
        ELSE (* 16-bit gate *)
                Push (FLAGS);
                Push (far pointer to return location); (* 2 words *)
                CS:IP ← Gate(CS:IP); (* segment descriptor information also loaded *)
                Push (ErrorCode); (* if any *)
    FI;
    CS(RPL) ← CPL;
    IF interrupt gate
        THEN
```

```
                    IF ← 0; FI;
                    TF ← 0;
                    NT ← 0;
                    VM ← 0;
                    RF ← 0;
        FI;
END;
```

Flags Affected

The EFLAGS register is pushed onto stack. The IF, TF, NT, AC, RF, and VM flags may be cleared, depending on the mode of operation of the processor when the INT instruction is executed (see "Operation" section.)

Protected Mode Exceptions

#GP(0)	If the instruction pointer in the IDT or in the interrupt-, trap-, or task gate is beyond the code segment limits.
#GP(selector)	If the segment selector in the interrupt-, trap-, or task gate is null.
	If a interrupt-, trap-, or task gate, code segment, or TSS segment selector index is outside its descriptor table limits.
	If the interrupt vector is outside the IDT limits.
	If an IDT descriptor is not an interrupt-, trap-, or task-descriptor.
	If an interrupt is generated by the INT*n* instruction and the DPL of an interrupt-, trap-, or task-descriptor is less than the CPL.
	If the segment selector in an interrupt- or trap-gate does not point to a segment descriptor for a code segment.
	If the segment selector for a TSS has its local/global bit set for local.
	If a TSS segment descriptor specifies that the TSS is busy or not available.
#SS(0)	If pushing the return address, flags, or error code onto the stack exceeds the bounds of the stack segment and no stack switch occurs.
#SS(selector)	If the SS register is being loaded and the segment pointed to is marked not present.
	If pushing the return address, flags, error code, or stack segment pointer exceeds the bounds of the stack segment.
#NP(selector)	If code segment, interrupt-, trap-, or task gate, or TSS is not present.
#TS(selector)	If the RPL of the stack segment selector in the TSS is not equal to the DPL of the code segment being accessed by the interrupt or trap gate.

> If DPL of the stack segment descriptor pointed to by the stack segment selector in the TSS is not equal to the DPL of the code segment descriptor for the interrupt or trap gate.
>
> If the stack segment selector in the TSS is null.
>
> If the stack segment for the TSS is not a writable data segment.
>
> If segment-selector index for stack segment is outside descriptor table limits.

#PF(fault-code)   If a page fault occurs.

Real Address Mode Exceptions

#GP   If a memory operand effective address is outside the CS, DS, ES, FS, or GS segment limit.

                    If the interrupt vector is outside the IDT limits.

#SS   If stack limit violation on push.

                    If pushing the return address, flags, or error code onto the stack exceeds the bounds of the stack segment when a stack switch occurs.

Virtual 8086 Mode Exceptions

#GP(0)   (For INTn instruction) If the IOPL is less than 3 and the DPL of the interrupt-, trap-, or task-gate descriptor is not equal to 3.

                    If the instruction pointer in the IDT or in the interrupt-, trap-, or task gate is beyond the code segment limits.

#GP(selector)   If the segment selector in the interrupt-, trap-, or task gate is null.

                    If a interrupt-, trap-, or task gate, code segment, or TSS segment selector index is outside its descriptor table limits.

                    If the interrupt vector is outside the IDT limits.

                    If an IDT descriptor is not an interrupt-, trap-, or task-descriptor.

                    If an interrupt is generated by the INTn instruction and the DPL of an interrupt-, trap-, or task-descriptor is less than the CPL.

                    If the segment selector in an interrupt- or trap-gate does not point to a segment descriptor for a code segment.

                    If the segment selector for a TSS has its local/global bit set for local.

#SS(selector)	If the SS register is being loaded and the segment pointed to is marked not present.
	If pushing the return address, flags, error code, stack segment pointer, or data segments exceeds the bounds of the stack segment.
#NP(selector)	If code segment, interrupt-, trap-, or task gate, or TSS is not present.
#TS(selector)	If the RPL of the stack segment selector in the TSS is not equal to the DPL of the code segment being accessed by the interrupt or trap gate.
	If DPL of the stack segment descriptor for the TSS's stack segment is not equal to the DPL of the code segment descriptor for the interrupt or trap gate.
	If the stack segment selector in the TSS is null.
	If the stack segment for the TSS is not a writable data segment.
	If segment-selector index for stack segment is outside descriptor table limits.
#PF(fault-code)	If a page fault occurs.
#BP	If the INT3 instruction is executed.
#OF	If the INTO instruction is executed and the OF flag is set.

INVD—Invalidate Internal Caches

Opcode	Instruction	Description
0F 08	INVD	Flush internal caches; initiate flushing of external caches.

Description

Invalidates (flushes) the processor's internal caches and issues a special-function bus cycle that directs external caches to also flush themselves. Data held in internal caches is not written back to main memory.

After executing this instruction, the processor does not wait for the external caches to complete their flushing operation before proceeding with instruction execution. It is the responsibility of hardware to respond to the cache flush signal.

The INVD instruction is a privileged instruction. When the processor is running in protected mode, the CPL of a program or procedure must be 0 to execute this instruction. This instruction is also implementation-dependent; its function may be implemented differently on future Intel Architecture processors.

Use this instruction with care. Data cached internally and not written back to main memory will be lost. Unless there is a specific requirement or benefit to flushing caches without writing back modified cache lines (for example, testing or fault recovery where cache coherency with main memory is not a concern), software should use the WBINVD instruction.

Operation

Flush(InternalCaches);
SignalFlush(ExternalCaches);
Continue (* Continue execution);

Flags Affected

None.

Protected Mode Exceptions

#GP(0)   If the current privilege level is not 0.

Real Address Mode Exceptions

None.

Virtual 8086 Mode Exceptions

#GP(0)   The INVD instruction cannot be executed at the virtual 8086 mode.

Intel Architecture Compatibility

This instruction is not supported on Intel Architecture processors earlier than the Intel486 processor.

INVLPG—Invalidate TLB Entry

Opcode	Instruction	Description
0F 01/7	INVLPG m	Invalidate TLB Entry for page that contains *m*

Description

Invalidates (flushes) the translation lookaside buffer (TLB) entry specified with the source operand. The source operand is a memory address. The processor determines the page that contains that address and flushes the TLB entry for that page.

The INVLPG instruction is a privileged instruction. When the processor is running in protected mode, the CPL of a program or procedure must be 0 to execute this instruction. This instruction is also implementation-dependent; its function may be implemented differently on future Intel Architecture processors.

The INVLPG instruction normally flushes the TLB entry only for the specified page; however, in some cases, it flushes the entire TLB. See Chapter 11, "MOV—Move to/from Control Registers" for further information on operations that flush the TLB.

Operation

Flush(RelevantTLBEntries);
Continue (* Continue execution);

Flags Affected

None.

Protected Mode Exceptions

#GP(0)   If the current privilege level is not 0.

#UD   Operand is a register.

Real Address Mode Exceptions

None.

Virtual 8086 Mode Exceptions

#GP(0)   The INVLPG instruction cannot be executed at the virtual 8086 mode.

Intel Architecture Compatibility

This instruction is not supported on Intel Architecture processors earlier than the Intel486 processor.

IRET/IRETD—Interrupt Return

Opcode	Instruction	Description
CF	IRET	Interrupt return (16-bit operand size)
CF	IRETD	Interrupt return (32-bit operand size)

Description

Returns program control from an exception or interrupt handler to a program or procedure that was interrupted by an exception, an external interrupt or, a software-generated interrupt, or returns from a nested task. IRET and IRETD are mnemonics for the same opcode. The IRETD mnemonic (interrupt return double) is intended for use when returning from an interrupt when using the 32-bit operand size; however, most assemblers use the IRET mnemonic interchangeably for both operand sizes.

In Real Address Mode, the IRET instruction preforms a far return to the interrupted program or procedure. During this operation, the processor pops the return instruction pointer, return code segment selector, and EFLAGS image from the stack to the EIP, CS, and EFLAGS registers, respectively, and then resumes execution of the interrupted program or procedure.

In Protected Mode, the action of the IRET instruction depends on the settings of the NT (nested task) and VM flags in the EFLAGS register and the VM flag in the EFLAGS image stored on the current stack. Depending on the setting of these flags, the processor performs the following types of interrupt returns:

- Return from virtual-8086 mode.

- Return to virtual-8086 mode.

- Intra-privilege level return.

- Inter-privilege level return.

- Return from nested task (task switch).

If the NT flag (EFLAGS register) is cleared, the IRET instruction performs a far return from the interrupt procedure, without a task switch. The code segment being returned to must be equally or less privileged than the interrupt handler routine (as indicated by the RPL field of the code segment selector popped from the stack). As with a real-address mode interrupt return, the IRET instruction pops the return instruction pointer, return code segment selector, and EFLAGS image from the stack to the EIP, CS, and EFLAGS registers, respectively, and then resumes execution of the interrupted program or procedure. If the return is to another privilege level, the IRET instruction also pops the stack pointer and SS from the stack, before resuming program execution. If the return is to virtual-8086 mode, the processor also pops the data segment registers from the stack.

If the NT flag is set, the IRET instruction performs a return from a nested task (switches from the called task back to the calling task) or reverses the operation of an interrupt or exception that caused a task switch. The updated state of the task executing the IRET instruction is saved in its TSS. If the task is reentered later, the code that follows the IRET instruction is executed.

Operation

```
IF PE = 0
    THEN
        GOTO REAL-ADDRESS-MODE:;
    ELSE
        GOTO PROTECTED-MODE;
FI;

REAL-ADDRESS-MODE;
    IF OperandSize = 32
        THEN
            IF top 12 bytes of stack not within stack limits THEN #SS; FI;
            IF instruction pointer not within code segment limits THEN #GP(0); FI;
            EIP ← Pop();
            CS ← Pop(); (* 32-bit pop, high-order 16-bits discarded *)
            tempEFLAGS ← Pop();
            EFLAGS ← (tempEFLAGS AND 257FD5H) OR (EFLAGS AND 1A0000H);
        ELSE (* OperandSize = 16 *)
            IF top 6 bytes of stack are not within stack limits THEN #SS; FI;
            IF instruction pointer not within code segment limits THEN #GP(0); FI;
            EIP ← Pop();
            EIP ← EIP AND 0000FFFFH;
            CS ← Pop(); (* 16-bit pop *)
            EFLAGS[15:0] ← Pop();
    FI;
END;

PROTECTED-MODE:
    IF VM = 1 (* Virtual-8086 mode: PE=1, VM=1 *)
        THEN
            GOTO RETURN-FROM-VIRTUAL-8086-MODE; (* PE=1, VM=1 *)
    FI;
    IF NT = 1
        THEN
            GOTO TASK-RETURN;( *PE=1, VM=0, NT=1 *)
    FI;
    IF OperandSize=32
        THEN
            IF top 12 bytes of stack not within stack limits
                THEN #SS(0)
            FI;
            tempEIP ← Pop();
            tempCS ← Pop();
            tempEFLAGS ← Pop();
        ELSE (* OperandSize = 16 *)
            IF top 6 bytes of stack are not within stack limits
                THEN #SS(0);
```

```
                    FI;
                    tempEIP ← Pop();
                    tempCS ← Pop();
                    tempEFLAGS ← Pop();
                    tempEIP ← tempEIP AND FFFFH;
                    tempEFLAGS ← tempEFLAGS AND FFFFH;
        FI;
        IF tempEFLAGS(VM) = 1 AND CPL=0
            THEN
                    GOTO RETURN-TO-VIRTUAL-8086-MODE;
                    (* PE=1, VM=1 in EFLAGS image *)
            ELSE
                    GOTO PROTECTED-MODE-RETURN;
                    (* PE=1, VM=0 in EFLAGS image *)
        FI;


RETURN-FROM-VIRTUAL-8086-MODE:
(* Processor is in virtual-8086 mode when IRET is executed and stays in virtual-8086 mode *)
    IF IOPL=3 (* Virtual mode: PE=1, VM=1, IOPL=3 *)
        THEN IF OperandSize = 32
            THEN
                    IF top 12 bytes of stack not within stack limits THEN #SS(0); FI;
                    IF instruction pointer not within code segment limits THEN #GP(0); FI;
                    EIP ← Pop();
                    CS ← Pop(); (* 32-bit pop, high-order 16-bits discarded *)
                    EFLAGS ← Pop();
                    (*VM,IOPL,VIP,and VIF EFLAGS bits are not modified by pop *)
            ELSE (* OperandSize = 16 *)
                    IF top 6 bytes of stack are not within stack limits THEN #SS(0); FI;
                    IF instruction pointer not within code segment limits THEN #GP(0); FI;
                    EIP ← Pop();
                    EIP ← EIP AND 0000FFFFH;
                    CS ← Pop(); (* 16-bit pop *)
                    EFLAGS[15:0] ← Pop(); (* IOPL in EFLAGS is not modified by pop *)
            FI;
        ELSE
                    #GP(0); (* trap to virtual-8086 monitor: PE=1, VM=1, IOPL<3 *)
    FI;
END;


RETURN-TO-VIRTUAL-8086-MODE:
(* Interrupted procedure was in virtual-8086 mode: PE=1, VM=1 in flags image *)
    IF top 24 bytes of stack are not within stack segment limits
        THEN #SS(0);
    FI;
    IF instruction pointer not within code segment limits
        THEN #GP(0);
```

```
        FI;
        CS ← tempCS;
        EIP ← tempEIP;
        EFLAGS ← tempEFLAGS
        TempESP ← Pop();
        TempSS ← Pop();
        ES ← Pop(); (* pop 2 words; throw away high-order word *)
        DS ← Pop(); (* pop 2 words; throw away high-order word *)
        FS ← Pop(); (* pop 2 words; throw away high-order word *)
        GS ← Pop(); (* pop 2 words; throw away high-order word *)
        SS:ESP ← TempSS:TempESP;
        (* Resume execution in Virtual 8086 mode *)
END;


TASK-RETURN: (* PE=1, VM=1, NT=1 *)
    Read segment selector in link field of current TSS;
    IF local/global bit is set to local
            OR index not within GDT limits
                THEN #GP(TSS selector);
    FI;
    Access TSS for task specified in link field of current TSS;
    IF TSS descriptor type is not TSS or if the TSS is marked not busy
        THEN #GP(TSS selector);
    FI;
    IF TSS not present
        THEN #NP(TSS selector);
    FI;
    SWITCH-TASKS (without nesting) to TSS specified in link field of current TSS;
    Mark the task just abandoned as NOT BUSY;
    IF EIP is not within code segment limit
        THEN #GP(0);
    FI;
END;


PROTECTED-MODE-RETURN: (* PE=1, VM=0 in flags image *)
    IF return code segment selector is null THEN GP(0); FI;
    IF return code segment selector addrsses descriptor beyond descriptor table limit
        THEN GP(selector; FI;
    Read segment descriptor pointed to by the return code segment selector
    IF return code segment descriptor is not a code segment THEN #GP(selector); FI;
    IF return code segment selector RPL < CPL THEN #GP(selector); FI;
    IF return code segment descriptor is conforming
        AND return code segment DPL > return code segment selector RPL
            THEN #GP(selector); FI;
    IF return code segment descriptor is not present THEN #NP(selector); FI:
    IF return code segment selector RPL > CPL
        THEN GOTO RETURN-OUTER-PRIVILEGE-LEVEL;
```

```
          ELSE GOTO RETURN-TO-SAME-PRIVILEGE-LEVEL
    FI;
END;

RETURN-TO-SAME-PRIVILEGE-LEVEL: (* PE=1, VM=0 in flags image, RPL=CPL *)
    IF EIP is not within code segment limits THEN #GP(0); FI;
    EIP ← tempEIP;
    CS ← tempCS; (* segment descriptor information also loaded *)
    EFLAGS (CF, PF, AF, ZF, SF, TF, DF, OF, NT) ← tempEFLAGS;
    IF OperandSize=32
        THEN
                EFLAGS(RF, AC, ID) ← tempEFLAGS;
    FI;
    IF CPL ≤ IOPL
        THEN
                EFLAGS(IF) ← tempEFLAGS;
    FI;
    IF CPL = 0
        THEN
                EFLAGS(IOPL) ← tempEFLAGS;
                IF OperandSize=32
                    THEN EFLAGS(VM, VIF, VIP) ← tempEFLAGS;
                FI;
    FI;
END;

RETURN-TO-OUTER-PRIVILGE-LEVEL:
    IF OperandSize=32
        THEN
                IF top 8 bytes on stack are not within limits THEN #SS(0); FI;
            ELSE (* OperandSize=16 *)
                IF top 4 bytes on stack are not within limits THEN #SS(0); FI;
    FI;
    Read return segment selector;
    IF stack segment selector is null THEN #GP(0); FI;
    IF return stack segment selector index is not within its descriptor table limits
            THEN #GP(SSselector); FI;
    Read segment descriptor pointed to by return segment selector;
    IF stack segment selector RPL ≠ RPL of the return code segment selector
        IF stack segment selector RPL ≠ RPL of the return code segment selector
        OR the stack segment descriptor does not indicate a a writable data segment;
        OR stack segment DPL ≠ RPL of the return code segment selector
                THEN #GP(SS selector);
        FI;
        IF stack segment is not present THEN #NP(SS selector); FI;
    IF tempEIP is not within code segment limit THEN #GP(0); FI;
    EIP ← tempEIP;
```

```
CS ← tempCS;
EFLAGS (CF, PF, AF, ZF, SF, TF, DF, OF, NT) ← tempEFLAGS;
IF OperandSize=32
     THEN
             EFLAGS(RF, AC, ID) ← tempEFLAGS;
FI;
IF CPO ≤ IOPL
     THEN
             EFLAGS(IF) ← tempEFLAGS;
FI;
IF CPL = 0
     THEN
             EFLAGS(IOPL) ← tempEFLAGS;
             IF OperandSize=32
                  THEN EFLAGS(VM, VIF, VIP) ← tempEFLAGS;
             FI;
FI;
CPL ← RPL of the return code segment selector;
FOR each of segment register (ES, FS, GS, and DS)
     DO;
             IF segment register points to data or non-conforming code segment
             AND CPL > segment descriptor DPL (* stored in hidden part of segment register *)
                  THEN (* segment register invalid *)
                          SegmentSelector ← 0; (* null segment selector *)
             FI;
     OD;
END:
```

Flags Affected

All the flags and fields in the EFLAGS register are potentially modified, depending on the mode of operation of the processor.

Protected Mode Exceptions

#GP(0)   If the return code or stack segment selector is null.

                    If the return instruction pointer is not within the return code segment limit.

#GP(selector)   If a segment selector index is outside its descriptor table limits.

                    If the return code segment selector RPL is greater than the CPL.

                    If the DPL of a conforming-code segment is greater than the return code segment selector RPL.

                    If the DPL for a nonconforming-code segment is not equal to the RPL of the code segment selector.

If the stack segment descriptor DPL is not equal to the RPL of the return code segment selector.

                If the stack segment is not a writable data segment.

                If the stack segment selector RPL is not equal to the RPL of the return code segment selector.

                If the segment descriptor for a code segment does not indicate it is a code segment.

                If the segment selector for a TSS has its local/global bit set for local.

                If a TSS segment descriptor specifies that the TSS is busy or not available.

#SS(0)	If the top bytes of stack are not within stack limits.
#NP(selector)	If the return code or stack segment is not present.
#PF(fault-code)	If a page fault occurs.
#AC(0)	If an unaligned memory reference occurs when the CPL is 3 and alignment checking is enabled.

Real Address Mode Exceptions

#GP	If the return instruction pointer is not within the return code segment limit.
#SS	If the top bytes of stack are not within stack limits.

Virtual 8086 Mode Exceptions

#GP(0)	If the return instruction pointer is not within the return code segment limit.
	IF IOPL not equal to 3
#PF(fault-code)	If a page fault occurs.
#SS(0)	If the top bytes of stack are not within stack limits.
#AC(0)	If an unaligned memory reference occurs and alignment checking is enabled.

Jcc—Jump if Condition Is Met

Opcode	Instruction	Description
77 cb	JA rel8	Jump short if above (CF=0 and ZF=0)
73 cb	JAE rel8	Jump short if above or equal (CF=0)
72 cb	JB rel8	Jump short if below (CF=1)
76 cb	JBE rel8	Jump short if below or equal (CF=1 or ZF=1)
72 cb	JC rel8	Jump short if carry (CF=1)
E3 cb	JCXZ rel8	Jump short if CX register is 0
E3 cb	JECXZ rel8	Jump short if ECX register is 0
74 cb	JE rel8	Jump short if equal (ZF=1)
7F cb	JG rel8	Jump short if greater (ZF=0 and SF=OF)
7D cb	JGE rel8	Jump short if greater or equal (SF=OF)
7C cb	JL rel8	Jump short if less (SF<>OF)
7E cb	JLE rel8	Jump short if less or equal (ZF=1 or SF<>OF)
76 cb	JNA rel8	Jump short if not above (CF=1 or ZF=1)
72 cb	JNAE rel8	Jump short if not above or equal (CF=1)
73 cb	JNB rel8	Jump short if not below (CF=0)
77 cb	JNBE rel8	Jump short if not below or equal (CF=0 and ZF=0)
73 cb	JNC rel8	Jump short if not carry (CF=0)
75 cb	JNE rel8	Jump short if not equal (ZF=0)
7E cb	JNG rel8	Jump short if not greater (ZF=1 or SF<>OF)
7C cb	JNGE rel8	Jump short if not greater or equal (SF<>OF)
7D cb	JNL rel8	Jump short if not less (SF=OF)
7F cb	JNLE rel8	Jump short if not less or equal (ZF=0 and SF=OF)
71 cb	JNO rel8	Jump short if not overflow (OF=0)
7B cb	JNP rel8	Jump short if not parity (PF=0)
79 cb	JNS rel8	Jump short if not sign (SF=0)
75 cb	JNZ rel8	Jump short if not zero (ZF=0)
70 cb	JO rel8	Jump short if overflow (OF=1)
7A cb	JP rel8	Jump short if parity (PF=1)
7A cb	JPE rel8	Jump short if parity even (PF=1)
7B cb	JPO rel8	Jump short if parity odd (PF=0)
78 cb	JS rel8	Jump short if sign (SF=1)
74 cb	JZ rel8	Jump short if zero (ZF = 1)
0F 87 cw/cd	JA rel16/32	Jump near if above (CF=0 and ZF=0)
0F 83 cw/cd	JAE rel16/32	Jump near if above or equal (CF=0)
0F 82 cw/cd	JB rel16/32	Jump near if below (CF=1)
0F 86 cw/cd	JBE rel16/32	Jump near if below or equal (CF=1 or ZF=1)
0F 82 cw/cd	JC rel16/32	Jump near if carry (CF=1)
0F 84 cw/cd	JE rel16/32	Jump near if equal (ZF=1)
0F 84 cw/cd	JZ rel16/32	Jump near if 0 (ZF=1)
0F 8F cw/cd	JG rel16/32	Jump near if greater (ZF=0 and SF=OF)

Opcode	Instruction	Description
0F 8D *cw/cd*	JGE *rel16/32*	Jump near if greater or equal (SF=OF)
0F 8C *cw/cd*	JL *rel16/32*	Jump near if less (SF<>OF)
0F 8E *cw/cd*	JLE *rel16/32*	Jump near if less or equal (ZF=1 or SF<>OF)
0F 86 *cw/cd*	JNA *rel16/32*	Jump near if not above (CF=1 or ZF=1)
0F 82 *cw/cd*	JNAE *rel16/32*	Jump near if not above or equal (CF=1)
0F 83 *cw/cd*	JNB *rel16/32*	Jump near if not below (CF=0)
0F 87 *cw/cd*	JNBE *rel16/32*	Jump near if not below or equal (CF=0 and ZF=0)
0F 83 *cw/cd*	JNC *rel16/32*	Jump near if not carry (CF=0)
0F 85 *cw/cd*	JNE *rel16/32*	Jump near if not equal (ZF=0)
0F 8E *cw/cd*	JNG *rel16/32*	Jump near if not greater (ZF=1 or SF<>OF)
0F 8C *cw/cd*	JNGE *rel16/32*	Jump near if not greater or equal (SF<>OF)
0F 8D *cw/cd*	JNL *rel16/32*	Jump near if not less (SF=OF)
0F 8F *cw/cd*	JNLE *rel16/32*	Jump near if not less or equal (ZF=0 and SF=OF)
0F 81 *cw/cd*	JNO *rel16/32*	Jump near if not overflow (OF=0)
0F 8B *cw/cd*	JNP *rel16/32*	Jump near if not parity (PF=0)
0F 89 *cw/cd*	JNS *rel16/32*	Jump near if not sign (SF=0)
0F 85 *cw/cd*	JNZ *rel16/32*	Jump near if not zero (ZF=0)
0F 80 *cw/cd*	JO *rel16/32*	Jump near if overflow (OF=1)
0F 8A *cw/cd*	JP *rel16/32*	Jump near if parity (PF=1)
0F 8A *cw/cd*	JPE *rel16/32*	Jump near if parity even (PF=1)
0F 8B *cw/cd*	JPO *rel16/32*	Jump near if parity odd (PF=0)
0F 88 *cw/cd*	JS *rel16/32*	Jump near if sign (SF=1)
0F 84 *cw/cd*	JZ *rel16/32*	Jump near if 0 (ZF=1)

Description

Checks the state of one or more of the status flags in the EFLAGS register (CF, OF, PF, SF, and ZF) and, if the flags are in the specified state (condition), performs a jump to the target instruction specified by the destination operand. A condition code (*cc*) is associated with each instruction to indicate the condition being tested for. If the condition is not satisfied, the jump is not performed and execution continues with the instruction following the J*cc* instruction.

The target instruction is specified with a relative offset (a signed offset relative to the current value of the instruction pointer in the EIP register). A relative offset (*rel8*, *rel16*, or *rel32*) is generally specified as a label in assembly code, but at the machine code level, it is encoded as a signed, 8-bit or 32-bit immediate value, which is added to the instruction pointer. Instruction coding is most efficient for offsets of −128 to +127. If the operand-size attribute is 16, the upper two bytes of the EIP register are cleared to 0s, resulting in a maximum instruction pointer size of 16 bits.

The conditions for each J*cc* mnemonic are given in the "Description" column of the above table. The terms "less" and "greater" are used for comparisons of signed integers and the terms "above" and "below" are used for unsigned integers.

Because a particular state of the status flags can sometimes be interpreted in two ways, two mnemonics are defined for some opcodes. For example, the JA (jump if above) instruction and the JNBE (jump if not below or equal) instruction are alternate mnemonics for the opcode 77H.

The J*cc* instruction does not support far jumps (jumps to other code segments). When the target for the conditional jump is in a different segment, use the opposite condition from the condition being tested for the J*cc* instruction, and then access the target with an unconditional far jump (JMP instruction) to the other segment. For example, the following conditional far jump is illegal:

```
JZ FARLABEL;
```

To accomplish this far jump, use the following two instructions:

```
JNZ BEYOND;
JMP FARLABEL;
BEYOND:
```

The JECXZ and JCXZ instructions differs from the other J*cc* instructions because they do not check the status flags. Instead they check the contents of the ECX and CX registers, respectively, for 0. These instructions are useful at the beginning of a conditional loop that terminates with a conditional loop instruction (such as LOOPNE). They prevent entering the loop when the ECX or CX register is equal to 0, which would cause the loop to execute 2^{32} or 64K times, respectively, instead of zero times.

All conditional jumps are converted to code fetches of one or two cache lines, regardless of jump address or cacheability.

Operation

```
IF condition
    THEN
         EIP ← EIP + SignExtend(DEST);
         IF OperandSize = 16
             THEN
                  EIP ← EIP AND 0000FFFFH;
         FI;
FI;
```

Flags Affected

None.

Protected Mode Exceptions

#GP(0)   If the offset being jumped to is beyond the limits of the CS segment.

Real Address Mode Exceptions

#GP   If the offset being jumped to is beyond the limits of the CS segment or is outside of the effective address space from 0 to FFFFH. This condition can occur if 32-address size override prefix is used.

Virtual 8086 Mode Exceptions

#GP(0)   If the offset being jumped to is beyond the limits of the CS segment or is outside of the effective address space from 0 to FFFFH. This condition can occur if 32-address size override prefix is used.

JMP—Jump

Opcode	Instruction	Description
EB cb	JMP rel8	Jump near, relative address
E9 cw	JMP rel16	Jump near, relative address
E9 cd	JMP rel32	Jump near, relative address
FF /4	JMP r/m16	Jump near, indirect address
FF /4	JMP r/m32	Jump near, indirect address
EA cd	JMP ptr16:16	Jump far, absolute address
EA cp	JMP ptr16:32	Jump far, absolute address
FF /5	JMP m16:16	Jump far, indirect address
FF /5	JMP m16:32	Jump far, indirect address

Description

Transfers program control to a different point in the instruction stream without recording return information. The destination (target) operand specifies the address of the instruction being jumped to. This operand can be an immediate value, a general-purpose register, or a memory location.

- Near jump—A jump to an instruction within the current code segment (the segment currently pointed to by the CS register), sometimes referred to as an intrasegment call.

- Far jump—A jump to an instruction located in a different segment than the current code segment, sometimes referred to as an intersegment call.

- Task switch—A jump to an instruction located in a different task. (This is a form of a far jump.)

A task switch can only be executed in protected mode (see Chapter 6 in the *Pentium® Pro Family Developer's Manual, Volume 3* for information on task switching with the JMP instruction).

When executing a near jump, the processor jumps to the address (within the current code segment) that is specified with the target operand. The target operand specifies either an absolute address (that is an offset from the base of the code segment) or a relative offset (a signed offset relative to the current value of the instruction pointer in the EIP register). An absolute address is specified directly in a register or indirectly in a memory location (*r/m16* or *r/m32* operand form). A relative offset (*rel8*, *rel16*, or *rel32*) is generally specified as a label in assembly code, but at the machine code level, it is encoded as a signed, 8-bit or 32-bit immediate value, which is added to the value in the EIP register (that is, to the instruction following the JMP instruction). The operand-size attribute determines the size of the target operand (16 or 32 bits) for absolute addresses. Absolute addresses are loaded directly into the EIP register. When a relative offset is specified, it is added to the value of the EIP register. If the operand-size attribute is 16, the upper two bytes of the EIP register are cleared to 0s, resulting in a maximum instruction pointer size of 16 bits. The CS register is not changed on near jumps.

When executing a far jump, the processor jumps to the code segment and address specified with the target operand. Here the target operand specifies an absolute far address either directly with a pointer (*ptr16:16* or *ptr16:32*) or indirectly with a memory location (*m16:16* or *m16:32*). With the pointer method, the segment and address of the called procedure is encoded in the instruction using a 4-byte (16-bit operand size) or 6-byte (32-bit operand size) far address immediate. With the indirect method, the target operand specifies a memory location that contains a 4-byte (16-bit operand size) or 6-byte (32-bit operand size) far address. The operand-size attribute determines the size of the offset (16 or 32 bits) in the far address. The far address is loaded directly into the CS and EIP registers. If the operand-size attribute is 16, the upper two bytes of the EIP register are cleared to 0s.

When the processor is operating in protected mode, a far jump can also be used to access a code segment through a call gate or to switch tasks. Here, the processor uses the segment selector part of the far address to access the segment descriptor for the segment being jumped to. Depending on the value of the type and access rights information in the segment selector, the JMP instructon can perform:

- A far jump to a conforming or non-conforming code segment (same mechanism as the far jump described in the previous paragraph, except that the processor checks the access rights of the code segment being jumped to).

- An far jump through a call gate.

- A task switch.

The JMP instruction cannot be used to perform inter-privilege level jumps.

When executing an far jump through a call gate, the segment selector specified by the target operand identifies the call gate. (The offset part of the target operand is ignored.) The processor then jumps to the code segment specified in the call gate descriptor and begins executing the instruction at the offset specified in the gate. No stack switch occurs. Here again, the target operand can specify the far address of the call gate and instruction either directly with a pointer (*ptr16:16* or *ptr16:32*) or indirectly with a memory location (*m16:16* or *m16:32*).

Executing a task switch with the JMP instruction, is similar to executing a jump through a call gate. Here the target operand specifies the segment selector of the task gate for the task being switched to. (The offset part of the target operand is ignored). The task gate in turn points to the TSS for the task, which contains the segment selectors for the task's code, data, and stack segments and the instruction pointer to the target instruction. One form of the JMP instruction allows the jump to be made directly to a TSS, without going through a task gate. See Chapter 13 in *Pentium® Pro Family Developer's Manual, Volume 3* the for detailed information on the mechanics of a task switch.

All branches are converted to code fetches of one or two cache lines, regardless of jump address or cacheability.

Operation

```
IF near jump
    THEN IF near relative jump
        THEN
            tempEIP ← EIP + DEST; (* EIP is instruction following JMP instruction*)
        ELSE (* near absolute jump *)
            tempEIP ← DEST;
    FI;
    IF tempEIP is beyond code segment limit THEN #GP(0); FI;
    IF OperandSize = 32
        THEN
            EIP ← tempEIP;
        ELSE (* OperandSize=16 *)
            EIP ← tempEIP AND 0000FFFFH;
    FI;
FI:

IF far jump AND (PE = 0 OR (PE = 1 AND VM = 1)) (* real address or virtual 8086 mode *)
    THEN
        tempEIP ← DEST(offset); (* DEST is ptr16:32 or [m16:32] *)
        IF tempEIP is beyond code segment limit THEN #GP(0); FI;
        CS ← DEST(segment selector); (* DEST is ptr16:32 or [m16:32] *)
        IF OperandSize = 32
            THEN
                EIP ← tempEIP; (* DEST is ptr16:32 or [m16:32] *)
            ELSE (* OperandSize = 16 *)
                EIP ← tempEIP AND 0000FFFFH; (* clear upper 16 bits *)
        FI;
FI;
IF far call AND (PE = 1 AND VM = 0) (* Protected mode, not virtual 8086 mode *)
    THEN
        IF effective address in the CS, DS, ES, FS, GS, or SS segment is illegal
            OR segment selector in target operand null
            THEN #GP(0);
        FI;
        IF segment selector index not within descriptor table limits
            THEN #GP(new selector);
        FI;
        Read type and access rights of segment descriptor;
        IF segment type is not a conforming or nonconforming code segment, call gate,
            task gate, or TSS THEN #GP(segment selector); FI;
        Depending on type and access rights
            GO TO CONFORMING-CODE-SEGMENT;
            GO TO NONCONFORMING-CODE-SEGMENT;
            GO TO CALL-GATE;
            GO TO TASK-GATE;
            GO TO TASK-STATE-SEGMENT;
```

```
        ELSE
             #GP(segment selector);
FI;


CONFORMING-CODE-SEGMENT:
    IF DPL > CPL THEN #GP(segment selector); FI;
    IF segment not present THEN #NP(segment selector); FI;
    tempEIP ← DEST(offset);
    IF OperandSize=16
         THEN tempEIP ← tempEIP AND 0000FFFFH;
    FI;
    IF tempEIP not in code segment limit THEN #GP(0); FI;
    CS ← DEST(SegmentSelector); (* segment descriptor information also loaded *)
    CS(RPL) ← CPL
    EIP ← tempEIP;
END;


NONCONFORMING-CODE-SEGMENT:
    IF (RPL > CPL) OR (DPL ≠ CPL) THEN #GP(code segment selector); FI;
    IF segment not present THEN #NP(segment selector); FI;
    IF instruction pointer outside code segment limit THEN #GP(0); FI;
    tempEIP ← DEST(offset);
    IF OperandSize=16
         THEN tempEIP ← tempEIP AND 0000FFFFH;
    FI;
    IF tempEIP not in code segment limit THEN #GP(0); FI;
    CS ← DEST(SegmentSelector); (* segment descriptor information also loaded *)
    CS(RPL) ← CPL
    EIP ← tempEIP;
END;


CALL-GATE:
    IF call gate DPL < CPL
         OR call gate DPL < call gate segment-selector RPL
             THEN #GP(call gate selector); FI;
    IF call gate not present THEN #NP(call gate selector); FI;
    IF call gate code-segment selector is null THEN #GP(0); FI;
    IF call gate code-segment selector index is outside descriptor table limits
         THEN #GP(code segment selector); FI;
    Read code segment descriptor;
    IF code-segment segment descriptor does not indicate a code segment
         OR code-segment segment descriptor is conforming and DPL > CPL
         OR code-segment segment descriptor is non-conforming and DPL ≠ CPL
             THEN #GP(code segment selector); FI;
    IF code segment is not present THEN #NP(code-segment selector); FI;
    IF instruction pointer is not within code-segment limit THEN #GP(0); FI;
    tempEIP ← DEST(offset);
```

```
    IF GateSize=16
        THEN tempEIP ← tempEIP AND 0000FFFFH;
    FI;
    IF tempEIP not in code segment limit THEN #GP(0); FI;
    CS ← DEST(SegmentSelector); (* segment descriptor information also loaded *)
    CS(RPL) ← CPL
    EIP ← tempEIP;
END;


TASK-GATE:
    IF task gate DPL < CPL
        OR task gate DPL < task gate segment-selector RPL
            THEN #GP(task gate selector); FI;
    IF task gate not present THEN #NP(gate selector); FI;
    Read the TSS segment selector in the task-gate descriptor;
    IF TSS segment selector local/global bit is set to local
        OR index not within GDT limits
        OR TSS descriptor specifies that the TSS is busy
            THEN #GP(TSS selector); FI;
    IF TSS not present THEN #NP(TSS selector); FI;
    SWITCH-TASKS to TSS;
    IF EIP not within code segment limit THEN #GP(0); FI;
END;


TASK-STATE-SEGMENT:
    IF TSS DPL < CPL
        OR TSS DPL < TSS segment-selector RPL
        OR TSS descriptor indicates TSS not available
            THEN #GP(TSS selector); FI;
    IF TSS is not present THEN #NP(TSS selector); FI;
    SWITCH-TASKS to TSS
    IF EIP not within code segment limit THEN #GP(0); FI;
END;
```

Flags Affected

All flags are affected if a task switch occurs; no flags are affected if a task switch does not occur.

Protected Mode Exceptions

#GP(0)   If offset in target operand, call gate, or TSS is beyond the code segment limits.

                If the segment selector in the destination operand, call gate, task gate, or TSS is null.

                If a memory operand effective address is outside the CS, DS, ES, FS, or GS segment limit.

If the DS, ES, FS, or GS register is used to access memory and it contains a null segment selector.

#GP(selector)   If segment selector index is outside descriptor table limits.

If the segment descriptor pointed to by the segment selector in the destination operand is not for a conforming-code segment, nonconforming-code segment, call gate, task gate, or task state segment.

If the DPL for a nonconforming-code segment is not equal to the CPL

(When not using a call gate.) If the RPL for the segment's segment selector is greater than the CPL.

If the DPL for a conforming-code segment is greater than the CPL.

If the DPL from a call-gate, task-gate, or TSS segment descriptor is less than the CPL or than the RPL of the call-gate, task-gate, or TSS's segment selector.

If the segment descriptor for selector in a call gate does not indicate it is a code segment.

If the segment descriptor for the segment selector in a task gate does not indicate available TSS.

If the segment selector for a TSS has its local/global bit set for local.

If a TSS segment descriptor specifies that the TSS is busy or not available.

#SS(0)   If a memory operand effective address is outside the SS segment limit.

#NP (selector)   If the code segment being accessed is not present.

If call gate, task gate, or TSS not present.

#PF(fault-code) If a page fault occurs.

#AC(0)   If alignment checking is enabled and an unaligned memory reference is made while the current privilege level is 3. (Only occurs when fetching target from memory.)

Real Address Mode Exceptions

#GP   If a memory operand effective address is outside the CS, DS, ES, FS, or GS segment limit.

If a memory operand effective address is outside the CS, DS, ES, FS, or GS segment limit.

#SS   If a memory operand effective address is outside the SS segment limit.

Virtual 8086 Mode Exceptions

#GP(0)	If the target operand is beyond the code segment limits.
	If a memory operand effective address is outside the CS, DS, ES, FS, or GS segment limit.
#SS(0)	If a memory operand effective address is outside the SS segment limit.
#PF(fault-code)	If a page fault occurs.
#AC(0)	If alignment checking is enabled and an unaligned memory reference is made. (Only occurs when fetching target from memory.)

LAHF—Load Status Flags into AH Register

Opcode	Instruction	Description
9F	LAHF	Load: AH = EFLAGS(SF:ZF:0:AF:0:PF:1:CF)

Description

Moves the low byte of the EFLAGS register (which includes status flags SF, ZF, AF, PF, and CF) to the AH register. Reserved bits 1, 3, and 5 of the EFLAGS register are set in the AH register as shown in the "Operation" below.

Operation

AH ← EFLAGS(SF:ZF:0:AF:0:PF:1:CF);

Flags Affected

None (that is, the state of the flags in the EFLAGS register are not affected).

Exceptions (All Operating Modes)

None.

LAR—Load Access Rights Byte

Opcode	Instruction	Description
0F 02 /r	LAR r16,r/m16	r16 ← r/m16 masked by FF00H
0F 02 /r	LAR r32,r/m32	r32 ← r/m32 masked by 00FxFF00H

Description

Loads the access rights from the segment descriptor specified by the second operand (source operand) into the first operand (destination operand) and sets the ZF flag in the EFLAGS register. The source operand (which can be a register or a memory location) contains the segment selector for the segment descriptor being accessed. The destination operand is a general-purpose register.

The processor performs access checks as part of the loading process. Once loaded in the destination register, software can preform additional checks on the access rights information.

When the operand size is 32 bits, the access rights for a segment descriptor comprise the type and DPL fields and the S, P, AVL, D/B, and G flags, all of which are located in the second doubleword (bytes 4 through 7) of the segment descriptor. The doubleword is masked by 00FXFF00H before it is loaded into the destination operand. When the operand size is 16 bits, the access rights comprise the type and DPL fields. Here, the two lower-order bytes of the doubleword are masked by FF00H before being loaded into the destination operand.

This instruction performs the following checks before it loads the access rights in the destination register:

- Checks that the segment selector is not null.

- Checks that the segment selector points to a descriptor that is within the limits of the GDT or LDT being accessed

- Checks that the descriptor type is valid for this instruction. All code and data segment descriptors are valid for (can be accessed with) the LAR instruction. The valid system segment and gate descriptor types are given in the following table.

- If the segment is not a conforming code segment, it checks that the specified segment descriptor is visible at the CPL (that is, if the CPL and the RPL of the segment selector are less than or equal to the DPL of the segment selector).

If the segment descriptor cannot be accessed or is an invalid type for the instruction, the ZF flag is cleared and no access rights are loaded in the destination operand.

The LAR instruction can only be executed in protected mode.

Type	Name	Valid
0	Reserved	No
1	Available 16-bit TSS	Yes
2	LDT	Yes
3	Busy 16-bit TSS	Yes
4	16-bit call gate	Yes
5	16-bit/32-bit task gate	Yes
6	16-bit trap gate	No
7	16-bit interrupt gate	No
8	Reserved	No
9	Available 32-bit TSS	Yes
A	Reserved	No
B	Busy 32-bit TSS	Yes
C	32-bit call gate	Yes
D	Reserved	No
E	32-bit trap gate	No
F	32-bit interrupt gate	No

Operation

```
IF SRC(Offset) > descriptor table limit THEN ZF ← 0; FI;
Read segment descriptor;
IF SegmentDescriptor(Type) ≠ conforming code segment
    AND (CPL > DPL) OR (RPL > DPL)
    OR Segment type is not valid for instruction
        THEN
            ZF ← 0
        ELSE
        IF OperandSize = 32
            THEN
                DEST ← [SRC] AND 00FxFF00H;
            ELSE (*OperandSize = 16*)
                DEST ← [SRC] AND FF00H;
        FI;
FI;
```

Flags Affected

The ZF flag is set to 1 if the access rights are loaded successfully; otherwise, it is cleared to 0.

Protected Mode Exceptions

#GP(0)	If a memory operand effective address is outside the CS, DS, ES, FS, or GS segment limit.
	If the DS, ES, FS, or GS register is used to access memory and it contains a null segment selector.
#SS(0)	If a memory operand effective address is outside the SS segment limit.
#PF(fault-code)	If a page fault occurs.
#AC(0)	If alignment checking is enabled and an unaligned memory reference is made while the current privilege level is 3. (Only occurs when fetching target from memory.)

Real Address Mode Exceptions

#UD	The LAR instruction is not recognized in real address mode.

Virtual 8086 Mode Exceptions

#UD	The LAR instruction cannot be executed in virtual 8086 mode.

LDS/LES/LFS/LGS/LSS—Load Far Pointer

Opcode	Instruction	Description
C5 /r	LDS r16,m16:16	Load DS:r16 with far pointer from memory
C5 /r	LDS r32,m16:32	Load DS:r32 with far pointer from memory
0F B2 /r	LSS r16,m16:16	Load SS:r16 with far pointer from memory
0F B2 /r	LSS r32,m16:32	Load SS:r32 with far pointer from memory
C4 /r	LES r16,m16:16	Load ES:r16 with far pointer from memory
C4 /r	LES r32,m16:32	Load ES:r32 with far pointer from memory
0F B4 /r	LFS r16,m16:16	Load FS:r16 with far pointer from memory
0F B4 /r	LFS r32,m16:32	Load FS:r32 with far pointer from memory
0F B5 /r	LGS r16,m16:16	Load GS:r16 with far pointer from memory
0F B5 /r	LGS r32,m16:32	Load GS:r32 with far pointer from memory

Description

Load a far pointer (segment selector and offset) from the second operand (source operand) into a segment register and the first operand (destination operand). The source operand specifies a 48-bit or a 32-bit pointer in memory depending on the current setting of the operand-size attribute (32 bits or 16 bits, respectively). The instruction opcode and the destination operand specify a segment register/general-purpose register pair. The 16-bit segment selector from the source operand is loaded into the segment register implied with the opcode (DS, SS, ES, FS, or GS). The 32-bit or 16-bit offset is loaded into the register specified with the destination operand.

If one of these instructions is executed in protected mode, additional information from the segment descriptor pointed to by the segment selector in the source operand is loaded in the hidden part of the selected segment register.

Also in protected mode, a null selector (values 0000 through 0003) can be loaded into DS, ES, FS, or GS registers without causing a protection exception. (Any subsequent reference to a segment whose corresponding segment register is loaded with a null selector, causes a general-protection exception (#GP) and no memory reference to the segment occurs.)

Operation

```
IF ProtectedMode
    THEN IF SS is loaded
        THEN IF SegementSelector = null
            THEN #GP(0);
        FI;
        ELSE IF Segment selector index is not within descriptor table limits
        OR Segment selector RPL ≠ CPL
        OR Access rights indicate nonwritable data segment
        OR DPL ≠ CPL
            THEN #GP(selector);
        FI;
```

```
        ELSE IF Segment marked not present
            THEN #SS(selector);
        FI;
        SS ← SegmentSelector(SRC);
        SS ← SegmentDescriptor([SRC]);
    ELSE IF DS, ES, FS, or GS is loaded with non-null segment selector
        THEN IF Segment selector index is not within descriptor table limits
        OR Access rights indicate segment neither data nor readable code segment
        OR (Segment is data or nonconforming-code segment
            AND both RPL and CPL > DPL)
            THEN #GP(selector);
        FI;
        ELSE IF Segment marked not present
            THEN #NP(selector);
        FI;
        SegmentRegister ← SegmentSelector(SRC) AND RPL;
        SegmentRegister ← SegmentDescriptor([SRC]);
    ELSE IF DS, ES, FS or GS is loaded with a null selector:
        SegmentRegister ← NullSelector;
        SegmentRegister(DescriptorValidBit) ← 0; (*hidden flag; not accessible by software*)
    FI;
FI;
IF (Real-Address or Virtual 8086 Mode)
    THEN
        SS ← SegmentSelector(SRC);
FI;
DEST ← Offset(SRC);
```

Flags Affected

None.

Protected Mode Exceptions

#UD   If source operand is not a memory location.

#GP(0)   If a null selector is loaded into the SS register.

               If a memory operand effective address is outside the CS, DS, ES, FS, or
               GS segment limit.

               If the DS, ES, FS, or GS register is used to access memory and it contains
               a null segment selector.

#GP(selector) If the SS register is being loaded and any of the following is true: the
               segment selector index is not within the descriptor table limits, the
               segment selector RPL is not equal to CPL, the segment is a nonwritable
               data segment, or DPL is not equal to CPL.

If the DS, ES, FS, or GS register is being loaded with a non-null segment selector and any of the following is true: the segment selector index is not within descriptor table limits, the segment is neither a data nor a readable code segment, or the segment is a data or nonconforming-code segment and both RPL and CPL are greater than DPL.

#SS(0)	If a memory operand effective address is outside the SS segment limit.
#SS(selector)	If the SS register is being loaded and the segment is marked not present.
#NP(selector)	If DS, ES, FS, or GS register is being loaded with a non-null segment selector and the segment is marked not present.
#PF(fault-code)	If a page fault occurs.
#AC(0)	If alignment checking is enabled and an unaligned memory reference is made while the current privilege level is 3.

Real Address Mode Exceptions

#GP	If a memory operand effective address is outside the CS, DS, ES, FS, or GS segment limit.
#SS	If a memory operand effective address is outside the SS segment limit.
#UD	If source operand is not a memory location.

Virtual 8086 Mode Exceptions

#UD	If source operand is not a memory location.
#GP(0)	If a memory operand effective address is outside the CS, DS, ES, FS, or GS segment limit.
#SS(0)	If a memory operand effective address is outside the SS segment limit.
#PF(fault-code)	If a page fault occurs.
#AC(0)	If alignment checking is enabled and an unaligned memory reference is made.

LEA—Load Effective Address

Opcode	Instruction	Description
8D /r	LEA r16,m	Store effective address for m in register r16
8D /r	LEA r32,m	Store effective address for m in register r32

Description

Computes the effective address of the second operand (the source operand) and stores it in the first operand (destination operand). The source operand is a memory address (offset part) specified with one of the processors addressing modes; the destination operand is a general-purpose register. The address-size and operand-size attributes affect the action performed by this instruction, as shown in the following table. The operand-size attribute of the instruction is determined by the chosen register; the address-size attribute is determined by the attribute of the code segment.

Operand Size	Address Size	Action Performed
16	16	16-bit effective address is calculated and stored in requested 16-bit register destination.
16	32	32-bit effective address is calculated. The lower 16 bits of the address are stored in the requested 16-bit register destination.
32	16	16-bit effective address is calculated. The 16-bit address is zero-extended and stored in the requested 32-bit register destination.
32	32	32-bit effective address is calculated and stored in the requested 32-bit register destination.

Different assemblers may use different algorithms based on the size attribute and symbolic reference of the source operand.

Operation

```
IF OperandSize = 16 AND AddressSize = 16
    THEN
        DEST ← EffectiveAddress(SRC); (* 16-bit address *)
    ELSE IF OperandSize = 16 AND AddressSize = 32
        THEN
            temp ← EffectiveAddress(SRC); (* 32-bit address *)
            DEST ← temp[0..15]; (* 16-bit address *)
    ELSE IF OperandSize = 32 AND AddressSize = 16
        THEN
            temp ← EffectiveAddress(SRC); (* 16-bit address *)
            DEST ← ZeroExtend(temp); (* 32-bit address *)
    ELSE IF OperandSize = 32 AND AddressSize = 32
        THEN
            DEST ← EffectiveAddress(SRC); (* 32-bit address *)
    FI;
FI;
```

Flags Affected

None.

Protected Mode Exceptions

#UD   If source operand is not a memory location.

Real Address Mode Exceptions

#UD   If source operand is not a memory location.

Virtual 8086 Mode Exceptions

#UD   If source operand is not a memory location.

LEAVE—High Level Procedure Exit

Opcode	Instruction	Description
C9	LEAVE	Set SP to BP, then pop BP
C9	LEAVE	Set ESP to EBP, then pop EBP

Description

Executes a return from a procedure or group of nested procedures established by an earlier ENTER instruction. The instruction copies the frame pointer (in the EBP register) into the stack pointer register (ESP), releasing the stack space used by a procedure for its local variables. The old frame pointer (the frame pointer for the calling procedure that issued the ENTER instruction) is then popped from the stack into the EBP register, restoring the calling procedure's frame.

A RET instruction is commonly executed following a LEAVE instruction to return program control to the calling procedure and remove any arguments pushed onto the stack by the procedure being returned from.

See Section 4.5., "Procedure Calls for Block-Structured Languages" for detailed information on the use of the ENTER and LEAVE instructions.

Operation

```
IF StackAddressSize = 32
    THEN
        ESP ← EBP;
    ELSE (* StackAddressSize = 16*)
        SP ← BP;
FI;
IF OperandSize = 32
    THEN
        EBP ← Pop();
    ELSE (* OperandSize = 16*)
        BP ← Pop();
FI;
```

Flags Affected

None.

Protected Mode Exceptions

#SS(0)   If the EBP register points to a location that is not within the limits of the current stack segment.

Real Address Mode Exceptions

#GP   If the EBP register points to a location outside of the effective address
               space from 0 to 0FFFFH.

Virtual 8086 Mode Exceptions

#GP(0)   If the EBP register points to a location outside of the effective address
               space from 0 to 0FFFFH.

LES—Load Full Pointer

See entry for LDS/LES/LFS/LGS/LSS.

LFS—Load Full Pointer

See entry for LDS/LES/LFS/LGS/LSS.

LGDT/LIDT—Load Global/Interrupt Descriptor Table Register

Opcode	Instruction	Description
0F 01 /2	LGDT *m16&32*	Load *m* into GDTR
0F 01 /3	LIDT *m16&32*	Load *m* into IDTR

Description

Loads the values in the source operand into the global descriptor table register (GDTR) or the interrupt descriptor table register (IDTR). The source operand is a pointer to 6 bytes of data in memory that contains the base address (a linear address) and the limit (size of table in bytes) of the global descriptor table (GDT) or the interrupt descriptor table (IDT). If operand-size attribute is 32 bits, a 16-bit limit (lower 2 bytes of the 6-byte data operand) and a 32-bit base address (upper 4 bytes of the data operand) are loaded into the register. If the operand-size attribute is 16 bits, a 16-bit limit (lower 2 bytes) and a 24-bit base address (third, fourth, and fifth byte) are loaded. Here, the high-order byte of the operand is not used and the high-order byte of the base address in the GDTR or IDTR is filled with zeros.

The LGDT and LIDT instructions are used only in operating-system software; they are not used in application programs. They are the only instructions that directly load a linear address (that is, not a segment-relative address) and a limit in protected mode. They are commonly executed in real-address mode to allow processor initialization prior to switching to protected mode.

See Chapter 11, "SGDT/SIDT—Store Global/Interrupt Descriptor Table Register" for information on storing the contents of the GDTR and IDTR.

Operation

```
IF instruction is LIDT
    THEN
        IF OperandSize = 16
            THEN
                IDTR(Limit) ← SRC[0:15];
                IDTR(Base) ← SRC[16:47] AND 00FFFFFFH;
            ELSE (* 32-bit Operand Size *)
                IDTR(Limit) ← SRC[0:15];
                IDTR(Base) ← SRC[16:47];
        FI;
    ELSE (* instruction is LGDT *)
        IF OperandSize = 16
            THEN
                GDTR(Limit) ← SRC[0:15];
                GDTR(Base) ← SRC[16:47] AND 00FFFFFFH;
            ELSE (* 32-bit Operand Size *)
                GDTR(Limit) ← SRC[0:15];
                GDTR(Base) ← SRC[16:47];
        FI;
```

FI;

Flags Affected

None.

Protected Mode Exceptions

#UD	If source operand is not a memory location.
#GP(0)	If the current privilege level is not 0.
	If a memory operand effective address is outside the CS, DS, ES, FS, or GS segment limit.
	If the DS, ES, FS, or GS register is used to access memory and it contains a null segment selector.
#SS(0)	If a memory operand effective address is outside the SS segment limit.
#PF(fault-code)	If a page fault occurs.

Real Address Mode Exceptions

#UD	If source operand is not a memory location.
#GP	If a memory operand effective address is outside the CS, DS, ES, FS, or GS segment limit.
#SS	If a memory operand effective address is outside the SS segment limit.

Virtual 8086 Mode Exceptions

#UD	If source operand is not a memory location.
#GP(0)	If a memory operand effective address is outside the CS, DS, ES, FS, or GS segment limit.
#SS(0)	If a memory operand effective address is outside the SS segment limit.
#PF(fault-code)	If a page fault occurs.

LGS—Load Full Pointer

See entry for LDS/LES/LFS/LGS/LSS.

LLDT—Load Local Descriptor Table Register

Opcode	Instruction	Description
0F 00 /2	LLDT *r/m16*	Load segment selector *r/m16* into LDTR

Description

Loads the source operand into the segment selector field of the local descriptor table register (LDTR). The source operand (a general-purpose register or a memory location) contains a segment selector that points to a local descriptor table (LDT). After the segment selector is loaded in the LDTR, the processor uses to segment selector to locate the segment descriptor for the LDT in the global descriptor table (GDT). It then loads the segment limit and base address for the LDT from the segment descriptor into the LDTR. The segment registers DS, ES, SS, FS, GS, and CS are not affected by this instruction, nor is the LDTR field in the task state segment (TSS) for the current task.

If the source operand is 0, the LDTR is marked invalid and all references to descriptors in the LDT (except by the LAR, VERR, VERW or LSL instructions) cause a general protection exception (#GP).

The operand-size attribute has no effect on this instruction.

The LLDT instruction is provided for use in operating-system software; it should not be used in application programs. Also, this instruction can only be executed in protected mode.

Operation

IF SRC(Offset) > descriptor table limit THEN #GP(segment selector); FI;
Read segment descriptor;
IF SegmentDescriptor(Type) ≠ LDT THEN #GP(segment selector); FI;
IF segment descriptor is not present THEN #NP(segment selector);
LDTR(SegmentSelector) ← SRC;
LDTR(SegmentDescriptor) ← GDTSegmentDescriptor;

Flags Affected

None.

Protected Mode Exceptions

#GP(0)	If the current privilege level is not 0.
	If a memory operand effective address is outside the CS, DS, ES, FS, or GS segment limit.
	If the DS, ES, FS, or GS register contains a null segment selector.
#GP(selector)	If the selector operand does not point into the Global Descriptor Table or if the entry in the GDT is not a Local Descriptor Table.
	Segment selector is beyond GDT limit.
#SS(0)	If a memory operand effective address is outside the SS segment limit.
#NP(selector)	If the LDT descriptor is not present.
#PF(fault-code)	If a page fault occurs.

Real Address Mode Exceptions

#UD	The LLDT instruction is not recognized in real address mode.

Virtual 8086 Mode Exceptions

#UD	The LLDT instruction is recognized in virtual 8086 mode.

LIDT—Load Interrupt Descriptor Table Register

See entry for LGDT/LIDT—Load Global Descriptor Table Register/Load Interrupt Descriptor Table Register.

LMSW—Load Machine Status Word

Opcode	Instruction	Description
0F 01 /6	LMSW *r/m16*	Loads *r/m16* in machine status word of CR0

Description

Loads the source operand into the machine status word, bits 0 through 15 of register CR0. The source operand can be a 16-bit general-purpose register or a memory location. Only the low-order 4 bits of the source operand (which contains the PE, MP, EM, and TS flags) are loaded into CR0. The PG, CD, NW, AM, WP, NE, and ET flags of CR0 are not affected. The operand-size attribute has no effect on this instruction.

If the PE flag of the source operand (bit 0) is set to 1, the instruction causes the processor to switch to protected mode. The PE flag in the CR0 register is a sticky bit. Once set to 1, the LMSW instruction cannot be used clear this flag and force a switch back to real address mode.

The LMSW instruction is provided for use in operating-system software; it should not be used in application programs. In protected or virtual 8086 mode, it can only be executed at CPL 0.

This instruction is provided for compatibility with the Intel 286 processor; programs and procedures intended to run on the Pentium Pro, Pentium, Intel486, and Intel386 processors should use the MOV (control registers) instruction to load the machine status word.

This instruction is a serializing instruction.

Operation

CR0[0:3] ← SRC[0:3];

Flags Affected

None.

Protected Mode Exceptions

#GP(0)	If the current privilege level is not 0.
	If a memory operand effective address is outside the CS, DS, ES, FS, or GS segment limit.
	If the DS, ES, FS, or GS register is used to access memory and it contains a null segment selector.
#SS(0)	If a memory operand effective address is outside the SS segment limit.
#PF(fault-code)	If a page fault occurs.

Real Address Mode Exceptions

#GP   If a memory operand effective address is outside the CS, DS, ES, FS, or
                 GS segment limit.

Virtual 8086 Mode Exceptions

#GP(0)   If the current privilege level is not 0.

                 If a memory operand effective address is outside the CS, DS, ES, FS, or
                 GS segment limit.

#SS(0)   If a memory operand effective address is outside the SS segment limit.

#PF(fault-code) If a page fault occurs.

LOCK—Assert LOCK# Signal Prefix

Opcode	Instruction	Description
F0	LOCK	Asserts LOCK# signal for duration of the accompanying instruction

Description

Causes the processor's LOCK# signal to be asserted during execution of the accompanying instruction (turns the instruction into an atomic instruction). In a multiprocessor environment, the LOCK# signal insures that the processor has exclusive use of any shared memory while the signal is asserted.

The LOCK prefix can be prepended only to the following instructions and to those forms of the instructions that use a memory operand: ADD, ADC, AND, BTC, BTR, BTS, CMPXCHG, DEC, INC, NEG, NOT, OR, SBB, SUB, XOR, XADD, and XCHG. An undefined opcode exception will be generated if the LOCK prefix is used with any other instruction. The XCHG instruction always asserts the LOCK# signal regardless of the presence or absence of the LOCK prefix.

The LOCK prefix is typically used with the BTS instruction to perform a read-modify-write operation on a memory location in shared memory environment.

The integrity of the LOCK prefix is not affected by the alignment of the memory field. Memory locking is observed for arbitrarily misaligned fields.

Operation

AssertLOCK#(DurationOfAccompaningInstruction)

Flags Affected

None.

Protected Mode Exceptions

#UD   If the LOCK prefix is used with an instruction not listed in the "Description" section above. Other exceptions can be generated by the instruction that the LOCK prefix is being applied to.

Real Address Mode Exceptions

#UD   If the LOCK prefix is used with an instruction not listed in the "Description" section above. Other exceptions can be generated by the instruction that the LOCK prefix is being applied to.

Virtual 8086 Mode Exceptions

#UD   If the LOCK prefix is used with an instruction not listed in the "Description" section above. Other exceptions can be generated by the instruction that the LOCK prefix is being applied to.

LODS/LODSB/LODSW/LODSD—Load String Operand

Opcode	Instruction	Description
AC	LODS DS:(E)SI	Load byte at address DS:(E)SI into AL
AD	LODS DS:SI	Load word at address DS:SI into AX
AD	LODS DS:ESI	Load doubleword at address DS:ESI into EAX
AC	LODSB	Load byte at address DS:(E)SI into AL
AD	LODSW	Load word at address DS:SI into AX
AD	LODSD	Load doubleword at address DS:ESI into EAX

Description

Load a byte, word, or doubleword from the source operand into the AL, AX, or EAX register, respectively. The source operand is a memory location at the address DS:ESI. (When the operand-size attribute is 16, the SI register is used as the source-index register.) The DS segment may be overridden with a segment override prefix.

The LODSB, LODSW, and LODSD mnemonics are synonyms of the byte, word, and double-word versions of the LODS instructions. (For the LODS instruction, "DS:ESI" must be explicitly specified in the instruction.)

After the byte, word, or doubleword is transfer from the memory location into the AL, AX, or EAX register, the ESI register is incremented or decremented automatically according to the setting of the DF flag in the EFLAGS register. (If the DF flag is 0, the ESI register is incremented; if the DF flag is 1, the ESI register is decremented.) The ESI register is incremented or decremented by 1 for byte operations, by 2 for word operations, or by 4 for doubleword operations.

The LODS, LODSB, LODSW, and LODSD instructions can be preceded by the REP prefix for block loads of ECX bytes, words, or doublewords. More often, however, these instructions are used within a LOOP construct, because further processing of the data moved into the register is usually necessary before the next transfer can be made. See Chapter 11, "REP/REPE/REPZ/REPNE /REPNZ—Repeat String Operation Prefix" for a description of the REP prefix.

Operation

```
IF (byte load)
    THEN
        AL ← SRC; (* byte load *)
            THEN IF DF = 0
                THEN (E)SI ← 1;
                ELSE (E)SI ← –1;
        FI;
    ELSE IF (word load)
        THEN
            AX ← SRC; (* word load *)
```

```
            THEN IF DF = 0
                THEN SI ← 2;
                ELSE SI ← –2;
            FI;
        ELSE (* doubleword transfer *)
            EAX ← SRC; (* doubleword load *)
                THEN IF DF = 0
                    THEN ESI ← 4;
                    ELSE ESI ← –4;
                FI;
        FI;
    FI;
FI;
```

Flags Affected

None.

Protected Mode Exceptions

#GP(0)   If a memory operand effective address is outside the CS, DS, ES, FS, or GS segment limit.

                    If the DS, ES, FS, or GS register contains a null segment selector.

#SS(0)   If a memory operand effective address is outside the SS segment limit.

#PF(fault-code)   If a page fault occurs.

#AC(0)   If alignment checking is enabled and an unaligned memory reference is made while the current privilege level is 3.

Real Address Mode Exceptions

#GP   If a memory operand effective address is outside the CS, DS, ES, FS, or GS segment limit.

#SS   If a memory operand effective address is outside the SS segment limit.

Virtual 8086 Mode Exceptions

#GP(0)   If a memory operand effective address is outside the CS, DS, ES, FS, or GS segment limit.

#SS(0)   If a memory operand effective address is outside the SS segment limit.

#PF(fault-code)   If a page fault occurs.

#AC(0)   If alignment checking is enabled and an unaligned memory reference is made.

LOOP/LOOP*cc*—Loop According to ECX Counter

Opcode	Instruction	Description
E2 *cb*	LOOP *rel8*	Decrement count; jump short if count ≠ 0
E1 *cb*	LOOPE *rel8*	Decrement count; jump short if count ≠ 0 and ZF=1
E1 *cb*	LOOPZ *rel8*	Decrement count; jump short if count ≠ 0 and ZF=1
E0 *cb*	LOOPNE *rel8*	Decrement count; jump short if count ≠ 0 and ZF=0
E0 *cb*	LOOPNZ *rel8*	Decrement count; jump short if count ≠ 0 and ZF=0

Description

Performs a loop operation using the ECX or CX register as a counter. Each time the LOOP instruction is executed, the count register is decremented, then checked for 0. If the count is 0, the loop is terminated and program execution continues with the instruction following the LOOP instruction. If the count is not zero, a near jump is performed to the destination (target) operand, which is presumably the instruction at the beginning of the loop. If the address-size attribute is 32 bits, the ECX register is used as the count register; otherwise the CX register is used.

The target instruction is specified with a relative offset (a signed offset relative to the current value of the instruction pointer in the EIP register). This offset is generally specified as a label in assembly code, but at the machine code level, it is encoded as a signed, 8-bit immediate value, which is added to the instruction pointer. Offsets of −128 to +127 are allowed with this instruction.

Some forms of the loop instruction (LOOP*cc*) also accept the ZF flag as a condition for terminating the loop before the count reaches zero. With these forms of the instruction, a condition code (*cc*) is associated with each instruction to indicate the condition being tested for. Here, the LOOP*cc* instruction itself does not affect the state of the ZF flag; the ZF flag is changed by other instructions in the loop.

All branches are converted to code fetches of one or two cache lines, regardless of jump address or cacheability.

Operation

```
IF AddressSize = 32
    THEN
        Count is ECX;
    ELSE (* AddressSize = 16 *)
        Count is CX;
FI;
Count ← Count − 1;

IF instruction in not LOOP
    THEN
        IF (instruction = LOOPE) OR (instruction = LOOPZ)
            THEN
```

```
                    IF (ZF =1) AND (Count ≠ 0)
                        THEN BranchCond ← 1;
                        ELSE BranchCond ← 0;
                    FI;
            FI;
            IF (instruction = LOOPNE) OR (instruction = LOOPNZ)
                    THEN
                        IF (ZF =0 ) AND (Count ≠ 0)
                            THEN BranchCond ← 1;
                            ELSE BranchCond ← 0;
                        FI;
            FI;
        ELSE (* instruction = LOOP *)
            IF (Count ≠ 0)
                THEN BranchCond ← 1;
                ELSE BranchCond ← 0;
            FI;
FI;
IF BranchCond = 1
    THEN
            EIP ← EIP + SignExtend(DEST);
            IF OperandSize = 16
                THEN
                        EIP ← EIP AND 0000FFFFH;
            FI;
    ELSE
            Terminate loop and continue program execution at EIP;
FI;
```

Flags Affected

None.

Protected Mode Exceptions

#GP(0)   If the offset jumped to is beyond the limits of the code segment.

Real Address Mode Exceptions

None.

Virtual 8086 Mode Exceptions

None.

LSL—Load Segment Limit

Opcode	Instruction	Description
0F 03 /r	LSL r16,r/m16	Load: r16 ← segment limit, selector r/m16
0F 03 /r	LSL r32,r/m32	Load: r32 ← segment limit, selector r/m32)

Description

Loads the unscrambled segment limit from the segment descriptor specified with the second operand (source operand) into the first operand (destination operand) and sets the ZF flag in the EFLAGS register. The source operand (which can be a register or a memory location) contains the segment selector for the segment descriptor being accessed. The destination operand is a general-purpose register.

The processor performs access checks as part of the loading process. Once loaded in the destination register, software can compare the segment limit with the offset of a pointer.

The segment limit is a 20-bit value contained in bytes 0 and 1 and in the first 4 bits of byte 6 of the segment descriptor. If the descriptor has a byte granular segment limit (the granularity flag is set to 0), the destination operand is loaded with a byte granular value (byte limit). If the descriptor has a page granular segment limit (the granularity flag is set to 1), the LSL instruction will translate the page granular limit (page limit) into a byte limit before loading it into the destination operand. The translation is performed by shifting the 20-bit "raw" limit left 12 bits and filling the low-order 12 bits with 1s.

When the operand size is 32 bits, the 32-bit byte limit is stored in the destination operand. When the operand size is 16 bits, a valid 32-bit limit is computed; however, the upper 16 bits are truncated and only the low-order 16 bits are loaded into the destination operand.

This instruction performs the following checks before it loads the segment limit into the destination register:

- Checks that the segment selector is not null.

- Checks that the segment selector points to a descriptor that is within the limits of the GDT or LDT being accessed

- Checks that the descriptor type is valid for this instruction. All code and data segment descriptors are valid for (can be accessed with) the LSL instruction. The valid special segment and gate descriptor types are given in the following table.

- If the segment is not a conforming code segment, the instruction checks that the specified segment descriptor is visible at the CPL (that is, if the CPL and the RPL of the segment selector are less than or equal to the DPL of the segment selector).

If the segment descriptor cannot be accessed or is an invalid type for the instruction, the ZF flag is cleared and no value is loaded in the destination operand.

Type	Name	Valid
0	Reserved	No
1	Available 16-bit TSS	Yes
2	LDT	Yes
3	Busy 16-bit TSS	Yes
4	16-bit call gate	No
5	16-bit/32-bit task gate	No
6	16-bit trap gate	No
7	16-bit interrupt gate	No
8	Reserved	No
9	Available 32-bit TSS	Yes
A	Reserved	No
B	Busy 32-bit TSS	Yes
C	32-bit call gate	No
D	Reserved	No
E	32-bit trap gate	No
F	32-bit interrupt gate	No

Operation

```
IF SRC(Offset) > descriptor table limit
    THEN ZF ← 0; FI;
Read segment descriptor;
IF SegmentDescriptor(Type) ≠ conforming code segment
    AND (CPL > DPL) OR (RPL > DPL)
    OR Segment type is not valid for instruction
        THEN
            ZF ← 0
        ELSE
            temp ← SegmentLimit([SRC]);
            IF (G = 1)
                THEN
                    temp ← ShiftLeft(12, temp) OR 00000FFFH;
            FI;
            IF OperandSize = 32
                THEN
                    DEST ← temp;
                ELSE (*OperandSize = 16*)
                    DEST ← temp AND FFFFH;
            FI;
FI;
```

Flags Affected

The ZF flag is set to 1 if the segment limit is loaded successfully; otherwise, it is cleared to 0.

Protected Mode Exceptions

#GP(0)	If a memory operand effective address is outside the CS, DS, ES, FS, or GS segment limit.
	If the DS, ES, FS, or GS register is used to access memory and it contains a null segment selector.
#SS(0)	If a memory operand effective address is outside the SS segment limit.
#PF(fault-code)	If a page fault occurs.
#AC(0)	If alignment checking is enabled and an unaligned memory reference is made while the current privilege level is 3.

Real Address Mode Exceptions

#UD	The LSL instruction is not recognized in real address mode.

Virtual 8086 Mode Exceptions

#UD	The LSL instruction is not recognized in virtual 8086 mode.

LSS—Load Full Pointer

See entry for LDS/LES/LFS/LGS/LSS.

int̲e̲l̲

LTR—Load Task Register

Opcode	Instruction	Description
0F 00 /3	LTR r/m16	Load r/m16 into TR

Description

Loads the source operand into the segment selector field of the task register. The source operand (a general-purpose register or a memory location) contains a segment selector that points to a task state segment (TSS). After the segment selector is loaded in the task register, the processor uses to segment selector to locate the segment descriptor for the TSS in the global descriptor table (GDT). It then loads the segment limit and base address for the TSS from the segment descriptor into the task register. The task pointed to by the task register is marked busy, but a switch to the task does not occur.

The LTR instruction is provided for use in operating-system software; it should not be used in application programs. It can only be executed in protected mode when the CPL is 0. It is commonly used in initialization code to establish the first task to be executed.

The operand-size attribute has no effect on this instruction.

Operation

```
IF SRC(Offset) > descriptor table limit OR IF SRC(type) ≠ global
    THEN #GP(segment selector);
FI;
Reat segment descriptor;
IF segment descriptor is not for an available TSS THEN #GP(segment selector); FI;
IF segment descriptor is not present THEN #NP(segment selector);
TSSsegmentDescriptor(busy) ← 1;
(* Locked read-modify-write operation on the entire descriptor when setting busy flag *)
TaskRegister(SegmentSelector) ← SRC;
TaskRegister(SegmentDescriptor) ← TSSSegmentDescriptor;
```

Flags Affected

None.

Protected Mode Exceptions

#GP(0)   If the current privilege level is not 0.

                If a memory operand effective address is outside the CS, DS, ES, FS, or GS segment limit.

                If the DS, ES, FS, or GS register is used to access memory and it contains a null segment selector.

#GP(selector)	If the source selector points to a segment that is not a TSS or to one for a task that is already busy.
	If the selector points to LDT or is beyond the GDT limit.
#NP(selector)	If the TSS is marked not present.
#SS(0)	If a memory operand effective address is outside the SS segment limit.
#PF(fault-code)	If a page fault occurs.

Real Address Mode Exceptions

#UD   The LTR instruction is not recognized in real address mode.

Virtual 8086 Mode Exceptions

#UD   The LTR instruction is not recognized in virtual 8086 mode.

MOV—Move

Opcode	Instruction	Description
88 /r	MOV r/m8,r8	Move r8 to r/m8
89 /r	MOV r/m16,r16	Move r16 to r/m16
89 /r	MOV r/m32,r32	Move r32 to r/m32
8A /r	MOV r8,r/m8	Move r/m8 to r8
8B /r	MOV r16,r/m16	Move r/m16 to r16
8B /r	MOV r32,r/m32	Move r/m32 to r32
8C /r	MOV r/m16,Sreg**	Move segment register to r/m16
8E /r	MOV Sreg,r/m16	Move r/m16 to segment register
A0	MOV AL,moffs8*	Move byte at (seg:offset) to AL
A1	MOV AX,moffs16*	Move word at (seg:offset) to AX
A1	MOV EAX,moffs32*	Move doubleword at (seg:offset) to EAX
A2	MOV moffs8*,AL	Move AL to (seg:offset)
A3	MOV moffs16*,AX	Move AX to (seg:offset)
A3	MOV moffs32*,EAX	Move EAX to (seg:offset)
B0+ rb	MOV r8,imm8	Move imm8 to r8
B8+ rw	MOV r16,imm16	Move imm16 to r16
B8+ rd	MOV r32,imm32	Move imm32 to r32
C6 /0	MOV r/m8,imm8	Move imm8 to r/m8
C7 /0	MOV r/m16,imm16	Move imm16 to r/m16
C7 /0	MOV r/m32,imm32	Move imm32 to r/m32

NOTES:

* The moffs8, moffs16, and moffs32 operands specify a simple offset relative to the segment base, where 8, 16, and 32 refer to the size of the data. The address-size attribute of the instruction determines the size of the offset, either 16 or 32 bits.

** In 32-bit mode, the assembler may require the use of the 16-bit operand size prefix (a byte with the value 66H preceding the instruction).

Description

Copies the second operand (source operand) to the first operand (destination operand). The source operand can be an immediate value, general-purpose register, segment register, or memory location; the destination register can be a general-purpose register, segment register, or memory location. Both operands must be the same size, which can be a byte, a word, or a doubleword.

The MOV instruction cannot be used to load the CS register. Attempting to do so results in an invalid opcode exception (#UD). To load the CS register, use the RET instruction.

If the destination operand is a segment register (DS, ES, FS, GS, or SS), the source operand must be a valid segment selector. In protected mode, moving a segment selector into a segment register automatically causes the segment descriptor information associated with that segment selector to be loaded into the hidden (shadow) part of the segment register. While loading this information, the segment selector and segment descriptor information is validated (see the "Operation" algorithm below). The segment descriptor data is obtained from the GDT or LDT entry for the specified segment selector.

A null segment selector (values 0000-0003) can be loaded into the DS, ES, FS, and GS registers without causing a protection exception. However, any subsequent attempt to reference a segment whose corresponding segment register is loaded with a null value causes a general protection exception (#GP) and no memory reference occurs.

Loading the SS register with a MOV instruction inhibits all interrupts until after the execution of the next instruction. This operation allows a stack pointer to be loaded into the ESP register with the next instruction (MOV ESP, *stack-pointer value*) before an interrupt occurs. The LSS instruction offers a more efficient method of loading the SS and ESP registers.

When moving data in 32-bit mode between a segment register and a 32-bit general-purpose register, the Pentium Pro processor does not require the use of a 16-bit operand size prefix; however, some assemblers do require this prefix. The processor assumes that the 16 least-significant bits of the general-purpose register are the destination or source operand. When moving a value from a segment selector to a 32-bit register, the processor fills the two high-order bytes of the register with zeros.

Operation

DEST ← SRC;

Loading a segment register while in protected mode results in special checks and actions, as described in the following listing. These checks are performed on the segment selector and the segment descriptor it points to.

```
IF SS is loaded;
    THEN
        IF segment selector is null
            THEN #GP(0);
        FI;
        IF segment selector index is outside descriptor table limits
            OR segment selector's RPL ≠ CPL
            OR segment is not a writable data segment
            OR DPL ≠ CPL
                THEN #GP(selector);
        FI;
        IF segment not marked present
            THEN #SS(selector);
    ELSE
        SS ← segment selector;
        SS ← segment descriptor;
    FI;
FI;
IF DS, ES, FS or GS is loaded with non-null selector;
THEN
    IF segment selector index is outside descriptor table limits
```

```
            OR segment is not a data or readable code segment
            OR ((segment is a data or nonconforming code segment)
                  AND (both RPL and CPL > DPL))
                       THEN #GP(selector);
            IF segment not marked present
                 THEN #NP(selector);
       ELSE
            SegmentRegister ← segment selector;
            SegmentRegister ← segment descriptor;
       FI;
FI;
IF DS, ES, FS or GS is loaded with a null selector;
    THEN
            SegmentRegister ← segment selector;
            SegmentRegister ← segment descriptor;
FI;
```

Flags Affected

None.

Protected Mode Exceptions

#GP(0)	If attempt is made to load SS register with null segment selector.
	If the destination operand is in a nonwritable segment.
	If a memory operand effective address is outside the CS, DS, ES, FS, or GS segment limit.
	If the DS, ES, FS, or GS register contains a null segment selector.
#GP(selector)	If segment selector index is outside descriptor table limits.
	If the SS register is being loaded and the segment selector's RPL and the segment descriptor's DPL are not equal to the CPL.
	If the SS register is being loaded and the segment pointed to is a nonwritable data segment.
	If the DS, ES, FS, or GS register is being loaded and the segment pointed to is not a data or readable code segment.
	If the DS, ES, FS, or GS register is being loaded and the segment pointed to is a data or nonconforming code segment, but both the RPL and the CPL are greater than the DPL.
#SS(0)	If a memory operand effective address is outside the SS segment limit.
#SS(selector)	If the SS register is being loaded and the segment pointed to is marked not present.

#NP   If the DS, ES, FS, or GS register is being loaded and the segment pointed to is marked not present.

#PF(fault-code)   If a page fault occurs.

#AC(0)   If alignment checking is enabled and an unaligned memory reference is made while the current privilege level is 3.

#UD   If attempt is made to load the CS register.

Real Address Mode Exceptions

#GP   If a memory operand effective address is outside the CS, DS, ES, FS, or GS segment limit.

#SS   If a memory operand effective address is outside the SS segment limit.

#UD   If attempt is made to load the CS register.

Virtual 8086 Mode Exceptions

#GP(0)   If a memory operand effective address is outside the CS, DS, ES, FS, or GS segment limit.

#SS(0)   If a memory operand effective address is outside the SS segment limit.

#PF(fault-code)   If a page fault occurs.

#AC(0)   If alignment checking is enabled and an unaligned memory reference is made.

#UD   If attempt is made to load the CS register.

MOV—Move to/from Control Registers

Opcode	Instruction	Description
0F 22 /r	MOV CR0,r32	Move r32 to CR0
0F 22 /r	MOV CR2,r32	Move r32 to CR2
0F 22 /r	MOV CR3,r32	Move r32 to CR3
0F 22 /r	MOV CR4,r32	Move r32 to CR4
0F 20 /r	MOV r32,CR0	Move CR0 to r32
0F 20 /r	MOV r32,CR2	Move CR2 to r32
0F 20 /r	MOV r32,CR3	Move CR3 to r32
0F 20 /r	MOV r32,CR4	Move CR4 to r32

Description

Moves the contents of a control register (CR0, CR2, CR3, or CR4) to a general-purpose register or vice versa. The operand size for these instructions is always 32 bits, regardless of the operand-size attribute. (See "Control Registers" in Chapter 2, *System Architecture Overview*, of the *Pentium® Pro Family Developer's Manual, Volume 3* for a detailed description of the flags and fields in the control registers.)

When loading a control register, a program should not attempt to change any of the reserved bits; that is, always set reserved bits to the value previously read.

At the opcode level, the *reg* field within the ModR/M byte specifies which of the control registers is loaded or read. The 2 bits in the *mod* field are always 11B. The *r/m* field specifies the general-purpose register loaded or read.

These instructions have the following side effects:

- When writing to control register CR3, all non-global TLB entries are flushed (see "Translation Lookaside Buffers (TLBs)") in Chapter 3, *Protected-Mode Memory Management*, of the *Pentium® Pro Family Developer's Manual, Volume 3*.

- When modifying any of the paging flags in the control registers (PE and PG in register CR0 and PGE, PSE, and PAE in register CR4), all TLB entries are flushed, including global entries. This operation is implementation specific for the Pentium Pro processor. Software should not depend on this functionality in future Intel Architecture processors.

- If the PG flag is set to 1 and control register CR4 is written to set the PAE flag to 1 (to enable the physical address extension mode), the pointers (PDPTRs) in the page-directory pointers table will be loaded into the processor (into internal, non-architectural registers).

- If the PAE flag is set to 1 and the PG flag set to 1, writing to control register CR3 will cause the PDPTRs to be reloaded into the processor.

- If the PAE flag is set to 1 and control register CR0 is written to set the PG flag, the PDPTRs are reloaded into the processor.

Operation

DEST ← SRC;

Flags Affected

The OF, SF, ZF, AF, PF, and CF flags are undefined.

Protected Mode Exceptions

#GP(0)   If the current privilege level is not 0.

If an attempt is made to write a 1 to any reserved bit in CR4.

If an attempt is made to write reserved bits in the page-directory pointers table (used in the extended physical addressing mode) when the PAE flag in control register CR4 and the PG flag in control register CR0 are set to 1.

Real Address Mode Exceptions

#GP   If an attempt is made to write a 1 to any reserved bit in CR4.

Virtual 8086 Mode Exceptions

#GP(0)   These instructions cannot be executed in virtual 8086 mode.

MOV—Move to/from Debug Registers

Opcode	Instruction	Description
0F 21/r	MOV r32, DR0-DR3	Move debug registers to r32
0F 21/r	MOV r32, DR4-DR5	Move debug registers to r32
0F 21/r	MOV r32, DR6-DR7	Move debug registers to r32
0F 23 /r	MOV DR0-DR3, r32	Move r32 to debug registers
0F 23 /r	MOV DR4-DR5, r32	Move r32 to debug registers
0F 23 /r	MOV DR6-DR7,r32	Move r32 to debug registers

Description

Moves the contents of two or more debug registers (DR0 through DR3, DR4 and DR5, or DR6 and DR7) to a general-purpose register or vice versa. The operand size for these instructions is always 32 bits, regardless of the operand-size attribute. (See Chapter 10, *Debugging and Performance Monitoring*, of the *Pentium® Pro Family Developer's Manual, Volume 3* for a detailed description of the flags and fields in the debug registers.)

The instructions must be executed at privilege level 0 or in real-address mode.

When the debug extension (DE) flag in register CR4 is clear, these instructions operate on debug registers in a manner that is compatible with Intel386 and Intel486 processors. In this mode, references to DR4 and DR5 refer to DR6 and DR7, respectively. When the DE set in CR4 is set, attempts to reference DR4 and DR5 result in an undefined opcode (#UD) exception.

At the opcode level, the *reg* field within the ModR/M byte specifies which of the debug registers is loaded or read. The two bits in the *mod* field are always 11. The *r/m* field specifies the general-purpose register loaded or read.

Operation

```
IF ((DE = 1)  and (SRC or DEST = DR4 or DR5))
THEN
    #UD;
ELSE
    DEST ← SRC;
```

Flags Affected

The OF, SF, ZF, AF, PF, and CF flags are undefined.

Protected Mode Exceptions

#GP(0)	If the current privilege level is not 0.
#UD	If the DE (debug extensions) bit of CR4 is set and a MOV instruction is executed involving DR4 or DR5.

#DB   If any debug register is accessed while the GD flag in debug register DR7
                    is set.

Real Address Mode Exceptions

#UD   If the DE (debug extensions) bit of CR4 is set and a MOV instruction is
                    executed involving DR4 or DR5.

#DB   If any debug register is accessed while the GD flag in debug register DR7
                    is set.

Virtual 8086 Mode Exceptions

#GP(0)   The debug registers cannot be loaded or read when in virtual 8086 mode.

MOVS/MOVSB/MOVSW/MOVSD—Move Data from String to String

Opcode	Instruction	Description
A4	MOVS ES:(E)DI, DS:(E)SI	Move byte at address DS:(E)SI to address ES:(E)DI
A5	MOVS ES:DI,DS:SI	Move word at address DS:SI to address ES:DI
A5	MOVS ES:EDI, DS:ESI	Move doubleword at address DS:ESI to address ES:EDI
A4	MOVSB	Move byte at address DS:(E)SI to address ES:(E)DI
A5	MOVSW	Move word at address DS:SI to address ES:DI
A5	MOVSD	Move doubleword at address DS:ESI to address ES:EDI

Description

Moves the byte, word, or doubleword specified with the second operand (source operand) to the location specified with the first operand (destination operand). The source operand specifies the memory location at the address DS:ESI and the destination operand specifies the memory location at address ES:EDI. (When the operand-size attribute is 16, the SI and DI register are used as the source-index and destination-index registers, respectively.) The DS segment may be overridden with a segment override prefix, but the ES segment cannot be overridden.

The MOVSB, MOVSW, and MOVSD mnemonics are synonyms of the byte, word, and doubleword versions of the MOVS instructions. They are simpler to use, but provide no type or segment checking. (For the MOVS instruction, "DS:ESI" and "ES:EDI" must be explicitly specified in the instruction.)

After the transfer, the ESI and EDI registers are incremented or decremented automatically according to the setting of the DF flag in the EFLAGS register. (If the DF flag is 0, the ESI and EDI register are incremented; if the DF flag is 1, the ESI and EDI register are decremented.) The registers are incremented or decremented by 1 for byte operations, by 2 for word operations, or by 4 for doubleword operations.

The MOVS, MOVSB, MOVSW, and MOVSD instructions can be preceded by the REP prefix (see Chapter 11, "REP/REPE/REPZ/REPNE /REPNZ—Repeat String Operation Prefix") for block moves of ECX bytes, words, or doublewords.

Operation

```
DEST ←SRC;
IF (byte move)
    THEN IF DF = 0
        THEN (E)DI ← 1;
        ELSE (E)DI ← −1;
    FI;
    ELSE IF (word move)
        THEN IF DF = 0
            THEN DI ← 2;
```

```
            ELSE DI ← –2;
        FI;
        ELSE (* doubleword move*)
            THEN IF DF = 0
                THEN EDI ← 4;
                ELSE EDI ← –4;
            FI;
    FI;
```

Flags Affected

None.

Protected Mode Exceptions

#GP(0)	If the destination is located in a nonwritable segment.
	If a memory operand effective address is outside the CS, DS, ES, FS, or GS segment limit.
	If the DS, ES, FS, or GS register contains a null segment selector.
#SS(0)	If a memory operand effective address is outside the SS segment limit.
#PF(fault-code)	If a page fault occurs.
#AC(0)	If alignment checking is enabled and an unaligned memory reference is made while the current privilege level is 3.

Real Address Mode Exceptions

#GP	If a memory operand effective address is outside the CS, DS, ES, FS, or GS segment limit.
#SS	If a memory operand effective address is outside the SS segment limit.

Virtual 8086 Mode Exceptions

#GP(0)	If a memory operand effective address is outside the CS, DS, ES, FS, or GS segment limit.
#SS(0)	If a memory operand effective address is outside the SS segment limit.
#PF(fault-code)	If a page fault occurs.
#AC(0)	If alignment checking is enabled and an unaligned memory reference is made.

MOVSX—Move with Sign-Extension

Opcode	Instruction	Description
0F BE /r	MOVSX r16,r/m8	Move byte to word with sign-extension
0F BE /r	MOVSX r32,r/m8	Move byte to doubleword, sign-extension
0F BF /r	MOVSX r32,r/m16	Move word to doubleword, sign-extension

Description

Copies the contents of the source operand (register or memory location) to the destination operand (register) and sign extends the value to 16 or 32 bits (see Figure 6-5). The size of the converted value depends on the operand-size attribute.

Operation

DEST ← SignExtend(SRC);

Flags Affected

None.

Protected Mode Exceptions

#GP(0)	If a memory operand effective address is outside the CS, DS, ES, FS, or GS segment limit.
	If the DS, ES, FS, or GS register contains a null segment selector.
#SS(0)	If a memory operand effective address is outside the SS segment limit.
#PF(fault-code)	If a page fault occurs.
#AC(0)	If alignment checking is enabled and an unaligned memory reference is made while the current privilege level is 3.

Real Address Mode Exceptions

#GP	If a memory operand effective address is outside the CS, DS, ES, FS, or GS segment limit.
#SS	If a memory operand effective address is outside the SS segment limit.

Virtual 8086 Mode Exceptions

#GP(0)	If a memory operand effective address is outside the CS, DS, ES, FS, or GS segment limit.
#SS(0)	If a memory operand effective address is outside the SS segment limit.
#PF(fault-code)	If a page fault occurs.

MOVZX—Move with Zero-Extend

Opcode	Instruction	Description
0F B6 /r	MOVZX r16,r/m8	Move byte to word with zero-extension
0F B6 /r	MOVZX r32,r/m8	Move byte to doubleword, zero-extension
0F B7 /r	MOVZX r32,r/m16	Move word to doubleword, zero-extension

Description

Copies the contents of the source operand (register or memory location) to the destination operand (register) and sign extends the value to 16 or 32 bits (see Figure 6-5). The size of the converted value depends on the operand-size attribute.

Copies the contents of the source operand (register or memory location) to the destination operand (register) and zero extends the value to 16 or 32 bits. The size of the converted value depends on the operand-size attribute.

Operation

DEST ← ZeroExtend(SRC);

Flags Affected

None.

Protected Mode Exceptions

#GP(0)	If a memory operand effective address is outside the CS, DS, ES, FS, or GS segment limit.
	If the DS, ES, FS, or GS register contains a null segment selector.
#SS(0)	If a memory operand effective address is outside the SS segment limit.
#PF(fault-code)	If a page fault occurs.
#AC(0)	If alignment checking is enabled and an unaligned memory reference is made while the current privilege level is 3.

Real Address Mode Exceptions

#GP	If a memory operand effective address is outside the CS, DS, ES, FS, or GS segment limit.
#SS	If a memory operand effective address is outside the SS segment limit.

Virtual 8086 Mode Exceptions

#GP(0)	If a memory operand effective address is outside the CS, DS, ES, FS, or GS segment limit.
#SS(0)	If a memory operand effective address is outside the SS segment limit.
#PF(fault-code)	If a page fault occurs.
#AC(0)	If alignment checking is enabled and an unaligned memory reference is made.

MUL—Unsigned Multiplication of AL, AX, or EAX

Opcode	Instruction	Description
F6 /4	MUL r/m8	Unsigned multiply (AX ← AL * r/m8)
F7 /4	MUL r/m16	Unsigned multiply (DX:AX ← AX * r/m16)
F7 /4	MUL r/m32	Unsigned multiply (EDX:EAX ← EAX * r/m32)

Description

Performs an unsigned multiplication of the first operand (destination operand) and the second operand (source operand) and stores the result in the destination operand. The destination operand is an implied operand located in register AL, AX or EAX (depending on the size of the operand); the source operand is located in a general-purpose register or a memory location. The action of this instruction and the location of the result depends on the opcode and the operand size as shown in the following table.

Operand Size	Source 1	Source 2	Destination
Byte	AL	r/m8	AX
Word	AX	r/m16	DX:AX
Doubleword	EAX	r/m32	EDX:EAX

The AH, DX, or EDX registers (depending on the operand size) contain the high-order bits of the product. If the contents of one of these registers are 0, the CF and OF flags are cleared; otherwise, the flags are set.

Operation

```
IF byte operation
    THEN
        AX ← AL * SRC
    ELSE (* word or doubleword operation *)
        IF OperandSize = 16
            THEN
                DX:AX ← AX * SRC
            ELSE (* OperandSize = 32 *)
                EDX:EAX ← EAX * SRC
        FI;
FI;
```

Flags Affected

The OF and CF flags are cleared to 0 if the upper half of the result is 0; otherwise, they are set to 1. The SF, ZF, AF, and PF flags are undefined.

Protected Mode Exceptions

#GP(0)   If a memory operand effective address is outside the CS, DS, ES, FS, or GS segment limit.

                If the DS, ES, FS, or GS register contains a null segment selector.

#SS(0)   If a memory operand effective address is outside the SS segment limit.

#PF(fault-code) If a page fault occurs.

#AC(0)   If alignment checking is enabled and an unaligned memory reference is made while the current privilege level is 3.

Real Address Mode Exceptions

#GP   If a memory operand effective address is outside the CS, DS, ES, FS, or GS segment limit.

#SS   If a memory operand effective address is outside the SS segment limit.

Virtual 8086 Mode Exceptions

#GP(0)   If a memory operand effective address is outside the CS, DS, ES, FS, or GS segment limit.

#SS(0)   If a memory operand effective address is outside the SS segment limit.

#PF(fault-code) If a page fault occurs.

#AC(0)   If alignment checking is enabled and an unaligned memory reference is made.

NEG—Two's Complement Negation

Opcode	Instruction	Description
F6 /3	NEG r/m8	Two's complement negate r/m8
F7 /3	NEG r/m16	Two's complement negate r/m16
F7 /3	NEG r/m32	Two's complement negate r/m32

Description

Replaces the value of operand (the destination operand) with its two's complement. The destination operand is located in a general-purpose register or a memory location.

Operation

```
IF DEST = 0
    THEN CF ← 0
    ELSE CF ← 1;
FI;
DEST ← – (DEST)
```

Flags Affected

The CF flag cleared to 0 if the source operand is 0; otherwise it is set to 1. The OF, SF, ZF, AF, and PF flags are set according to the result.

Protected Mode Exceptions

#GP(0)	If the destination is located in a nonwritable segment.
	If a memory operand effective address is outside the CS, DS, ES, FS, or GS segment limit.
	If the DS, ES, FS, or GS register contains a null segment selector.
#SS(0)	If a memory operand effective address is outside the SS segment limit.
#PF(fault-code)	If a page fault occurs.
#AC(0)	If alignment checking is enabled and an unaligned memory reference is made while the current privilege level is 3.

Real Address Mode Exceptions

#GP	If a memory operand effective address is outside the CS, DS, ES, FS, or GS segment limit.
#SS	If a memory operand effective address is outside the SS segment limit.

Virtual 8086 Mode Exceptions

#GP(0)	If a memory operand effective address is outside the CS, DS, ES, FS, or GS segment limit.
#SS(0)	If a memory operand effective address is outside the SS segment limit.
#PF(fault-code)	If a page fault occurs.
#AC(0)	If alignment checking is enabled and an unaligned memory reference is made.

NOP—No Operation

Opcode	Instruction	Description
90	NOP	No operation

Description

Performs no operation. This instruction is a one-byte instruction that takes up space in the instruction stream but does not affect the machine context, except the EIP register.

The NOP instruction is an alias mnemonic for the XCHG EAX, EAX instruction.

Flags Affected

None.

Exceptions (All Operating Modes)

None.

NOT—One's Complement Negation

Opcode	Instruction	Description
F6 /2	NOT *r/m8*	Reverse each bit of *r/m8*
F7 /2	NOT *r/m16*	Reverse each bit of *r/m16*
F7 /2	NOT *r/m32*	Reverse each bit of *r/m32*

Description

Performs a bitwise NOT operation (1's complement) on the destination operand and stores the result in the destination operand location. The destination operand can be a register or a memory location.

Operation

DEST ← NOT DEST;

Flags Affected

None.

Protected Mode Exceptions

#GP(0)	If the destination operand points to a nonwritable segment.
	If a memory operand effective address is outside the CS, DS, ES, FS, or GS segment limit.
	If the DS, ES, FS, or GS register contains a null segment selector.
#SS(0)	If a memory operand effective address is outside the SS segment limit.
#PF(fault-code)	If a page fault occurs.
#AC(0)	If alignment checking is enabled and an unaligned memory reference is made while the current privilege level is 3.

Real Address Mode Exceptions

#GP	If a memory operand effective address is outside the CS, DS, ES, FS, or GS segment limit.
#SS	If a memory operand effective address is outside the SS segment limit.

Virtual 8086 Mode Exceptions

#GP(0)	If a memory operand effective address is outside the CS, DS, ES, FS, or GS segment limit.
#SS(0)	If a memory operand effective address is outside the SS segment limit.
#PF(fault-code)	If a page fault occurs.
#AC(0)	If alignment checking is enabled and an unaligned memory reference is made.

OR—Logical Inclusive OR

Opcode	Instruction	Description
0C ib	OR AL,imm8	AL OR imm8
0D iw	OR AX,imm16	AX OR imm16
0D id	OR EAX,imm32	EAX OR imm32
80 /1 ib	OR r/m8,imm8	r/m8 OR imm8
81 /1 iw	OR r/m16,imm16	r/m16 OR imm16
81 /1 id	OR r/m32,imm32	r/m32 OR imm32
83 /1 ib	OR r/m16,imm8	r/m16 OR imm8
83 /1 ib	OR r/m32,imm8	r/m32 OR imm8
08 /r	OR r/m8,r8	r/m8 OR r8
09 /r	OR r/m16,r16	r/m16 OR r16
09 /r	OR r/m32,r32	r/m32 OR r32
0A /r	OR r8,r/m8	r8 OR r/m8
0B /r	OR r16,r/m16	r16 OR r/m16
0B /r	OR r32,r/m32	r32 OR r/m32

Description

Performs a bitwise OR operation on the destination (first) and source (second) operands and stores the result in the destination operand location. The source operand can be an immediate, a register, or a memory location; the destination operand can be a register or a memory location.

Operation

DEST ← DEST OR SRC;

Flags Affected

The OF and CF flags are cleared; the SF, ZF, and PF flags are set according to the result. The state of the AF flag is undefined.

Protected Mode Exceptions

#GP(0)	If the destination operand points to a nonwritable segment.
	If a memory operand effective address is outside the CS, DS, ES, FS, or GS segment limit.
	If the DS, ES, FS, or GS register contains a null segment selector.
#SS(0)	If a memory operand effective address is outside the SS segment limit.
#PF(fault-code)	If a page fault occurs.
#AC(0)	If alignment checking is enabled and an unaligned memory reference is made while the current privilege level is 3.

Real Address Mode Exceptions

#GP	If a memory operand effective address is outside the CS, DS, ES, FS, or GS segment limit.
#SS	If a memory operand effective address is outside the SS segment limit.

Virtual 8086 Mode Exceptions

#GP(0)	If a memory operand effective address is outside the CS, DS, ES, FS, or GS segment limit.
#SS(0)	If a memory operand effective address is outside the SS segment limit.
#PF(fault-code)	If a page fault occurs.
#AC(0)	If alignment checking is enabled and an unaligned memory reference is made.

OUT—Output to Port

Opcode	Instruction	Description
E6 *ib*	OUT *imm8*, AL	Output byte AL to *imm8* I/O port address
E7 *ib*	OUT *imm8*, AX	Output word AX to *imm8* I/O port address
E7 *ib*	OUT *imm8*, EAX	Output doubleword EAX to *imm8* I/O port address
EE	OUT DX, AL	Output byte AL to I/O port address in DX
EF	OUT DX, AX	Output word AX to I/O port address in DX
EF	OUT DX, EAX	Output doubleword EAX to I/O port address in DX

Description

Copies the value from the second operand (source operand) to the I/O port specified with the destination operand (first operand). The source operand can be register AL, AX, or EAX, depending on the size of the port being accessed (8, 16, or 32 bits, respectively); the destination operand can be a byte-immediate or the DX register. Using a byte immediate allows I/O port addresses 0 to 255 to be accessed; using the DX register as a source operand allows I/O ports from 0 to 65,535 to be accessed.

When accessing an 8-bit I/O port, the opcode determines the port size; when accessing a 16- and 32-bit I/O port, the operand-size attribute determines the port size.

At the machine code level, I/O instructions are shorter when accessing 8-bit I/O ports. Here, the upper eight bits of the port address will be 0.

This instruction is only useful for accessing I/O ports located in the processor's I/O address space. See Chapter 8, *Input/Output*, for more information on accessing I/O ports in the I/O address space.

Operation

```
IF ((PE = 1) AND ((VM = 1) OR (CPL > IOPL)))
    THEN (* Protected mode or virtual-8086 mode with CPL > IOPL *)
        IF (Any I/O Permission Bit for I/O port being accessed = 1)
            THEN #GP(0);
        FI;
    ELSE ( * Real-address mode or protected mode with CPL ≤ IOPL *)
    (* or virtual-8086 mode with all I/O permission bits for I/O port cleared *)
        DEST ← SRC; (* Writes to selected I/O port *)
FI;
```

Flags Affected

None.

Protected Mode Exceptions

#GP(0)   If the CPL is greater than (has less privilege) the I/O privilege level (IOPL) and any of the corresponding I/O permission bits in TSS for the I/O port being accessed is 1.

Real Address Mode Exceptions

None.

Virtual 8086 Mode Exceptions

#GP(0)   If any of the I/O permission bits in the TSS for the I/O port being accessed is 1.

INSTRUCTION SET REFERENCE

OUTS/OUTSB/OUTSW/OUTSD—Output String to Port

Opcode	Instruction	Description
6E	OUTS DX, DS:(E)SI	Output byte at address DS:(E)SI to I/O port in DX
6F	OUTS DX, DS:SI	Output word at address DS:SI to I/O port in DX
6F	OUTS DX, DS:ESI	Output doubleword at address DS:ESI to I/O port in DX
6E	OUTSB	Output byte at address DS:(E)SI to I/O port in DX
6F	OUTSW	Output word at address DS:SI to I/O port in DX
6F	OUTSD	Output doubleword at address DS:ESI to I/O port in DX

Description

Copies data from the second operand (source operand) to the I/O port specified with the first operand (destination operand). The source operand is a memory location at the address DS:ESI. (When the operand-size attribute is 16, the SI register is used as the source-index register.) The DS register may be overridden with a segment override prefix.

The destination operand must be the DX register, allowing I/O port addresses from 0 to 65,535 to be accessed. When accessing an 8-bit I/O port, the opcode determines the port size; when accessing a 16- and 32-bit I/O port, the operand-size attribute determines the port size.

The OUTSB, OUTSW and OUTSD mnemonics are synonyms of the byte, word, and double-word versions of the OUTS instructions. (For the OUTS instruction, "DS:ESI" must be explicitly specified in the instruction.)

After the byte, word, or doubleword is transfer from the memory location to the I/O port, the ESI register is incremented or decremented automatically according to the setting of the DF flag in the EFLAGS register. (If the DF flag is 0, the ESI register is incremented; if the DF flag is 1, the EDI register is decremented.) The ESI register is incremented or decremented by 1 for byte operations, by 2 for word operations, or by 4 for doubleword operations.

The OUTS, OUTSB, OUTSW, and OUTSD instructions can be preceded by the REP prefix for block input of ECX bytes, words, or doublewords. See Chapter 11, "REP/REPE/REPZ/REPNE /REPNZ—Repeat String Operation Prefix" for a description of the REP prefix.

After an OUTS, OUTSB, OUTSW, or OUTSD instruction is executed, the processor ensures that the EWBE# pin has been sampled active before beginning to execute the next instruction. Note that the instruction may be prefetched if EWBE# is not active, but it will not execute until EWBE# is sampled active.

This instruction is only useful for accessing I/O ports located in the processor's I/O address space. See Chapter 8, *Input/Output*, for more information on accessing I/O ports in the I/O address space.

Operation

```
IF ((PE = 1) AND ((VM = 1) OR (CPL > IOPL)))
    THEN (* Protected mode or virtual-8086 mode with CPL > IOPL *)
```

```
                IF (Any I/O Permission Bit for I/O port being accessed = 1)
                    THEN #GP(0);
            FI;
        ELSE ( * I/O operation is allowed *)
            DEST ← SRC; (* Writes to I/O port *)
            IF (byte operation)
                THEN IF DF = 0
                    THEN (E)DI ← 1;
                    ELSE (E)DI ← −1;
                FI;
                ELSE IF (word operation)
                    THEN IF DF = 0
                        THEN DI ← 2;
                        ELSE DI ← −2;
                    FI;
                    ELSE (* doubleword operation *)
                        THEN IF DF = 0
                            THEN EDI ← 4;
                            ELSE EDI ← −4;
                        FI;
                FI;
            FI;
FI;
```

Flags Affected

None.

Protected Mode Exceptions

#GP(0)	If the CPL is greater than (has less privilege) the I/O privilege level (IOPL) and any of the corresponding I/O permission bits in TSS for the I/O port being accessed is 1.
	If the destination is located in a nonwritable segment.
	If a memory operand effective address is outside the limit of the ES segment.
	If the ES register contains a null segment selector.
	If an illegal memory operand effective address in the ES segments is given.
#PF(fault-code)	If a page fault occurs.
#AC(0)	If alignment checking is enabled and an unaligned memory reference is made while the current privilege level is 3.

Real Address Mode Exceptions

#GP   If a memory operand effective address is outside the CS, DS, ES, FS, or GS segment limit.

#SS   If a memory operand effective address is outside the SS segment limit.

Virtual 8086 Mode Exceptions

#GP(0)   If any of the I/O permission bits in the TSS for the I/O port being accessed is 1.

#PF(fault-code)   If a page fault occurs.

#AC(0)   If alignment checking is enabled and an unaligned memory reference is made.

POP—Pop a Value from the Stack

Opcode	Instruction	Description
8F /0	POP m16	Pop top of stack into m16; increment stack pointer
8F /0	POP m32	Pop top of stack into m32; increment stack pointer
58+ rw	POP r16	Pop top of stack into r16; increment stack pointer
58+ rd	POP r32	Pop top of stack into r32; increment stack pointer
1F	POP DS	Pop top of stack into DS; increment stack pointer
07	POP ES	Pop top of stack into ES; increment stack pointer
17	POP SS	Pop top of stack into SS; increment stack pointer
0F A1	POP FS	Pop top of stack into FS; increment stack pointer
0F A9	POP GS	Pop top of stack into GS; increment stack pointer

Description

Loads the value from the top of the procedure stack to the location specified with the destination operand and then increments the stack pointer. The destination operand can be a general-purpose register, memory location, or segment register.

The current address-size attribute for the stack segment and the operand-size attribute determine the amount the stack pointer is incremented (see the "Operation" below). For example, if 32-bit addressing and operands are being used, the ESP register (stack pointer) is incremented by 4 and, if 16-bit addressing and operands are being used, the SP register (stack pointer for 16-bit addressing) is incremented by 2. The B flag in the stack segment's segment descriptor determines the stack's address-size attribute.

If the destination operand is one of the segment registers DS, ES, FS, GS, or SS, the value loaded into the register must be a valid segment selector. In protected mode, popping a segment selector into a segment register automatically causes the descriptor information associated with that segment selector to be loaded into the hidden (shadow) part of the segment register and causes the selector and the descriptor information to be validated (see the "Operation" below).

A null value (0000-0003) may be popped into the DS, ES, FS, or GS register without causing a general protection fault. However, any subsequent attempt to reference a segment whose corresponding segment register is loaded with a null value causes a general protection exception (#GP). In this situation, no memory reference occurs and the saved value of the segment register is null.

The POP instruction cannot pop a value into the CS register. To load the CS register, use the RET instruction.

A POP SS instruction inhibits all interrupts, including the NMI interrupt, until after execution of the next instruction. This action allows sequential execution of POP SS and MOV ESP, EBP instructions without the danger of having an invalid stack during an interrupt. However, use of the LSS instruction is the preferred method of loading the SS and ESP registers.

If the ESP register is used as a base register for addressing a destination operand in memory, the POP instructions computes the effective address of the operand after it increments the ESP register.

The POP ESP instruction increments the stack pointer (ESP) before data at the old top of stack is written into the destination.

Operation

```
IF StackAddrSize = 32
    THEN
        IF OperandSize = 32
            THEN
                DEST ← SS:ESP; (* copy a doubleword *)
                ESP ← ESP + 4;
            ELSE (* OperandSize = 16*)
                DEST ← SS:ESP; (* copy a word *)
            ESP ← ESP + 2;
        FI;
    ELSE (* StackAddrSize = 16* )
        IF OperandSize = 16
            THEN
                DEST ← SS:SP; (* copy a word *)
                SP ← SP + 2;
            ELSE (* OperandSize = 32 *)
                DEST ← SS:SP; (* copy a doubleword *)
                SP ← SP + 4;
        FI;
FI;
```

Loading a segment register while in protected mode results in special checks and actions, as described in the following listing. These checks are performed on the segment selector and the segment descriptor it points to.

```
IF SS is loaded;
    THEN
        IF segment selector is null
            THEN #GP(0);
        FI;
        IF segment selector index is outside descriptor table limits
            OR segment selector's RPL ≠ CPL
            OR segment is not a writable data segment
            OR DPL ≠ CPL
                THEN #GP(selector);
        FI;
        IF segment not marked present
            THEN #SS(selector);
    ELSE
        SS ← segment selector;
```

```
                SS ← segment descriptor;
        FI;
FI;
IF DS, ES, FS or GS is loaded with non-null selector;
THEN
    IF segment selector index is outside descriptor table limits
        OR segment is not a data or readable code segment
        OR ((segment is a data or nonconforming code segment)
            AND (both RPL and CPL > DPL))
                THEN #GP(selector);
        IF segment not marked present
            THEN #NP(selector);
    ELSE
        SegmentRegister ← segment selector;
        SegmentRegister ← segment descriptor;
    FI;
FI;
IF DS, ES, FS or GS is loaded with a null selector;
    THEN
        SegmentRegister ← segment selector;
        SegmentRegister ← segment descriptor;
FI;
```

Flags Affected

None.

Protected Mode Exceptions

#GP(0) If attempt is made to load SS register with null segment selector.

If the destination operand is in a nonwritable segment.

If a memory operand effective address is outside the CS, DS, ES, FS, or GS segment limit.

If the DS, ES, FS, or GS register is used to access memory and it contains a null segment selector.

#GP(selector) If segment selector index is outside descriptor table limits.

If the SS register is being loaded and the segment selector's RPL and the segment descriptor's DPL are not equal to the CPL.

If the SS register is being loaded and the segment pointed to is a nonwritable data segment.

If the DS, ES, FS, or GS register is being loaded and the segment pointed to is not a data or readable code segment.

If the DS, ES, FS, or GS register is being loaded and the segment pointed to is a data or nonconforming code segment, but both the RPL and the CPL are greater than the DPL.

#SS(0)	If the current top of stack is not within the stack segment.
	If a memory operand effective address is outside the SS segment limit.
#SS(selector)	If the SS register is being loaded and the segment pointed to is marked not present.
#NP	If the DS, ES, FS, or GS register is being loaded and the segment pointed to is marked not present.
#PF(fault-code)	If a page fault occurs.
#AC(0)	If an unaligned memory reference is made while the current privilege level is 3 and alignment checking is enabled.

Real Address Mode Exceptions

#GP	If a memory operand effective address is outside the CS, DS, ES, FS, or GS segment limit.

Virtual 8086 Mode Exceptions

#GP(0)	If a memory operand effective address is outside the CS, DS, ES, FS, or GS segment limit.
#PF(fault-code)	If a page fault occurs.
#AC(0)	If an unaligned memory reference is made while alignment checking is enabled.

POPA/POPAD—Pop All General-Purpose Registers

Opcode	Instruction	Description
61	POPA	Pop DI, SI, BP, BX, DX, CX, and AX
61	POPAD	Pop EDI, ESI, EBP, EBX, EDX, ECX, and EAX

Description

Pops doublewords (POPAD) or words (POPA) from the procedure stack into the general-purpose registers. The registers are loaded in the following order: EDI, ESI, EBP, EBX, EDX, ECX, and EAX (if the current operand-size attribute is 32) and DI, SI, BP, BX, DX, CX, and AX (if the operand-size attribute is 16). (These instructions reverse the operation of the PUSHA/PUSHAD instructions.) The value on the stack for the ESP or SP register is ignored. Instead, the ESP or SP register is incremented after each register is loaded (see the "Operation" below).

The POPA (pop all) and POPAD (pop all double) mnemonics reference the same opcode. The POPA instruction is intended for use when the operand-size attribute is 16 and the POPAD instruction for when the operand-size attribute is 32. Some assemblers may force the operand size to 16 when POPA is used and to 32 when POPAD is used. Others may treat these mnemonics as synonyms (POPA/POPAD) and use the current setting of the operand-size attribute to determine the size of values to be popped from the stack, regardless of the mnemonic used.

Operation

```
IF OperandSize = 32 (* instruction = POPAD *)
THEN
    EDI ← Pop();
    ESI ← Pop();
    EBP ← Pop();
    increment ESP by 4 (* skip next 4 bytes of stack *)
    EBX ← Pop();
    EDX ← Pop();
    ECX ← Pop();
    EAX ← Pop();
ELSE (* OperandSize = 16, instruction = POPA *)
    DI ← Pop();
    SI ← Pop();
    BP ← Pop();
    increment ESP by 2 (* skip next 2 bytes of stack *)
    BX ← Pop();
    DX ← Pop();
    CX ← Pop();
    AX ← Pop();
FI;
```

Flags Affected

None.

Protected Mode Exceptions

#SS(0)	If the starting or ending stack address is not within the stack segment.
#PF(fault-code)	If a page fault occurs.

Real Address Mode Exceptions

#GP	If a memory operand effective address is outside the CS, DS, ES, FS, or GS segment limit.
#SS	If a memory operand effective address is outside the SS segment limit.

Virtual 8086 Mode Exceptions

#GP(0)	If a memory operand effective address is outside the CS, DS, ES, FS, or GS segment limit.
#SS(0)	If a memory operand effective address is outside the SS segment limit.
#PF(fault-code)	If a page fault occurs.

POPF/POPFD—Pop Stack into EFLAGS Register

Opcode	Instruction	Description
9D	POPF	Pop top of stack into EFLAGS
9D	POPFD	Pop top of stack into EFLAGS

Description

Pops a doubleword (POPFD) from the top of the stack (if the current operand-size attribute is 32) and stores the value in the EFLAGS register or pops a word from the top of the stack (if the operand-size attribute is 16) and stores it in the lower 16 bits of the EFLAGS register. (These instructions reverse the operation of the PUSHF/PUSHFD instructions.)

The POPF (pop flags) and POPFD (pop flags double) mnemonics reference the same opcode. The POPF instruction is intended for use when the operand-size attribute is 16 and the POPFD instruction for when the operand-size attribute is 32. Some assemblers may force the operand size to 16 when POPF is used and to 32 when POPFD is used. Others may treat these mnemonics as synonyms (POPF/POPFD) and use the current setting of the operand-size attribute to determine the size of values to be popped from the stack, regardless of the mnemonic used.

The effect of the POPF/POPFD instructions on the EFLAGS register changes slightly, depending on the mode of operation of the processor. When the processor is operating in protected mode at privilege level 0 (or in real-address mode, which is equivalent to privilege level 0), all the non-reserved flags in the EFLAGS register except the VIP and VIF flags can be modified. The VIP and VIF flags are cleared.

When operating in protected mode, but with a privilege level greater an 0, all the flags can be modified except the IOPL field and the VIP and VIF flags. Here, the IOPL flags are masked and the VIP and VIF flags are cleared.

When operating in virtual-8086 mode, the I/O privilege level (IOPL) must be equal to 3 to use POPF/POPFD instructions and the VM, RF, IOPL, VIP, and VIF flags are masked. If the IOPL is less than 3, the POPF/POPFD instructions cause a general protection exception (#GP).

See Section 3.6.3., "EFLAGS Register" for information about the EFLAGS registers.

The IOPL is altered only when executing at privilege level 0. The interrupt flag is altered only when executing at a level at least as privileged as the IOPL. (Real-address mode is equivalent to privilege level 0.) If a POPF/POPFD instruction is executed with insufficient privilege, an exception does not occur, but the privileged bits do not change.

Operation

```
IF VM=0 (* Not in Virtual-8086 Mode *)
    THEN IF CPL=0
        THEN
            IF OperandSize = 32;
                THEN
                    EFLAGS ← Pop();
```

```
                    (* All non-reserved flags except VIP and VIF can be modified; *)
                    (* VIP and VIF are cleared *)
              ELSE (* OperandSize = 16 *)
                    EFLAGS[15:0] ← Pop(); (* All non-reserved flags can be modified; *)
          FI;
      ELSE (* CPL > 0 *)
          IF OperandSize = 32;
              THEN
                    EFLAGS ← Pop()
                    (* All non-reserved bits except IOPL, VIP, and VIF can be modified; *)
                    (* IOPL is masked; VIP and VIF are cleared *)
              ELSE (* OperandSize = 16 *)
                    EFLAGS[15:0] ← Pop();
                    (* All non-reserved bits except IOPL can be modified; IOPL is masked *)
          FI;
  FI;
  ELSE  (* In Virtual-8086 Mode *)
      IF IOPL=3
          THEN IF OperandSize=32
              THEN
                    EFLAGS ← Pop()
                    (* All non-reserved bits except VM, RF, IOPL, VIP, and VIF *)
                    (* can be modified; VM, RF, IOPL, VIP, and VIF are masked*)
              ELSE
                    EFLAGS[15:0] ← Pop()
                    (* All non-reserved bits except IOPL can be modified; IOPL is masked*)
          FI;
          ELSE (* IOPL < 3 *)
              #GP(0);  (* trap to virtual-8086 monitor *)
      FI;
  FI;
FI;
```

Flags Affected

All flags except the reserved bits.

Protected Mode Exceptions

#SS(0)   If the top of stack is not within the stack segment.

Real Address Mode Exceptions

#GP   If a memory operand effective address is outside the CS, DS, ES, FS, or
                    GS segment limit.

#SS   If a memory operand effective address is outside the SS segment limit.

Virtual 8086 Mode Exceptions

#GP(0)   If a memory operand effective address is outside the CS, DS, ES, FS, or GS segment limit.

If the I/O privilege level is less than 3.

If an attempt is made to execute the POPF/POPFD instruction with an operand-size override prefix.

#SS(0)   If a memory operand effective address is outside the SS segment limit.

PUSH—Push Word or Doubleword Onto the Stack

Opcode	Instruction	Description
FF /6	PUSH r/m16	Push r/m16
FF /6	PUSH r/m32	Push r/m32
50+rw	PUSH r16	Push r16
50+rd	PUSH r32	Push r32
6A	PUSH imm8	Push imm8
68	PUSH imm16	Push imm16
68	PUSH imm32	Push imm32
0E	PUSH CS	Push CS
16	PUSH SS	Push SS
1E	PUSH DS	Push DS
06	PUSH ES	Push ES
0F A0	PUSH FS	Push FS
0F A8	PUSH GS	Push GS

Description

Decrements the stack pointer and then stores the source operand on the top of the procedure stack. The current address-size attribute for the stack segment and the operand-size attribute determine the amount the stack pointer is decremented (see the "Operation" below). For example, if 32-bit addressing and operands are being used, the ESP register (stack pointer) is decremented by 4 and, if 16-bit addressing and operands are being used, the SP register (stack pointer for 16-bit addressing) is decremented by 2. Pushing 16-bit operands when the stack address-size attribute is 32 can result in a misaligned the stack pointer (that is, the stack pointer not aligned on a doubleword boundary).

The PUSH ESP instruction pushes the value of the ESP register as it existed before the instruction was executed. Thus, if a PUSH instruction uses a memory operand in which the ESP register is used as a base register for computing the operand address, the effective address of the operand is computed before the ESP register is decremented.

In the real-address mode, if the ESP or SP register is 1 when the PUSH instruction is executed, the processor shuts down due to a lack of stack space. No exception is generated to indicate this condition.

Operation

```
IF StackAddrSize = 32
THEN
    IF OperandSize = 32
        THEN
            ESP ← ESP – 4;
            SS:ESP ← SRC; (* push doubleword *)
        ELSE (* OperandSize = 16*)
```

```
                ESP ← ESP – 2;
                SS:ESP ← SRC; (* push word *)
        FI;
ELSE (* StackAddrSize = 16*)
    IF OperandSize = 16
        THEN
                SP ← SP – 2;
                 SS:SP ← SRC; (* push word *)
        ELSE (* OperandSize = 32*)
                SP ← SP – 4;
                SS:SP ← SRC; (* push doubleword *)
    FI;
FI;
```

Flags Affected

None.

Protected Mode Exceptions

#GP(0)   If a memory operand effective address is outside the CS, DS, ES, FS, or GS segment limit.

If the DS, ES, FS, or GS register is used to access memory and it contains a null segment selector.

#SS(0)   If a memory operand effective address is outside the SS segment limit.

#PF(fault-code)   If a page fault occurs.

#AC(0)   If alignment checking is enabled and an unaligned memory reference is made while the current privilege level is 3.

Real Address Mode Exceptions

#GP   If a memory operand effective address is outside the CS, DS, ES, FS, or GS segment limit.

#SS   If a memory operand effective address is outside the SS segment limit.

If the new value of the SP or ESP register is outside the stack segment limit.

Virtual 8086 Mode Exceptions

#GP(0)   If a memory operand effective address is outside the CS, DS, ES, FS, or GS segment limit.

#SS(0)   If a memory operand effective address is outside the SS segment limit.

#PF(fault-code)   If a page fault occurs.

#AC(0)   If alignment checking is enabled and an unaligned memory reference is made.

Intel Architecture Compatibility

For Intel Architecture processors from the Intel 286 on, the PUSH ESP instruction pushes the value of the ESP register as it existed before the instruction was executed. (This is also true in the real-address and virtual-8086 modes.) For the Intel 8086 processor, the PUSH SP instruction pushes the new value of the SP register (that is the value after it has been decremented by 2).

PUSHA/PUSHAD—Push All General-Purpose Registers

Opcode	Instruction	Description
60	PUSHA	Push AX, CX, DX, BX, original SP, BP, SI, and DI
60	PUSHAD	Push EAX, ECX, EDX, EBX, original ESP, EBP, ESI, and EDI

Description

Push the contents of the general-purpose registers onto the procedure stack. The registers are stored on the stack in the following order: EAX, ECX, EDX, EBX, EBP, ESP (original value), EBP, ESI, and EDI (if the current operand-size attribute is 32) and AX, CX, DX, BX, SP (original value), BP, SI, and DI (if the operand-size attribute is 16). (These instructions perform the reverse operation of the POPA/POPAD instructions.) The value pushed for the ESP or SP register is its value before prior to pushing the first register (see the "Operation" below).

The PUSHA (push all) and PUSHAD (push all double) mnemonics reference the same opcode. The PUSHA instruction is intended for use when the operand-size attribute is 16 and the PUSHAD instruction for when the operand-size attribute is 32. Some assemblers may force the operand size to 16 when PUSHA is used and to 32 when PUSHAD is used. Others may treat these mnemonics as synonyms (PUSHA/PUSHAD) and use the current setting of the operand-size attribute to determine the size of values to be pushed from the stack, regardless of the mnemonic used.

In the real-address mode, if the ESP or SP register is 1, 3, or 5 when the PUSHA/PUSHAD instruction is executed, the processor shuts down due to a lack of stack space. No exception is generated to indicate this condition.

Operation

```
IF OperandSize = 32 (* PUSHAD instruction *)
    THEN
        Temp ← (ESP);
        Push(EAX);
        Push(ECX);
        Push(EDX);
        Push(EBX);
        Push(Temp);
        Push(EBP);
        Push(ESI);
        Push(EDI);
    ELSE (* OperandSize = 16, PUSHA instruction *)
        Temp ← (SP);
        Push(AX);
        Push(CX);
        Push(DX);
        Push(BX);
        Push(Temp);
```

```
        Push(BP);
        Push(SI);
        Push(DI);
FI;
```

Flags Affected

None.

Protected Mode Exceptions

#SS(0)   If the starting or ending stack address is outside the stack segment limit.

#PF(fault-code)   If a page fault occurs.

Real Address Mode Exceptions

#GP   If the ESP or SP register contains 7, 9, 11, 13, or 15.

Virtual 8086 Mode Exceptions

#GP(0)   If the ESP or SP register contains 7, 9, 11, 13, or 15.

#PF(fault-code)   If a page fault occurs.

PUSHF/PUSHFD—Push EFLAGS Register onto the Stack

Opcode	Instruction	Description
9C	PUSHF	Push EFLAGS
9C	PUSHFD	Push EFLAGS

Description

Decrement the stack pointer by 4 (if the current operand-size attribute is 32) and push the entire contents of the EFLAGS register onto the procedure stack or decrement the stack pointer by 2 (if the operand-size attribute is 16) push the lower 16 bits of the EFLAGS register onto the stack. (These instructions reverse the operation of the POPF/POPFD instructions.) See Section 3.6.3., "EFLAGS Register" for information about the EFLAGS registers.

When copying the entire EFLAGS register to the stack, bits 16 and 17, called the VM and RF flags, are not copied. Instead, the values for these flags are cleared in the EFLAGS image stored on the stack.

The PUSHF (push flags) and PUSHFD (push flags double) mnemonics reference the same opcode. The PUSHF instruction is intended for use when the operand-size attribute is 16 and the PUSHFD instruction for when the operand-size attribute is 32. Some assemblers may force the operand size to 16 when PUSHF is used and to 32 when PUSHFD is used. Others may treat these mnemonics as synonyms (PUSHF/PUSHFD) and use the current setting of the operand-size attribute to determine the size of values to be pushed from the stack, regardless of the mnemonic used.

When the I/O privilege level (IOPL) is less than 3 in virtual-8086 mode, the PUSHF/PUSHFD instructions causes a general protection exception (#GP). The IOPL is altered only when executing at privilege level 0. The interrupt flag is altered only when executing at a level at least as privileged as the IOPL. (Real-address mode is equivalent to privilege level 0.) If a PUSHF/PUSHFD instruction is executed with insufficient privilege, an exception does not occur, but the privileged bits do not change.

In the real-address mode, if the ESP or SP register is 1, 3, or 5 when the PUSHA/PUSHAD instruction is executed, the processor shuts down due to a lack of stack space. No exception is generated to indicate this condition.

Operation

```
IF VM=0 (* Not in Virtual-8086 Mode *)
    THEN
        IF OperandSize = 32
            THEN
                push(EFLAGS AND 00FCFFFFH);
                (* VM and RF EFLAG bits are cleared in image stored on the stack*)
            ELSE
                push(EFLAGS); (* Lower 16 bits only *)
        FI;
```

```
    ELSE (* In Virtual-8086 Mode *)
        IF IOPL=3
            THEN
                IF OperandSize = 32
                    THEN push(EFLAGS AND 0FCFFFFH);
                        (* VM and RF EFLAGS bits are cleared in image stored on the stack*)
                ELSE push(EFLAGS); (* Lower 16 bits only *)
            FI;
        ELSE
            #GP(0); (* Trap to virtual-8086 monitor *)
        FI;
FI;
```

Flags Affected

None.

Protected Mode Exceptions

#SS(0)   If the new value of the ESP register is outside the stack segment boundary.

Real Address Mode Exceptions

None.

Virtual 8086 Mode Exceptions

#GP(0)   If the I/O privilege level is less than 3.

RCL/RCR/ROL/ROR—Rotate

Opcode	Instruction	Description
D0 /2	RCL r/m8,1	Rotate 9 bits (CF,r/m8) left once
D2 /2	RCL r/m8,CL	Rotate 9 bits (CF,r/m8) left CL times
C0 /2 ib	RCL r/m8,imm8	Rotate 9 bits (CF,r/m8) left imm8 times
D1 /2	RCL r/m16,1	Rotate 17 bits (CF,r/m16) left once
D3 /2	RCL r/m16,CL	Rotate 17 bits (CF,r/m16) left CL times
C1 /2 ib	RCL r/m16,imm8	Rotate 17 bits (CF,r/m16) left imm8 times
D1 /2	RCL r/m32,1	Rotate 33 bits (CF,r/m32) left once
D3 /2	RCL r/m32,CL	Rotate 33 bits (CF,r/m32) left CL times
C1 /2 ib	RCL r/m32,imm8	Rotate 33 bits (CF,r/m32) left imm8 times
D0 /3	RCR r/m8,1	Rotate 9 bits (CF,r/m8) right once
D2 /3	RCR r/m8,CL	Rotate 9 bits (CF,r/m8) right CL times
C0 /3 ib	RCR r/m8,imm8	Rotate 9 bits (CF,r/m8) right imm8 times
D1 /3	RCR r/m16,1	Rotate 17 bits (CF,r/m16) right once
D3 /3	RCR r/m16,CL	Rotate 17 bits (CF,r/m16) right CL times
C1 /3 ib	RCR r/m16,imm8	Rotate 17 bits (CF,r/m16) right imm8 times
D1 /3	RCR r/m32,1	Rotate 33 bits (CF,r/m32) right once
D3 /3	RCR r/m32,CL	Rotate 33 bits (CF,r/m32) right CL times
C1 /3 ib	RCR r/m32,imm8	Rotate 33 bits (CF,r/m32) right imm8 times
D0 /0	ROL r/m8,1	Rotate 8 bits r/m8 left once
D2 /0	ROL r/m8,CL	Rotate 8 bits r/m8 left CL times
C0 /0 ib	ROL r/m8,imm8	Rotate 8 bits r/m8 left imm8 times
D1 /0	ROL r/m16,1	Rotate 16 bits r/m16 left once
D3 /0	ROL r/m16,CL	Rotate 16 bits r/m16 left CL times
C1 /0 ib	ROL r/m16,imm8	Rotate 16 bits r/m16 left imm8 times
D1 /0	ROL r/m32,1	Rotate 32 bits r/m32 left once
D3 /0	ROL r/m32,CL	Rotate 32 bits r/m32 left CL times
C1 /0 ib	ROL r/m32,imm8	Rotate 32 bits r/m32 left imm8 times
D0 /1	ROR r/m8,1	Rotate 8 bits r/m8 right once
D2 /1	ROR r/m8,CL	Rotate 8 bits r/m8 right CL times
C0 /1 ib	ROR r/m8,imm8	Rotate 8 bits r/m16 right imm8 times
D1 /1	ROR r/m16,1	Rotate 16 bits r/m16 right once
D3 /1	ROR r/m16,CL	Rotate 16 bits r/m16 right CL times
C1 /1 ib	ROR r/m16,imm8	Rotate 16 bits r/m16 right imm8 times
D1 /1	ROR r/m32,1	Rotate 32 bits r/m32 right once
D3 /1	ROR r/m32,CL	Rotate 32 bits r/m32 right CL times
C1 /1 ib	ROR r/m32,imm8	Rotate 32 bits r/m32 right imm8 times

Description

Shifts (rotates) the bits of the first operand (destination operand) the number of bit positions specified in the second operand (count operand) and stores the result in the destination operand. The destination operand can be a register or a memory location; the count operand is an unsigned integer that can be an immediate or a value in the CL register. The processor restricts the count to a number between 0 and 31 by masking all the bits in the count operand except the 5 least-significant bits.

The rotate left (ROL) and rotate through carry left (RCL) instructions shift all the bits toward more-significant bit positions, except for the most-significant bit, which is rotated to the least-significant bit location (see Figure 6-10). The rotate right (ROR) and rotate through carry right (RCR) instructions shift all the bits toward less significant bit positions, except for the least-significant bit, which is rotated to the most-significant bit location (see Figure 6-10).

The RCL and RCR instructions include the CF flag in the rotation. The RCL instruction shifts the CF flag into the least-significant bit and shifts the most-significant bit into the CF flag (see Figure 6-10). The RCR instruction shifts the CF flag into the most-significant bit and shifts the least-significant bit into the CF flag (see Figure 6-10). For the ROL and ROR instructions, the original value of the CF flag is not a part of the result, but the CF flag receives a copy of the bit that was shifted from one end to the other.

The OF flag is defined only for the 1-bit rotates; it is undefined in all other cases. For left rotates, the OF flag is set to the exclusive OR of the CF bit (after the rotate) and the most-significant bit of the result. For right rotates, the OF flag is set to the exclusive OR of the two most-significant bits of the result.

Operation

```
SIZE ← OperandSize
CASE (determine count) OF
    SIZE = 8:    tempCOUNT ← (COUNT AND 1FH) MOD 9;
    SIZE = 16:   tempCOUNT ← (COUNT AND 1FH) MOD 17;
    SIZE = 32:   tempCOUNT ← COUNT AND 1FH;
ESAC;
(* ROL instruction operation *)
WHILE (tempCOUNT ≠ 0)
    DO
        tempCF ← MSB(DEST);
        DEST ← (DEST * 2) + tempCF;
        tempCOUNT ← tempCOUNT – 1;
    OD;
ELIHW;
CF ← tempCF;
IF COUNT = 1
    THEN OF ← MSB(DEST) XOR CF;
    ELSE OF is undefined;
FI;
(* ROR instruction operation *)
WHILE (tempCOUNT ≠ 0)
```

```
    DO
        tempCF ← LSB(SRC);
        DEST ← (DEST / 2) + (tempCF * 2^SIZE);
        tempCOUNT ← tempCOUNT – 1;
    OD;
IF COUNT = 1
    THEN OF ← MSB(DEST) XOR MSB – 1(DEST);
    ELSE OF is undefined;
FI;
(* RCL instruction operation *)
WHILE (tempCOUNT ≠ 0)
    DO
        tempCF ← MSB(DEST);
        DEST ← (DEST * 2) + tempCF;
        tempCOUNT ← tempCOUNT – 1;
    OD;
ELIHW;
CF ← tempCF;
IF COUNT = 1
    THEN OF ← MSB(DEST) XOR CF;
    ELSE OF is undefined;
FI;
(* RCR instruction operation *)
WHILE (tempCOUNT ≠ 0)
    DO
        tempCF ← LSB(SRC);
        DEST ← (DEST / 2) + (tempCF * 2^SIZE);
        tempCOUNT ← tempCOUNT – 1;
    OD;
IF COUNT = 1
IF COUNT = 1
    THEN OF ← MSB(DEST) XOR MSB – 1(DEST);
    ELSE OF is undefined;
FI;
```

Flags Affected

The CF flag contains the value of the bit shifted into it. The OF flag is affected only for single-bit rotates (see "Description" above); it is undefined for multi-bit rotates. The SF, ZF, AF, and PF flags are not affected.

Protected Mode Exceptions

#GP(0)   If the source operand is located in a nonwritable segment.

                If a memory operand effective address is outside the CS, DS, ES, FS, or GS segment limit.

                If the DS, ES, FS, or GS register contains a null segment selector.

#SS(0)   If a memory operand effective address is outside the SS segment limit.

#PF(fault-code) If a page fault occurs.

#AC(0)   If alignment checking is enabled and an unaligned memory reference is made while the current privilege level is 3.

Real Address Mode Exceptions

#GP   If a memory operand effective address is outside the CS, DS, ES, FS, or GS segment limit.

#SS   If a memory operand effective address is outside the SS segment limit.

Virtual 8086 Mode Exceptions

#GP(0)   If a memory operand effective address is outside the CS, DS, ES, FS, or GS segment limit.

#SS(0)   If a memory operand effective address is outside the SS segment limit.

#PF(fault-code) If a page fault occurs.

#AC(0)   If alignment checking is enabled and an unaligned memory reference is made.

Intel Architecture Compatibility

The 8086 does not mask the rotation count. All Intel Architecture processors from the Intel386 processor on do mask the rotation count in all operating modes.

RDMSR—Read from Model Specific Register

Opcode	Instruction	Description
0F 32	RDMSR	Load MSR specified by ECX into EDX:EAX

Description

Loads the contents of a 64-bit model specific register (MSR) specified in the ECX register into registers EDX:EAX. The EDX register is loaded with the high-order 32 bits of the MSR and the EAX register is loaded with the low-order 32 bits. If less than 64 bits are implemented in the MSR being read, the values returned to EDX:EAX in unimplemented bit locations are undefined.

This instruction must be executed at privilege level 0 or in real-address mode; otherwise, a general protection exception #GP(0) will be generated. Specifying a reserved or unimplemented MSR address in ECX will also cause a general protection exception.

The MSRs control functions for testability, execution tracing, performance-monitoring and machine check errors. Appendix C, *Model-Specific Registers (MSRs)*, in the *Pentium® Pro Family Developer's Manual, Volume 3* lists all the MSRs that can be read with this instruction and their addresses.

The CPUID instruction should be used to determine whether MSRs are supported (EDX[5]=1) before using this instruction.

Operation

EDX:EAX ← MSR[ECX];

Flags Affected

None.

Protected Mode Exceptions

#GP(0)   If the current privilege level is not 0.

                    If the value in ECX specifies a reserved or unimplemented MSR address.

Real Address Mode Exceptions

#GP   If the current privilege level is not 0

                    If the value in ECX specifies a reserved or unimplemented MSR address.

Virtual 8086 Mode Exceptions

#GP(0)   The RDMSR instruction is not recognized in virtual 8086 mode.

Intel Architecture Compatibility

The MSRs and the ability to read them with the RDMSR instruction were introduced into the Intel Architecture with the Pentium processor. Execution of this instruction by an Intel Architecture processor earlier than the Pentium processor results in an invalid opcode exception #UD.

RDPMC—Read Performance-Monitoring Counters

Opcode	Instruction	Description
0F 33	RDPMC	Read performance-monitoring counter specified by ECX into EDX:EAX

Description

Loads the contents of the 40-bit performance-monitoring counter specified in the ECX register into registers EDX:EAX. The EDX register is loaded with the high-order 8 bits of the counter and the EAX register is loaded with the low-order 32 bits. The Pentium Pro processor has two performance-monitoring counters (0 and 1), which are specified by placing 0000H or 0001H, respectively, in the ECX register.

The RDPMC instruction allows application code running at a privilege level of 1, 2, or 3 to read the performance-monitoring counters if the PCE flag in the CR4 register is set. This instruction is provided to allow performance monitoring by application code without incurring the overhead of a call to an operating-system procedure.

The performance-monitoring counters are event counters that can be programmed to count events such as the number of instructions decoded, number of interrupts received, or number of cache loads. Appendix B, *Performance Monitoring Counters*, in the *Pentium® Pro Family Developer's Manual, Volume 3* lists all the events that can be counted.

The RDPMC instruction does not serialize instruction execution. That is, it does not imply that all the events caused by the preceding instructions have been completed or that events caused by subsequent instructions have not begun. If an exact event count is desired, software must use a serializing instruction (such as the CPUID instruction) before and/or after the execution of the RDPCM instruction.

The RDPMC instruction can execute in 16-bit addressing mode or virtual 8086 mode; however, the full contents of the ECX register are used to determine the counter to access and a full 40-bit result is returned (the low-order 32 bits in the EAX register and the high-order 9 bits in the EDX register).

Operation

```
IF (ECX = 0 OR 1) AND ((CR4.PCE = 1) OR ((CR4.PCE = 0) AND (CPL=0)))
    THEN
        EDX:EAX ← PMC[ECX];
    ELSE (* ECX is not 0 or 1 and/or CR4.PCE is 0 and CPL is 1, 2, or 3 *)
        #GP(0)
FI;
```

Flags Affected

None.

Protected Mode Exceptions

#GP(0)   If the current privilege level is not 0 and the PCE flag in the CR4 register is clear.

If the value in the ECX register is not 0 or 1.

Real Address Mode Exceptions

#GP   If the PCE flag in the CR4 register is clear.

If the value in the ECX register is not 0 or 1.

Virtual 8086 Mode Exceptions

#GP(0)   If the PCE flag in the CR4 register is clear.

If the value in the ECX register is not 0 or 1.

RDTSC—Read Time-Stamp Counter

Opcode	Instruction	Description
0F 31	RDTSC	Read time-stamp counter into EDX:EAX

Description

Loads the current value of the processor's time-stamp counter into the EDX:EAX registers. The time-stamp counter is contained in a 64-bit MSR. The high-order 32 bits of the MSR are loaded into the EDX register, and the low-order 32 bits are loaded into the EAX register. The processor increments the time-stamp counter MSR every clock cycle and resets it to 0 whenever the processor is reset.

The time stamp disable (TSD) flag in register CR4 restricts the use of the RDTSC instruction. When the TSD flag is clear, the RDTSC instruction can be executed at any privilege level; when the flag is set, the instruction can only be executed at privilege level 0. The time-stamp counter can also be read with the RDMSR instruction.

The RDTSC instruction is not serializing instruction. Thus, it does not necessarily wait until all previous instructions have been executed before reading the counter. Similarly, subsequent instructions may begin execution before the read operation is performed.

This instruction was introduced into the Intel Architecture in the Pentium processor.

Operation

```
IF (CR4.TSD = 0) OR ((CR4.TSD = 1) AND (CPL=0))
    THEN
        EDX:EAX ← TimeStampCounter;
    ELSE (* CR4 is 1 and CPL is 1, 2, or 3 *)
        #GP(0)
FI;
```

Flags Affected

None.

Protected Mode Exceptions

#GP(0)   If the TSD flag in register CR4 is set and the CPL is greater than 0.

Real Address Mode Exceptions

#GP   If the TSD flag in register CR4 is set.

Virtual 8086 Mode Exceptions

#GP(0)   If the TSD flag in register CR4 is set.

REP/REPE/REPZ/REPNE/REPNZ—Repeat String Operation Prefix

Opcode	Instruction	Description
F3 6C	REP INS r/m8, DX	Input ECX bytes from port DX into ES:[EDI]
F3 6D	REP INS r/m16,DX	Input ECX words from port DX into ES:[EDI]
F3 6D	REP INS r/m32,DX	Input ECX doublewords from port DX into ES:[EDI]
F3 A4	REP MOVS m8,m8	Move ECX bytes from DS:[ESI] to ES:[EDI]
F3 A5	REP MOVS m16,m16	Move ECX words from DS:[ESI] to ES:[EDI]
F3 A5	REP MOVS m32,m32	Move ECX doublewords from DS:[ESI] to ES:[EDI]
F3 6E	REP OUTS DX,r/m8	Output ECX bytes from DS:[ESI] to port DX
F3 6F	REP OUTS DX,r/m16	Output ECX words from DS:[ESI] to port DX
F3 6F	REP OUTS DX,r/m32	Output ECX doublewords from DS:[ESI] to port DX
F3 AC	REP LODS AL	Load ECX bytes from DS:[ESI] to AL
F3 AD	REP LODS AX	Load ECX words from DS:[ESI] to AX
F3 AD	REP LODS EAX	Load ECX doublewords from DS:[ESI] to EAX
F3 AA	REP STOS m8	Fill ECX bytes at ES:[EDI] with AL
F3 AB	REP STOS m16	Fill ECX words at ES:[EDI] with AX
F3 AB	REP STOS m32	Fill ECX doublewords at ES:[EDI] with EAX
F3 A6	REPE CMPS m8,m8	Find nonmatching bytes in ES:[EDI] and DS:[ESI]
F3 A7	REPE CMPS m16,m16	Find nonmatching words in ES:[EDI] and DS:[ESI]
F3 A7	REPE CMPS m32,m32	Find nonmatching doublewords in ES:[EDI] and DS:[ESI]
F3 AE	REPE SCAS m8	Find non-AL byte starting at ES:[EDI]
F3 AF	REPE SCAS m16	Find non-AX word starting at ES:[EDI]
F3 AF	REPE SCAS m32	Find non-EAX doubleword starting at ES:[EDI]
F2 A6	REPNE CMPS m8,m8	Find matching bytes in ES:[EDI] and DS:[ESI]
F2 A7	REPNE CMPS m16,m16	Find matching words in ES:[EDI] and DS:[ESI]
F2 A7	REPNE CMPS m32,m32	Find matching doublewords in ES:[EDI] and DS:[ESI]
F2 AE	REPNE SCAS m8	Find AL, starting at ES:[EDI]
F2 AF	REPNE SCAS m16	Find AX, starting at ES:[EDI]
F2 AF	REPNE SCAS m32	Find EAX, starting at ES:[EDI]

Description

Repeats a string instruction the number of times specified in the count register (ECX) or until the indicated condition of the ZF flag is no longer met. The REP (repeat), REPE (repeat while equal), REPNE (repeat while not equal), REPZ (repeat while zero), and REPNZ (repeat while not zero) mnemonics are prefixes that can be added to one of the string instructions. The REP prefix can be added to the INS, OUTS, MOVS, LODS, and STOS instructions, and the REPE, REPNE, REPZ, and REPNZ prefixes can be added to the CMPS and SCAS instructions. (The REPZ and REPNZ prefixes are synonymous forms of the REPE and REPNE prefixes, respectively.) The behavior of the REP prefix is undefined when used with non-string instructions.

The REP prefixes apply only to one string instruction at a time. To repeat a block of instructions, use the LOOP instruction or another looping construct.

All of these repeat prefixes cause the associated instruction to be repeated until the count in register ECX is decremented to 0 (see the following table). The REPE, REPNE, REPZ, and REPNZ prefixes also check the state of the ZF flag after each iteration and terminate the repeat loop if the ZF flag is not in the specified state. When both termination conditions are tested, the cause of a repeat termination can be determined either by testing the ECX register with a JECXZ instruction or by testing the ZF flag with a JZ, JNZ, and JNE instruction.

Repeat Conditions

Repeat Prefix	Termination Condition 1	Termination Condition 2
REP	ECX=0	None
REPE/REPZ	ECX=0	ZF=0
REPNE/REPNZ	ECX=0	ZF=1

When the REPE/REPZ and REPNE/REPNZ prefixes are used, the ZF flag does not require initialization because both the CMPS and SCAS instructions affect the ZF flag according to the results of the comparisons they make.

A repeating string operation can be suspended by an exception or interrupt. When this happens, the state of the registers is preserved to allow the string operation to be resumed upon a return from the exception or interrupt handler. The source and destination registers point to the next string elements to be operated on, the EIP register points to the string instruction, and the ECX register has the value it held following the last successful iteration of the instruction. This mechanism allows long string operations to proceed without affecting the interrupt response time of the system.

When a page fault occurs during CMPS or SCAS instructions that are prefixed with REPNE, the EFLAGS value is restored to the state prior to the execution of the instruction. Since SCAS and CMPS do not use EFLAGS as an input, the processor can resume the instruction after the page fault handler.

Use the REP INS and REP OUTS instructions with caution. Not all I/O ports can handle the rate at which these instructions execute.

A REP STOS instruction is the fastest way to initialize a large block of memory.

Operation

```
IF AddressSize = 16
    THEN
        use CX for CountReg;
    ELSE (* AddressSize = 32 *)
        use ECX for CountReg;
FI;
WHILE CountReg ≠ 0
    DO
        service pending interrupts (if any);
        execute associated string instruction;
        CountReg ← CountReg − 1;
        IF CountReg = 0
            THEN exit WHILE loop
        FI;
        IF (repeat prefix is REPZ or REPE) AND (ZF=0)
        OR (repeat prefix is REPNZ or REPNE) AND (ZF=1)
            THEN exit WHILE loop
        FI;
    OD;
```

Flags Affected

None; however, the CMPS and SCAS instructions do set the status flags in the EFLAGS register.

Exceptions (All Operating Modes)

None; however, exceptions can be generated by the instruction a repeat prefix is associated with.

RET—Return from Procedure

Opcode	Instruction	Description
C3	RET	Near return to calling procedure
CB	RET	Far return to calling procedure
C2 *iw*	RET *imm16*	Near return to calling procedure and pop *imm16* bytes from stack
CA *iw*	RET *imm16*	Far return to calling procedure and pop *imm16* bytes from stack

Description

Transfers program control to a return address located on the top of the stack. The address is usually placed on the stack by a CALL instruction, and the return is made to the instruction that follows the CALL instruction.

The optional source operand specifies the number of stack bytes to be released after the return address is popped; the default is none. This operand can be used to release parameters from the stack that were passed to the called procedure and are no longer needed.

The RET instruction can be used to execute three different types of returns:

- Near return—A return to a calling procedure within the current code segment (the segment currently pointed to by the CS register), sometimes referred to as an intrasegment return.

- Far return—A return to a calling procedure located in a different segment than the current code segment, sometimes referred to as an intersegment return.

- Inter-privilege-level far return—A far return to a different privilege level than that of the currently executing program or procedure.

The inter-privilege-level return type can only be executed in protected mode. See Section 4.3., "Calling Procedures Using CALL and RET" for detailed information on near, far, and inter-privilege-level returns.

When executing a near return, the processor pops the return instruction pointer (offset) from the top of the procedure stack into the EIP register and begins program execution at the new instruction pointer. The CS register is unchanged.

When executing a far return, the processor pops the return instruction pointer from the top of the procedure stack into the EIP register, then pops the segment selector from the top of the stack into the CS register. The processor then begins program execution in the new code segment at the new instruction pointer.

The mechanics of an inter-privilege-level far return are similar to an intersegment return, except that the processor examines the privilege levels and access rights of the code and stack segments being returned to determine if the control transfer is allowed to be made. The DS, ES, FS, and GS segment registers are cleared by the RET instruction during an inter-privilege-level return if they refer to segments that are not allowed to be accessed at the new privilege level. Since a stack switch also occurs on an inter-privilege level return, the ESP and SS registers are loaded from the stack.

Operation

```
(* Near return *)
IF instruction = near return
    THEN;
        IF OperandSize = 32
            THEN
                IF top 12 bytes of stack not within stack limits THEN #SS(0); FI;
                EIP ← Pop();
            ELSE (* OperandSize = 16 *)
                IF top 6 bytes of stack not within stack limits
                    THEN #SS(0)
                FI;
                tempEIP ← Pop();
                tempEIP ← tempEIP AND 0000FFFFH;
                IF tempEIP not within code segment limits THEN #GP(0); FI;
                EIP ← tempEIP;
        FI;
    IF instruction has immediate operand
        THEN IF StackAddressSize=32
            THEN
                ESP ← ESP + SRC;
            ELSE (* StackAddressSize=16 *)
                SP ← SP + SRC;
        FI;
    FI;

(* Real-address mode or virtual-8086 mode *)
IF ((PE = 0) OR (PE = 1 AND VM = 1)) AND instruction = far return
    THEN;
        IF OperandSize = 32
            THEN
                IF top 12 bytes of stack not within stack limits THEN #SS(0); FI;
                EIP ← Pop();
                CS ← Pop(); (* 32-bit pop, high-order 16-bits discarded *)
            ELSE (* OperandSize = 16 *)
                IF top 6 bytes of stack not within stack limits THEN #SS(0); FI;
                tempEIP ← Pop();
                tempEIP ← tempEIP AND 0000FFFFH;
                IF tempEIP not within code segment limits THEN #GP(0); FI;
                EIP ← tempEIP;
                CS ← Pop(); (* 16-bit pop *)
        FI;
    IF instruction has immediate operand THEN SP ← SP + (SRC AND FFFFH); FI;
FI;
```

```
(* Protected mode, not virtual 8086 mode *)
IF (PE = 1 AND VM = 0) AND instruction = far RET
    THEN
        IF OperandSize = 32
            THEN
                IF second doubleword on stack is not within stack limits THEN #SS(0); FI;
            ELSE (* OperandSize = 16 *)
                IF second word on stack is not within stack limits THEN #SS(0); FI;
        FI;
    IF return code segment selector is null THEN GP(0); FI;
    IF return code segment selector addrsses descriptor beyond diescriptor table limit
        THEN GP(selector; FI;
    Obtain descriptor to which return code segment selector points from descriptor table
    IF return code segment descriptor is nat a code segment THEN #GP(selector); FI;
    if return code segment selector RPL < CPL THEN #GP(selector); FI;
    IF return code segment descriptor is condorming
        AND return code segment DPL > return code segment selector RPL
            THEN #GP(selector); FI;
    IF return code segment descriptor is not present THEN #NP(selector); FI:
    IF return code segment selector RPL > CPL
        THEN GOTO RETURN-OUTER-PRIVILEGE-LEVEL;
        ELSE GOTO RETURN-TO-SAME-PRIVILEGE-LEVEL
    FI;
END;FI;


RETURN-SAME-PRIVILEGE-LEVEL:
    IF the return instruction pointer is not within ther return code segment limit
        THEN #GP(0);
    FI;
    IF OperandSize=32
        THEN
            EIP ← Pop();
            CS ← Pop(); (* 32-bit pop, high-order 16-bits discarded *)
            ESP ← ESP + SRC;
        ELSE (* OperandSize=16 *)
            EIP ← Pop();
            EIP ← EIP AND 0000FFFFH;
            CS ← Pop(); (* 16-bit pop *)
            ESP ← ESP + SRC;
    FI;


RETURN-OUTER-PRIVILEGE-LEVEL:
    IF top (16 + SRC) bytes of stack are not within stack limits (OperandSize=32)
        OR top (8 + SRC) bytes of stack are not within stack limits (OperandSize=16)
            THEN #SS(0); FI;
    FI;
    Read return segment selector;
```

IF stack segment selector is null THEN #GP(0); FI;
IF return stack segment selector index is not within its descriptor table limits
  THEN #GP(selector); FI;
Read segment descriptor pointed to by return segment selector;
IF stack segment selector RPL ≠ RPL of the return code segment selector
 OR stack segment is not a writable data segment
  OR stack segment descriptor DPL ≠ RPL of the return code segment selector
   THEN #GP(selector); FI;
  IF stack segment not present THEN #SS(StackSegmentSelector); FI;
IF the return instruction pointer is not within the return code segment limit THEN #GP(0); FI:
 CPL ← ReturnCodeSegmentSelector(RPL);
IF OperandSize=32
 THEN
   EIP ← Pop();
   CS ← Pop(); (* 32-bit pop, high-order 16-bits discarded *)
   (* segment descriptor information also loaded *)
   CS(RPL) ← CPL;
   ESP ← ESP + SRC;
   tempESP ← Pop();
   tempSS ← Pop(); (* 32-bit pop, high-order 16-bits discarded *)
   (* segment descriptor information also loaded *)
   ESP ← tempESP;
   SS ← tempSS;
  ELSE (* OperandSize=16 *)
   EIP ← Pop();
   EIP ← EIP AND 0000FFFFH;
   CS ← Pop(); (* 16-bit pop; segment descriptor information also loaded *)
   CS(RPL) ← CPL;
   ESP ← ESP + SRC;
   tempESP ← Pop();
   tempSS ← Pop(); (* 16-bit pop; segment descriptor information also loaded *)
   (* segment descriptor information also loaded *)
   ESP ← tempESP;
   SS ← tempSS;
FI;
FOR each of segment register (ES, FS, GS, and DS)
 DO;
   IF segment register points to data or non-conforming code segment
   AND CPL > segment descriptor DPL; (* DPL in hidden part of segment register *)
    THEN (* segment register invalid *)
     SegmentSelector ← 0; (* null segment selector *)
   FI;
 OD;
For each of ES, FS, GS, and DS
DO

```
                IF segment selector index is not within descriptor table limits
                    OR segment descriptor indicates the segment is not a data or
                        readable code segment
                    OR if the segment is a data or non-conforming code segment and the segment
                        descriptor's DPL < CPL or RPL of code segment's segment selector
                        THEN
                            segment selector register ← null selector;
        OD;
```

Flags Affected

None.

Protected Mode Exceptions

#GP(0)	If the return code or stack segment selector null.
	If the return instruction pointer is not within the return code segment limit
#GP(selector)	If the RPL of the return code segment selector is less then the CPL.
	If the return code or stack segment selector index is not within its descriptor table limits.
	If the return code segment descriptor does not indicate a code segment.
	If the return code segment is non-conforming and the segment selector's DPL is not equal to the RPL of the code segment's segment selector
	If the return code segment is conforming and the segment selector's DPL greater than the RPL of the code segment's segment selector
	If the stack segment is not a writable data segment.
	If the stack segment selector RPL is not equal to the RPL of the return code segment selector.
	If the stack segment descriptor DPL is not equal to the RPL of the return code segment selector.
#SS(0)	If the top bytes of stack are not within stack limits.
	If the return stack segment is not present.
#NP(selector)	If the return code segment is not present.
#PF(fault-code)	If a page fault occurs.
#AC(0)	If an unaligned memory access occurs when the CPL is 3 and alignment checking is enabled.

Real Address Mode Exceptions

#GP	If the return instruction pointer is not within the return code segment limit
#SS	If the top bytes of stack are not within stack limits.

Virtual 8086 Mode Exceptions

#GP(0)	If the return instruction pointer is not within the return code segment limit
#SS(0)	If the top bytes of stack are not within stack limits.
#PF(fault-code)	If a page fault occurs.
#AC(0)	If an unaligned memory access occurs when alignment checking is enabled.

ROL/ROR—Rotate

See entry for RCL/RCR/ROL/ROR.

®

RSM—Resume from System Management Mode

Opcode	Instruction	Description
0F AA	RSM	Resume operation of interrupted program

Description

Returns program control from system management mode (SMM) to the application program or operating system procedure that was interrupted when the processor received an SSM interrupt. The processor's state is restored from the dump created upon entering SMM. If the processor detects invalid state information during state restoration, it enters the shutdown state. The following invalid information can cause a shutdown:

- Any reserved bit of CR4 is set to 1.

- Any illegal combination of bits in CR0, such as (PG=1 and PE=0) or (NW=1 and CD=0).

- (Intel Pentium and Intel486 processors only.) The value stored in the state dump base field is not a 32-KByte aligned address.

The contents of the model-specific registers are not affected by a return from SMM.

See Chapter 9 in the *Pentium® Pro Family Developer's Manual, Volume 3* for more information about SMM and the behavior of the RSM instruction.

Operation

ReturnFromSSM;
ProcessorState ← Restore(SSMDump);

Flags Affected

All.

Protected Mode Exceptions

#UD   If an attempt is made to execute this instruction when the processor is not in SMM.

Real Address Mode Exceptions

#UD   If an attempt is made to execute this instruction when the processor is not in SMM.

Virtual 8086 Mode Exceptions

#UD   If an attempt is made to execute this instruction when the processor is not in SMM.

SAHF—Store AH into Flags

Opcode	Instruction	Clocks	Description
9E	SAHF	2	Loads SF, ZF, AF, PF, and CF from AH into EFLAGS register

Description

Loads the SF, ZF, AF, PF, and CF flags of the EFLAGS register with values from the corresponding bits in the AH register (bits 7, 6, 4, 2, and 0, respectively). Bits 1, 3, and 5 of register AH are ignored; the corresponding reserved bits (1, 3, and 5) in the EFLAGS registers are set as shown in the "Operation" below

Operation

EFLAGS(SF:ZF:0:AF:0:PF:1:CF) ← AH;

Flags Affected

The SF, ZF, AF, PF, and CF flags are loaded with values from the AH register. Bits 1, 3, and 5 of the EFLAGS register are set to 1, 0, and 0, respectively.

Exceptions (All Operating Modes)

None.

SAL/SAR/SHL/SHR—Shift Instructions

Opcode	Instruction	Description
D0 /4	SAL r/m8,1	Multiply r/m8 by 2, once
D2 /4	SAL r/m8,CL	Multiply r/m8 by 2, CL times
C0 /4 ib	SAL r/m8,imm8	Multiply r/m8 by 2, imm8 times
D1 /4	SAL r/m16,1	Multiply r/m16 by 2, once
D3 /4	SAL r/m16,CL	Multiply r/m16 by 2, CL times
C1 /4 ib	SAL r/m16,imm8	Multiply r/m16 by 2, imm8 times
D1 /4	SAL r/m32,1	Multiply r/m32 by 2, once
D3 /4	SAL r/m32,CL	Multiply r/m32 by 2, CL times
C1 /4 ib	SAL r/m32,imm8	Multiply r/m32 by 2, imm8 times
D0 /7	SAR r/m8,1	Signed divide* r/m8 by 2, once
D2 /7	SAR r/m8,CL	Signed divide* r/m8 by 2, CL times
C0 /7 ib	SAR r/m8,imm8	Signed divide* r/m8 by 2, imm8 times
D1 /7	SAR r/m16,1	Signed divide* r/m16 by 2, once
D3 /7	SAR r/m16,CL	Signed divide* r/m16 by 2, CL times
C1 /7 ib	SAR r/m16,imm8	Signed divide* r/m16 by 2, imm8 times
D1 /7	SAR r/m32,1	Signed divide* r/m32 by 2, once
D3 /7	SAR r/m32,CL	Signed divide* r/m32 by 2, CL times
C1 /7 ib	SAR r/m32,imm8	Signed divide* r/m32 by 2, imm8 times
D0 /4	SHL r/m8,1	Multiply r/m8 by 2, once
D2 /4	SHL r/m8,CL	Multiply r/m8 by 2, CL times
C0 /4 ib	SHL r/m8,imm8	Multiply r/m8 by 2, imm8 times
D1 /4	SHL r/m16,1	Multiply r/m16 by 2, once
D3 /4	SHL r/m16,CL	Multiply r/m16 by 2, CL times
C1 /4 ib	SHL r/m16,imm8	Multiply r/m16 by 2, imm8 times
D1 /4	SHL r/m32,1	Multiply r/m32 by 2, once
D3 /4	SHL r/m32,CL	Multiply r/m32 by 2, CL times
C1 /4 ib	SHL r/m32,imm8	Multiply r/m32 by 2, imm8 times
D0 /5	SHR r/m8,1	Unsigned divide r/m8 by 2, once
D2 /5	SHR r/m8,CL	Unsigned divide r/m8 by 2, CL times
C0 /5 ib	SHR r/m8,imm8	Unsigned divide r/m8 by 2, imm8 times
D1 /5	SHR r/m16,1	Unsigned divide r/m16 by 2, once
D3 /5	SHR r/m16,CL	Unsigned divide r/m16 by 2, CL times
C1 /5 ib	SHR r/m16,imm8	Unsigned divide r/m16 by 2, imm8 times
D1 /5	SHR r/m32,1	Unsigned divide r/m32 by 2, once
D3 /5	SHR r/m32,CL	Unsigned divide r/m32 by 2, CL times
C1 /5 ib	SHR r/m32,imm8	Unsigned divide r/m32 by 2, imm8 times

NOTE:

* Not the same form of division as IDIV; rounding is toward negative infinity.

Description

Shift the bits in the first operand (destination operand) to the left or right by the number of bits specified in the second operand (count operand). Bits shifted beyond the destination operand boundary are first shifted into the CF flag, then discarded. At the end of the shift operation, thc CF flag contains the last bit shifted out of the destination operand.

The destination operand can be a register or a memory location. The count operand can be an immediate value or register CL. The count is masked to 5 bits, which limits the count range to from 0 to 31. A special opcode encoding is provide for a count of 1.

The shift arithmetic left (SAL) and shift logical left (SHL) instructions perform the same operation; they shift the bits in the destination operand to the left (toward more significant bit locations). For each shift count, the most significant bit of the destination operand is shifted into the CF flag, and the least significant bit is cleared (see Figure 6-6).

The shift arithmetic right (SAR) and shift logical right (SHR) instructions shift the bits of the destination operand to the right (toward less significant bit locations). For each shift count, the least significant bit of the destination operand is shifted into the CF flag, and the most significant bit is either set or cleared depending on the instruction type. The SHR instruction clears the most significant bit (see Figure 6-7); the SAR instruction sets or clears the most significant bit to correspond to the sign (most significant bit) of the original value in the destination operand. In effect, the SAR instruction fills the empty bit position's shifted value with the sign of the unshifted value (see Figure 6-8).

The SAR and SHR instructions can be used to perform signed or unsigned division, respectively, of the destination operand by powers of 2. For example, using the SAR instruction shift a signed integer 1 bit to the right divides the value by 2.

Using the SAR instruction to perform a division operation does not produce the same result as the IDIV instruction. The quotient from the IDIV instruction is rounded toward zero, whereas the "quotient" of the SAR instruction is rounded toward negative infinity. This difference is apparent only for negative numbers. For example, when the IDIV instruction is used to divide -9 by 4, the result is -2 with a remainder of -1. If the SAR instruction is used to shift -9 right by two bits, the result is -3 and the "remainder" is +3; however, the SAR instruction stores only the most significant bit of the remainder (in the CF flag).

The OF flag is affected only on 1-bit shifts. For left shifts, the OF flag is cleared to 0 if the most-significant bit of the result is the same as the CF flag (that is, the top two bits of the original operand were the same); otherwise, it is set to 1. For the SAR instruction, the OF flag is cleared for all 1-bit shifts. For the SHR instruction, the OF flag is set to the most-significant bit of the original operand.

Operation

tempCOUNT ← COUNT;
tempDEST ← DEST;
WHILE (tempCOUNT ≠ 0)
DO
   IF instruction is SAL or SHL
      THEN
         CF ← MSB(DEST);
      ELSE (* instruction is SAR or SHR *)
         CF ← LSB(DEST);
   FI;
   IF instruction is SAL or SHL
      THEN
         DEST ← DEST * 2;
      ELSE
        IF instruction is SAR
           THEN
              DEST ← DEST / 2 (*Signed divide, rounding toward negative infinity*);
           ELSE (* instruction is SHR *)
              DEST ← DEST / 2 ; (* Unsigned divide *);
        FI;
   FI;
   temp ← temp − 1;
OD;
(* Determine overflow for the various instructions *)
IF COUNT = 1
   THEN
      IF instruction is SAL or SHL
         THEN
            OF ← MSB(DEST) XOR CF;
        ELSE
         IF instruction is SAR
           THEN
              OF ← 0;
           ELSE (* instruction is SHR *)
              OF ← MSB(tempDEST);
         FI;
      FI;
   ELSE
      OF ← undefined;
FI;

Flags Affected

The CF flag contains the value of the last bit shifted out of the destination operand; it is undefined for SHL and SHR instructions count is greater than or equal to the size of the destination operand. The OF flag is affected only for 1-bit shifts (see "Description" above); otherwise, it is undefined. The SF, ZF, and PF flags are set according to the result. If the count is 0, the flags are not affected.

Protected Mode Exceptions

#GP(0)	If the destination is located in a nonwritable segment.
	If a memory operand effective address is outside the CS, DS, ES, FS, or GS segment limit.
	If the DS, ES, FS, or GS register contains a null segment selector.
#SS(0)	If a memory operand effective address is outside the SS segment limit.
#PF(fault-code)	If a page fault occurs.
#AC(0)	If alignment checking is enabled and an unaligned memory reference is made while the current privilege level is 3.

Real Address Mode Exceptions

#GP	If a memory operand effective address is outside the CS, DS, ES, FS, or GS segment limit.
#SS	If a memory operand effective address is outside the SS segment limit.

Virtual 8086 Mode Exceptions

#GP(0)	If a memory operand effective address is outside the CS, DS, ES, FS, or GS segment limit.
#SS(0)	If a memory operand effective address is outside the SS segment limit.
#PF(fault-code)	If a page fault occurs.
#AC(0)	If alignment checking is enabled and an unaligned memory reference is made.

Intel Architecture Compatibility

The 8086 does not mask the shift count. All Intel Architecture processors from the Intel386 processor on do mask the rotation count in all operating modes.

SBB—Integer Subtraction with Borrow

Opcode	Instruction	Description
1C *ib*	SBB AL,*imm8*	Subtract with borrow *imm8* from AL
1D *iw*	SBB AX,*imm16*	Subtract with borrow *imm16* from AX
1D *id*	SBB EAX,*imm32*	Subtract with borrow *imm32* from EAX
80 /3 *ib*	SBB *r/m8,imm8*	Subtract with borrow *imm8* from *r/m8*
81 /3 *iw*	SBB *r/m16,imm16*	Subtract with borrow *imm16* from *r/m16*
81 /3 *id*	SBB *r/m32,imm32*	Subtract with borrow *imm32* from *r/m32*
83 /3 *ib*	SBB *r/m16,imm8*	Subtract with borrow sign-extended *imm8* from *r/m16*
83 /3 *ib*	SBB *r/m32,imm8*	Subtract with borrow sign-extended *imm8* from *r/m32*
18 /*r*	SBB *r/m8,r8*	Subtract with borrow *r8* from *r/m8*
19 /*r*	SBB *r/m16,r16*	Subtract with borrow *r16* from *r/m16*
19 /*r*	SBB *r/m32,r32*	Subtract with borrow *r32* from *r/m32*
1A /*r*	SBB *r8,r/m8*	Subtract with borrow *r/m8* from *r8*
1B /*r*	SBB *r16,r/m16*	Subtract with borrow *r/m16* from *r16*
1B /*r*	SBB *r32,r/m32*	Subtract with borrow *r/m32* from *r32*

Description

Adds the source operand (second operand) and the carry (CF) flag, and subtracts the result from the destination operand (first operand). The result of the subtraction is stored in the destination operand. The destination operand can be a register or a memory location; the source operand can be an immediate, a register, or a memory location. The state of the CF flag represents a borrow from a previous subtraction.

When an immediate value is used as an operand, it is sign-extended to the length of the destination operand format.

The SBB instruction does not distinguish between signed or unsigned operands. Instead, the processor evaluates the result for both data types and sets the OF and CF flags to indicate a borrow in the signed or unsigned result, respectively. The SF flag indicates the sign of the signed result.

The SBB instruction is usually executed as part of a multibyte or multiword subtraction in which a SUB instruction is followed by a SBB instruction.

Operation

DEST ← DEST – (SRC + CF);

Flags Affected

The OF, SF, ZF, AF, PF, and CF flags are set according to the result.

Protected Mode Exceptions

#GP(0)	If the destination is located in a nonwritable segment.
	If a memory operand effective address is outside the CS, DS, ES, FS, or GS segment limit.
	If the DS, ES, FS, or GS register contains a null segment selector.
#SS(0)	If a memory operand effective address is outside the SS segment limit.
#PF(fault-code)	If a page fault occurs.
#AC(0)	If alignment checking is enabled and an unaligned memory reference is made while the current privilege level is 3.

Real Address Mode Exceptions

#GP	If a memory operand effective address is outside the CS, DS, ES, FS, or GS segment limit.
#SS	If a memory operand effective address is outside the SS segment limit.

Virtual 8086 Mode Exceptions

#GP(0)	If a memory operand effective address is outside the CS, DS, ES, FS, or GS segment limit.
#SS(0)	If a memory operand effective address is outside the SS segment limit.
#PF(fault-code)	If a page fault occurs.
#AC(0)	If alignment checking is enabled and an unaligned memory reference is made.

SCAS/SCASB/SCASW/SCASD—Scan String Data

Opcode	Instruction	Description
AE	SCAS ES:(E)DI	Compare AL with byte at ES:(E)DI and set status flags
AF	SCAS ES:DI	Compare AX with word at ES:DI and set status flags
AF	SCAS ES:EDI	Compare EAX with doubleword at ES:EDI and set status flags
AE	SCASB	Compare AL with byte at ES:(E)DI and set status flags
AF	SCASW	Compare AX with word at ES:DI and set status flags
AF	SCASD	Compare EAX with doubleword at ES:EDI and set status flags

Description

Compares the byte, word, or double word specified with the source operand with the value in the AL, AX, or EAX register, respectively, and sets the status flags in the EFLAGS register according to the results. The source operand specifies the memory location at the address ES:EDI. (When the operand-size attribute is 16, the DI register is used as the source-index register.) The ES segment cannot be overridden with a segment override prefix.

The SCASB, SCASW, and SCASD mnemonics are synonyms of the byte, word, and double-word versions of the SCAS instructions. They are simpler to use, but provide no type or segment checking. (For the SCAS instruction, "ES:EDI" must be explicitly specified in the instruction.)

After the comparison, the EDI register is incremented or decremented automatically according to the setting of the DF flag in the EFLAGS register. (If the DF flag is 0, the EDI register is incremented; if the DF flag is 1, the EDI register is decremented.) The EDI register is incremented or decremented by 1 for byte operations, by 2 for word operations, or by 4 for doubleword operations.

The SCAS, SCASB, SCASW, and SCASD instructions can be preceded by the REP prefix for block comparisons of ECX bytes, words, or doublewords. More often, however, these instructions will be used in a LOOP construct that takes some action based on the setting of the status flags before the next comparison is made. See Chapter 11, "REP/REPE/REPZ/REPNE /REPNZ—Repeat String Operation Prefix" for a description of the REP prefix.

Operation

```
IF (byte cmparison)
    THEN
        temp ← AL − SRC;
        SetStatusFlags(temp);
            THEN IF DF = 0
                THEN (E)DI ← 1;
                ELSE (E)DI ← −1;
        FI;
    ELSE IF (word comparison)
        THEN
            temp ← AX − SRC;
```

```
            SetStatusFlags(temp)
                THEN IF DF = 0
                    THEN DI ← 2;
                    ELSE DI ← –2;
                FI;
        ELSE (* doubleword comparison *)
            temp ← EAX – SRC;
            SetStatusFlags(temp)
                THEN IF DF = 0
                    THEN EDI ← 4;
                    ELSE EDI ← –4;
                FI;
    FI;
FI;
```

Flags Affected

The OF, SF, ZF, AF, PF, and CF flags are set according to the temporary result of the comparison.

Protected Mode Exceptions

#GP(0)   If a memory operand effective address is outside the limit of the ES segment.

If the ES register contains a null segment selector.

If an illegal memory operand effective address in the ES segment is given.

#PF(fault-code)   If a page fault occurs.

#AC(0)   If alignment checking is enabled and an unaligned memory reference is made while the current privilege level is 3.

Real Address Mode Exceptions

#GP   If a memory operand effective address is outside the CS, DS, ES, FS, or GS segment limit.

#SS   If a memory operand effective address is outside the SS segment limit.

Virtual 8086 Mode Exceptions

#GP(0)   If a memory operand effective address is outside the CS, DS, ES, FS, or GS segment limit.

#SS(0)   If a memory operand effective address is outside the SS segment limit.

#PF(fault-code)   If a page fault occurs.

#AC(0)   If alignment checking is enabled and an unaligned memory reference is made.

SETcc—Set Byte on Condition

Opcode	Instruction	Description
0F 97	SETA r/m8	Set byte if above (CF=0 and ZF=0)
0F 93	SETAE r/m8	Set byte if above or equal (CF=0)
0F 92	SETB r/m8	Set byte if below (CF=1)
0F 96	SETBE r/m8	Set byte if below or equal (CF=1 or (ZF=1)
0F 92	SETC r/m8	Set if carry (CF=1)
0F 94	SETE r/m8	Set byte if equal (ZF=1)
0F 9F	SETG r/m8	Set byte if greater (ZF=0 and SF=OF)
0F 9D	SETGE r/m8	Set byte if greater or equal (SF=OF)
0F 9C	SETL r/m8	Set byte if less (SF<>OF)
0F 9E	SETLE r/m8	Set byte if less or equal (ZF=1 or SF<>OF)
0F 96	SETNA r/m8	Set byte if not above (CF=1 or ZF=1)
0F 92	SETNAE r/m8	Set byte if not above or equal (CF=1)
0F 93	SETNB r/m8	Set byte if not below (CF=0)
0F 97	SETNBE r/m8	Set byte if not below or equal (CF=0 and ZF=0)
0F 93	SETNC r/m8	Set byte if not carry (CF=0)
0F 95	SETNE r/m8	Set byte if not equal (ZF=0)
0F 9E	SETNG r/m8	Set byte if not greater (ZF=1 or SF<>OF)
0F 9C	SETNGE r/m8	Set if not greater or equal (SF<>OF)
0F 9D	SETNL r/m8	Set byte if not less (SF=OF)
0F 9F	SETNLE r/m8	Set byte if not less or equal (ZF=0 and SF=OF)
0F 91	SETNO r/m8	Set byte if not overflow (OF=0)
0F 9B	SETNP r/m8	Set byte if not parity (PF=0)
0F 99	SETNS r/m8	Set byte if not sign (SF=0)
0F 95	SETNZ r/m8	Set byte if not zero (ZF=0)
0F 90	SETO r/m8	Set byte if overflow (OF=1)
0F 9A	SETP r/m8	Set byte if parity (PF=1)
0F 9A	SETPE r/m8	Set byte if parity even (PF=1)
0F 9B	SETPO r/m8	Set byte if parity odd (PF=0)
0F 98	SETS r/m8	Set byte if sign (SF=1)
0F 94	SETZ r/m8	Set byte if zero (ZF=1)

Description

Set the destination operand to the value 0 or 1, depending on the settings of the status flags (CF, SF, OF, ZF, and PF) in the EFLAGS register. The destination operand points to a byte register or a byte in memory. The condition code suffix (cc) indicates the condition being tested for.

The terms "above" and "below" are associated with the CF flag and refer to the relationship between two unsigned integer values. The terms "greater" and "less" are associated with the SF and OF flags and refer to the relationship between two signed integer values.

Many of the SET*cc* instruction opcodes have alternate mnemonics. For example, the SETG (set byte if greater) and SETNLE (set if not less or equal) both have the same opcode and test for the same condition: ZF equals 0 and SF equals OF. These alternate mnemonics are provided to make code more intelligible. Appendix B, *EFLAGS Condition Codes*, shows the alternate mnemonics for various test conditions.

Some languages represent a logical one as an integer with all bits set. This representation can be arrived at by choosing the mutually exclusive condition for the SET*cc* instruction, then decrementing the result. For example, to test for overflow, use the SETNO instruction, then decrement the result.

Operation

```
IF condition
    THEN DEST ← 1
    ELSE DEST ← 0;
FI;
```

Flags Affected

None.

Protected Mode Exceptions

#GP(0)   If the destination is located in a nonwritable segment.

                If a memory operand effective address is outside the CS, DS, ES, FS, or GS segment limit.

                If the DS, ES, FS, or GS register contains a null segment selector.

#SS(0)   If a memory operand effective address is outside the SS segment limit.

#PF(fault-code) If a page fault occurs.

#AC(0)   If alignment checking is enabled and an unaligned memory reference is made while the current privilege level is 3.

Real Address Mode Exceptions

#GP   If a memory operand effective address is outside the CS, DS, ES, FS, or GS segment limit.

#SS   If a memory operand effective address is outside the SS segment limit.

Virtual 8086 Mode Exceptions

#GP(0)	If a memory operand effective address is outside the CS, DS, ES, FS, or GS segment limit.
#SS(0)	If a memory operand effective address is outside the SS segment limit.
#PF(fault-code)	If a page fault occurs.
#AC(0)	If alignment checking is enabled and an unaligned memory reference is made.

SGDT/SIDT—Store Global/Interrupt Descriptor Table Register

Opcode	Instruction	Description
0F 01 /0	SGDT *m*	Store GDTR to *m*
0F 01 /1	SIDT *m*	Store IDTR to *m*

Description

Stores the contents of the global descriptor table register (GDTR) or the interrupt descriptor table register (IDTR) in the destination operand. The destination operand is a pointer to 6-byte memory location. If the operand-size attribute is 32 bits, the 16-bit limit field of the register is stored in the lower 2 bytes of the memory location and the 32-bit base address is stored in the upper 4 bytes. If the operand-size attribute is 16 bits, the limit is stored in the lower 2 bytes and the 24-bit base address is stored in the third, fourth, and fifth byte, with the sixth byte is filled with 0s.

The SGDT and SIDT instructions are useful only in operating-system software; however, they can be used in application programs.

See Chapter 11, "LGDT/LIDT—Load Global/Interrupt Descriptor Table Register" for information on loading the GDTR and IDTR.

Operation

```
IF instruction is IDTR
    THEN
        IF OperandSize = 16
            THEN
                DEST[0:15] ← IDTR(Limit);
                DEST[16:39] ← IDTR(Base); (* 24 bits of base address loaded; *)
                DEST[40:47] ← 0;
            ELSE (* 32-bit Operand Size *)
                DEST[0:15] ← IDTR(Limit);
                DEST[16:47] ← IDTR(Base); (* full 32-bit base address loaded *)
        FI;
    ELSE (* instruction is SGDT *)
        IF OperandSize = 16
            THEN
                DEST[0:15] ← GDTR(Limit);
                DEST[16:39] ← GDTR(Base); (* 24 bits of base address loaded; *)
                DEST[40:47] ← 0;
            ELSE (* 32-bit Operand Size *)
                DEST[0:15] ← GDTR(Limit);
                DEST[16:47] ← GDTR(Base); (* full 32-bit base address loaded *)
        FI;
FI;
```

INSTRUCTION SET REFERENCE

Flags Affected

None.

Protected Mode Exceptions

#UD	If the destination operand is a register.
#GP(0)	If the destination is located in a nonwritable segment.
	If a memory operand effective address is outside the CS, DS, ES, FS, or GS segment limit.
	If the DS, ES, FS, or GS register is used to access memory and it contains a null segment selector.
#SS(0)	If a memory operand effective address is outside the SS segment limit.
#PF(fault-code)	If a page fault occurs.
#AC(0)	If an unaligned memory access occurs when the CPL is 3 and alignment checking is enabled.

Real Address Mode Exceptions

#UD	If the destination operand is a register.
#GP	If a memory operand effective address is outside the CS, DS, ES, FS, or GS segment limit.
#SS	If a memory operand effective address is outside the SS segment limit.

Virtual 8086 Mode Exceptions

#UD	If the destination operand is a register.
#GP(0)	If a memory operand effective address is outside the CS, DS, ES, FS, or GS segment limit.
#SS(0)	If a memory operand effective address is outside the SS segment limit.
#PF(fault-code)	If a page fault occurs.
#AC(0)	If an unaligned memory access occurs when alignment checking is enabled.

Intel Architecture Compatibility

The 16-bit forms of the SGDT and SIDT instructions are compatible with the Intel 286 processor, if the upper 8 bits are not referenced. The Intel 286 processor fills these bits with 1s; the Pentium Pro processor fills these bits with 0s.

SHL/SHR—Shift Instructions

See entry for SAL/SAR/SHL/SHR.

SHLD—Double Precision Shift Left

Opcode	Instruction	Description
0F A4	SHLD r/m16,r16,imm8	Shift r/m16 to left imm8 places while shifting bits from r16 in from the right
0F A5	SHLD r/m16,r16,CL	Shift r/m16 to left CL places while shifting bits from r16 in from the right
0F A4	SHLD r/m32,r32,imm8	Shift r/m32 to left imm8 places while shifting bits from r32 in from the right
0F A5	SHLD r/m32,r32,CL	Shift r/m32 to left CL places while shifting bits from r32 in from the right

Description

Shifts the first operand (destination operand) to the left the number of bits specified by the third operand (count operand). The second operand (source operand) provides bits to shift in from the right (starting with bit 0 of the destination operand). The destination operand can be a register or a memory location; the source operand is a register. The count operand is an unsigned integer that can be an immediate byte or the contents of the CL register. Only bits 0 through 4 of the count are used, which masks the count to a value between 0 and 31. If the count is greater than the operand size, the result in the destination operand is undefined.

If the count is 1 or greater, the CF flag is filled with the last bit shifted out of the destination operand. For a 1-bit shift, the OF flag is set if a sign change occurred; otherwise, it is cleared. If the count operand is 0, the flags are not affected.

The SHLD instruction is useful for multiprecision shifts of 64 bits or more.

Operation

```
COUNT ← COUNT MOD 32;
SIZE ← OperandSize
IF COUNT = 0
    THEN
        no operation
    ELSE
        IF COUNT ≥ SIZE
            THEN (* Bad parameters *)
                DEST is undefined;
                CF, OF, SF, ZF, AF, PF are undefined;
            ELSE (* Perform the shift *)
                CF ← BIT[DEST, SIZE – COUNT];
                (* Last bit shifted out on exit *)
                FOR i ← SIZE – 1 DOWNTO COUNT
                DO
                    Bit(DEST, i) ← Bit(DEST, i – COUNT);
                OD;
                FOR i ← COUNT – 1 DOWNTO 0
```

```
                    DO
                        BIT[DEST, i] ← BIT[SRC, i – COUNT + SIZE];
                    OD;
          FI;
FI;
```

Flags Affected

If the count is 1 or greater, the CF flag is filled with the last bit shifted out of the destination operand and the SF, ZF, and PF flags are set according to the value of the result. For a 1-bit shift, the OF flag is set if a sign change occurred; otherwise, it is cleared. For shifts greater than 1 bit, the OF flag is undefined. If a shift occurs, the AF flag is undefined. If the count operand is 0, the flags are not affected. If the count is greater than the operand size, the flags are undefined.

Protected Mode Exceptions

#GP(0)	If the destination is located in a nonwritable segment.
	If a memory operand effective address is outside the CS, DS, ES, FS, or GS segment limit.
	If the DS, ES, FS, or GS register contains a null segment selector.
#SS(0)	If a memory operand effective address is outside the SS segment limit.
#PF(fault-code)	If a page fault occurs.
#AC(0)	If alignment checking is enabled and an unaligned memory reference is made while the current privilege level is 3.

Real Address Mode Exceptions

#GP	If a memory operand effective address is outside the CS, DS, ES, FS, or GS segment limit.
#SS	If a memory operand effective address is outside the SS segment limit.

Virtual 8086 Mode Exceptions

#GP(0)	If a memory operand effective address is outside the CS, DS, ES, FS, or GS segment limit.
#SS(0)	If a memory operand effective address is outside the SS segment limit.
#PF(fault-code)	If a page fault occurs.
#AC(0)	If alignment checking is enabled and an unaligned memory reference is made.

SHRD—Double Precision Shift Right

Opcode	Instruction	Description
0F AC	SHRD r/m16,r16,imm8	Shift r/m16 to right imm8 places while shifting bits from r16 in from the left
0F AD	SHRD r/m16,r16,CL	Shift r/m16 to right CL places while shifting bits from r16 in from the left
0F AC	SHRD r/m32,r32,imm8	Shift r/m32 to right imm8 places while shifting bits from r32 in from the left
0F AD	SHRD r/m32,r32,CL	Shift r/m32 to right CL places while shifting bits from r32 in from the left

Description

Shifts the first operand (destination operand) to the right the number of bits specified by the third operand (count operand). The second operand (source operand) provides bits to shift in from the left (starting with the most significant bit of the destination operand). The destination operand can be a register or a memory location; the source operand is a register. The count operand is an unsigned integer that can be an immediate byte or the contents of the CL register. Only bits 0 through 4 of the count are used, which masks the count to a value between 0 and 31. If the count is greater than the operand size, the result in the destination operand is undefined.

If the count is 1 or greater, the CF flag is filled with the last bit shifted out of the destination operand. For a 1-bit shift, the OF flag is set if a sign change occurred; otherwise, it is cleared. If the count operand is 0, the flags are not affected.

The SHRD instruction is useful for multiprecision shifts of 64 bits or more.

Operation

```
COUNT ← COUNT MOD 32;
SIZE ← OperandSize
IF COUNT = 0
    THEN
        no operation
    ELSE
        IF COUNT ≥ SIZE
            THEN (* Bad parameters *)
                DEST is undefined;
                CF, OF, SF, ZF, AF, PF are undefined;
            ELSE (* Perform the shift *)
                CF ← BIT[DEST, COUNT − 1]; (* last bit shifted out on exit *)
                FOR i ← 0 TO SIZE − 1 − COUNT
                    DO
                        BIT[DEST, i] ← BIT[DEST, i − COUNT];
                    OD;
                FOR i ← SIZE − COUNT TO SIZE − 1
                    DO
```

$$BIT[DEST,i] \leftarrow BIT[inBits,i+COUNT - SIZE];$$
OD;

    FI;

FI;

Flags Affected

If the count is 1 or greater, the CF flag is filled with the last bit shifted out of the destination operand and the SF, ZF, and PF flags are set according to the value of the result. For a 1-bit shift, the OF flag is set if a sign change occurred; otherwise, it is cleared. For shifts greater than 1 bit, the OF flag is undefined. If a shift occurs, the AF flag is undefined. If the count operand is 0, the flags are not affected. If the count is greater than the operand size, the flags are undefined.

Protected Mode Exceptions

#GP(0)	If the destination is located in a nonwritable segment.
	If a memory operand effective address is outside the CS, DS, ES, FS, or GS segment limit.
	If the DS, ES, FS, or GS register contains a null segment selector.
#SS(0)	If a memory operand effective address is outside the SS segment limit.
#PF(fault-code)	If a page fault occurs.
#AC(0)	If alignment checking is enabled and an unaligned memory reference is made while the current privilege level is 3.

Real Address Mode Exceptions

#GP	If a memory operand effective address is outside the CS, DS, ES, FS, or GS segment limit.
#SS	If a memory operand effective address is outside the SS segment limit.

Virtual 8086 Mode Exceptions

#GP(0)	If a memory operand effective address is outside the CS, DS, ES, FS, or GS segment limit.
#SS(0)	If a memory operand effective address is outside the SS segment limit.
#PF(fault-code)	If a page fault occurs.
#AC(0)	If alignment checking is enabled and an unaligned memory reference is made.

SIDT—Store Interrupt Descriptor Table Register

See entry for SGDT/SIDT.

SLDT—Store Local Descriptor Table Register

Opcode	Instruction	Description
0F 00 /0	SLDT r/m16	Stores segment selector from LDTR in r/m16
0F 00 /0	SLDT r/m32	Store segment selector from LDTR in low-order 16 bits of r/m32; high-order 16 bits are undefined

Description

Stores the segment selector from the local descriptor table register (LDTR) in the destination operand. The destination operand can be a general-purpose register or a memory location. The segment selector stored with this instruction points to the LDT.

When the destination operand is a 32-bit register, the 16-bit segment selector is copied into the lower 16 bits of the register and the upper 16 bits of the register are cleared to 0s. With the destination operand is a memory location, the segment selector is written to memory as a 16-bit quantity, regardless of the operand size.

The SLDT instruction is only useful in operating-system software; however, it can be used in application programs. Also, this instruction can only be executed in protected mode.

Operation

DEST ← LDTR(SegmentSelector);

Flags Affected

None.

Protected Mode Exceptions

#GP(0)	If the destination is located in a nonwritable segment.
	If a memory operand effective address is outside the CS, DS, ES, FS, or GS segment limit.
	If the DS, ES, FS, or GS register is used to access memory and it contains a null segment selector.
#SS(0)	If a memory operand effective address is outside the SS segment limit.
#PF(fault-code)	If a page fault occurs.
#AC(0)	If alignment checking is enabled and an unaligned memory reference is made while the current privilege level is 3.

Real Address Mode Exceptions

#UD	The SLDT instruction is not recognized in real address mode.

Virtual 8086 Mode Exceptions

#UD   The SLDT instruction is not recognized in virtual 8086 mode.

SMSW—Store Machine Status Word

Opcode	Instruction	Description
0F 01 /4	SMSW r/m16	Store machine status word to r/m16
0F 01 /4	SMSW r32/m16	Store machine status word in low-order 16 bits of r32/m16; high-order 16 bits of r32 are undefined

Description

Stores the machine status word (bits 0 through 15 of control register CR0) into the destination operand. The destination operand can be a 16-bit general-purpose register or a memory location.

When the destination operand is a 32-bit register, the low-order 16 bits of register CR0 are copied into the low-order 16 bits of the register and the upper 16 bits of the register are undefined. With the destination operand is a memory location, the low-order 16 bits of register CR0 are written to memory as a 16-bit quantity, regardless of the operand size.

The SMSW instruction is only useful in operating-system software; however, it is not a privileged instruction and can be used in application programs.

This instruction is provided for compatibility with the Intel 286 processor; programs and procedures intended to run on the Pentium Pro, Pentium, Intel486, and Intel386 processors should use the MOV (control registers) instruction to load the machine status word.

Operation

DEST ← CR0[15:0]; (* MachineStatusWord *);

Flags Affected

None.

Protected Mode Exceptions

#GP(0)	If the destination is located in a nonwritable segment.
	If a memory operand effective address is outside the CS, DS, ES, FS, or GS segment limit.
	If the DS, ES, FS, or GS register is used to access memory and it contains a null segment selector.
#SS(0)	If a memory operand effective address is outside the SS segment limit.
#PF(fault-code)	If a page fault occurs.
#AC(0)	If alignment checking is enabled and an unaligned memory reference is made while the current privilege level is 3.

Real Address Mode Exceptions

#GP   If a memory operand effective address is outside the CS, DS, ES, FS, or GS segment limit.

Virtual 8086 Mode Exceptions

#GP(0)   If a memory operand effective address is outside the CS, DS, ES, FS, or GS segment limit.

#PF(fault-code)   If a page fault occurs.

#AC(0)   If alignment checking is enabled and an unaligned memory reference is made.

STC—Set Carry Flag

Opcode	Instruction	Description
F9	STC	Set CF flag

Description

Sets the CF flag in the EFLAGS register.

Operation

CF ← 1;

Flags Affected

The CF flag is set. The OF, ZF, SF, AF, and PF flags are unaffected.

Exceptions (All Operating Modes)

None.

STD—Set Direction Flag

Opcode	Instruction	Description
FD	STD	Set DF flag

Description

Sets the DF flag in the EFLAGS register. When the DF flag is set to 1, string operations decrement the index registers (ESI and/or EDI).

Operation

DF ← 1;

Flags Affected

The DF flag is set. The CF, OF, ZF, SF, AF, and PF flags are unaffected.

Operation

DF ← 1;

Exceptions (All Operating Modes)

None.

STI—Set Interrupt Flag

Opcode	Instruction	Description
FB	STI	Set interrupt flag; interrupts enabled at the end of the next instruction

Description

Sets the interrupt flag (IF) in the EFLAGS register. After the IF flag is set, the processor begins responding to external maskable interrupts after the next instruction is executed. If the STI instruction is followed by a CLI instruction (which clears the IF flag) the effect of the STI instruction is negated.

The IF flag and the STI and CLI instruction have no affect on the generation of exceptions and NMI interrupts.

The following decision table indicates the action of the STI instruction (bottom of the table) depending on the processor's mode of operating and the CPL and IOPL of the currently running program or procedure (top of the table).

PE =	0	1	1	1
VM =	X	0	0	1
CPL	X	≤ IOPL	> IOPL	=3
IOPL	X	X	X	=3
IF ← 1	Y	Y	N	Y
#GP(0)	N	N	Y	N

NOTES:

X Don't care

N Action in Column 1 not taken

Y Action in Column 1 taken

Operation

```
IF PE=0  (* Executing in real-address mode *)
    THEN
        IF ← 1;  (* Set Interrupt Flag *)
    ELSE  (* Executing in protected mode or virtual-8086 mode *)
        IF VM=0  (* Executing in protected mode*)
            THEN
                IF IOPL = 3
                    THEN
                        IF ← 1;
                    ELSE
                        IF  CPL ≤ IOPL
                            THEN
                                IF ← 1;
                            ELSE
                                #GP(0);
                        FI;
                FI;
            ELSE  (* Executing in Virtual-8086 mode *)
                #GP(0); (* Trap to virtual-8086 monitor *)
        FI;
FI;
```

Flags Affected

The IF flag is set to 1.

Protected Mode Exceptions

#GP(0)   If the CPL is greater (has less privilege) than the IOPL of the current
                    program or procedure.

Real Address Mode Exceptions

None.

Virtual 8086 Mode Exceptions

#GP(0)   If the CPL is greater (has less privilege) than the IOPL of the current
                    program or procedure.

STOS/STOSB/STOSW/STOSD—Store String Data

Opcode	Instruction	Description
AA	STOS ES:(E)DI	Store AL at address ES:(E)DI
AB	STOS ES:DI	Store AX at address ES:DI
AB	STOS ES:EDI	Store EAX at address ES:EDI
AA	STOSB	Store AL at address ES:(E)DI
AB	STOSW	Store AX at address ES:DI
AB	STOSD	Store EAX at address ES:EDI

Description

Stores a byte, word, or doubleword from the AL, AX, or EAX register, respectively, into the destination operand. The destination operand is a memory location at the address ES:EDI. (When the operand-size attribute is 16, the DI register is used as the source-index register.) The ES segment cannot be overridden with a segment override prefix.

The STOSB, STOSW, and STOSD mnemonics are synonyms of the byte, word, and doubleword versions of the STOS instructions. They are simpler to use, but provide no type or segment checking. (For the STOS instruction, "ES:EDI" must be explicitly specified in the instruction.)

After the byte, word, or doubleword is transfer from the AL, AX, or EAX register to the memory location, the EDI register is incremented or decremented automatically according to the setting of the DF flag in the EFLAGS register. (If the DF flag is 0, the EDI register is incremented; if the DF flag is 1, the EDI register is decremented.) The EDI register is incremented or decremented by 1 for byte operations, by 2 for word operations, or by 4 for doubleword operations.

The STOS, STOSB, STOSW, and STOSD instructions can be preceded by the REP prefix for block loads of ECX bytes, words, or doublewords. More often, however, these instructions are used within a LOOP construct, because data needs to be moved into the AL, AX, or EAX register before it can be stored. See Chapter 11, "REP/REPE/REPZ/REPNE /REPNZ—Repeat String Operation Prefix" for a description of the REP prefix.

Operation

```
IF (byte store)
    THEN
        DEST ← AL;
            THEN IF DF = 0
                THEN (E)DI ← 1;
                ELSE (E)DI ← –1;
            FI;
    ELSE IF (word store)
        THEN
            DEST ← AX;
                THEN IF DF = 0
                    THEN DI ← 2;
```

```
                    ELSE DI ← –2;
           FI;
     ELSE (* doubleword store *)
           DEST ← EAX;
                THEN IF DF = 0
                     THEN EDI ← 4;
                     ELSE EDI ← –4;
                FI;
   FI;
FI;
```

Flags Affected

None.

Protected Mode Exceptions

#GP(0)   If the destination is located in a nonwritable segment.

                    If a memory operand effective address is outside the limit of the ES
                    segment.

                    If the ES register contains a null segment selector.

#PF(fault-code)   If a page fault occurs.

#AC(0)   If alignment checking is enabled and an unaligned memory reference is
                    made while the current privilege level is 3.

Real Address Mode Exceptions

#GP   If a memory operand effective address is outside the CS, DS, ES, FS, or
                    GS segment limit.

#SS   If a memory operand effective address is outside the SS segment limit.

Virtual 8086 Mode Exceptions

#GP(0)   If a memory operand effective address is outside the CS, DS, ES, FS, or
                    GS segment limit.

#SS(0)   If a memory operand effective address is outside the SS segment limit.

#PF(fault-code)   If a page fault occurs.

#AC(0)   If alignment checking is enabled and an unaligned memory reference is
                    made.

STR—Store Task Register

Opcode	Instruction	Description
0F 00 /1	STR r/m16	Stores segment selector from TR in r/m16

Description

Stores the segment selector from the task register (TR) in the destination operand. The destination operand can be a general-purpose register or a memory location. The segment selector stored with this instruction points to the task state segment (TSS) for the currently running task.

When the destination operand is a 32-bit register, the 16-bit segment selector is copied into the lower 16 bits of the register and the upper 16 bits of the register are cleared to 0s. With the destination operand is a memory location, the segment selector is written to memory as a 16-bit quantity, regardless of operand size.

The STR instruction is useful only in operating-system software. It can only be executed in protected mode.

Operation

DEST ← TR(SegmentSelector);

Flags Affected

None.

Protected Mode Exceptions

#GP(0)	If the destination is a memory operand that is located in a nonwritable segment or if the effective address is outside the CS, DS, ES, FS, or GS segment limit.
	If the DS, ES, FS, or GS register is used to access memory and it contains a null segment selector.
#SS(0)	If a memory operand effective address is outside the SS segment limit.
#PF(fault-code)	If a page fault occurs.
#AC(0)	If alignment checking is enabled and an unaligned memory reference is made while the current privilege level is 3.

Real Address Mode Exceptions

#UD	The STR instruction is not recognized in real address mode.

Virtual 8086 Mode Exceptions

#UD	The STR instruction is not recognized in virtual 8086 mode.

SUB—Integer Subtraction

Opcode	Instruction	Description
2C *ib*	SUB AL,*imm8*	Subtract *imm8* from AL
2D *iw*	SUB AX,*imm16*	Subtract *imm16* from AX
2D *id*	SUB EAX,*imm32*	Subtract *imm32* from EAX
80 /5 *ib*	SUB *r/m8,imm8*	Subtract *imm8* from *r/m8*
81 /5 *iw*	SUB *r/m16,imm16*	Subtract *imm16* from *r/m16*
81 /5 *id*	SUB *r/m32,imm32*	Subtract *imm32* from *r/m32*
83 /5 *ib*	SUB *r/m16,imm8*	Subtract sign-extended *imm8* from *r/m16*
83 /5 *ib*	SUB *r/m32,imm8*	Subtract sign-extended *imm8* from *r/m32*
28 /r	SUB *r/m8,r8*	Subtract *r8* from *r/m8*
29 /r	SUB *r/m16,r16*	Subtract *r16* from *r/m16*
29 /r	SUB *r/m32,r32*	Subtract *r32* from *r/m32*
2A /r	SUB *r8,r/m8*	Subtract *r/m8* from *r8*
2B /r	SUB *r16,r/m16*	Subtract *r/m16* from *r16*
2B /r	SUB *r32,r/m32*	Subtract *r/m32* from *r32*

Description

Subtracts the second operand (source operand) from the first operand (destination operand) and stores the result in the destination operand. The destination operand can be a register or a memory location; the source operand can be an immediate, register, or memory location. When an immediate value is used as an operand, it is sign-extended to the length of the destination operand format.

The SUB instruction does not distinguish between signed or unsigned operands. Instead, the processor evaluates the result for both data types and sets the OF and CF flags to indicate a borrow in the signed or unsigned result, respectively. The SF flag indicates the sign of the signed result.

Operation

DEST ← DEST − SRC;

Flags Affected

The OF, SF, ZF, AF, PF, and CF flags are set according to the result.

Protected Mode Exceptions

#GP(0)   If the destination is located in a nonwritable segment.

If a memory operand effective address is outside the CS, DS, ES, FS, or GS segment limit.

If the DS, ES, FS, or GS register contains a null segment selector.

#SS(0)   If a memory operand effective address is outside the SS segment limit.

#PF(fault-code)   If a page fault occurs.

#AC(0)   If alignment checking is enabled and an unaligned memory reference is made while the current privilege level is 3.

Real Address Mode Exceptions

#GP   If a memory operand effective address is outside the CS, DS, ES, FS, or GS segment limit.

#SS   If a memory operand effective address is outside the SS segment limit.

Virtual 8086 Mode Exceptions

#GP(0)   If a memory operand effective address is outside the CS, DS, ES, FS, or GS segment limit.

#SS(0)   If a memory operand effective address is outside the SS segment limit.

#PF(fault-code)   If a page fault occurs.

#AC(0)   If alignment checking is enabled and an unaligned memory reference is made.

TEST—Logical Compare

Opcode	Instruction	Description
A8 *ib*	TEST AL,*imm8*	AND *imm8* with AL; set SF, ZF, PF according to result
A9 *iw*	TEST AX,*imm16*	AND *imm16* with AX; set SF, ZF, PF according to result
A9 *id*	TEST EAX,*imm32*	AND *imm32* with EAX; set SF, ZF, PF according to result
F6 /0 *ib*	TEST *r/m8*,*imm8*	AND *imm8* with *r/m8*; set SF, ZF, PF according to result
F7 /0 *iw*	TEST *r/m16*,*imm16*	AND *imm16* with *r/m16*; set SF, ZF, PF according to result
F7 /0 *id*	TEST *r/m32*,*imm32*	AND *imm32* with *r/m32*; set SF, ZF, PF according to result
84 /*r*	TEST *r/m8*,*r8*	AND *r8* with *r/m8*; set SF, ZF, PF according to result
85 /*r*	TEST *r/m16*,*r16*	AND *r16* with *r/m16*; set SF, ZF, PF according to result
85 /*r*	TEST *r/m32*,*r32*	AND *r32* with *r/m32*; set SF, ZF, PF according to result

Description

Computes the bit-wise logical AND of first operand (source 1 operand) and the second operand (source 2 operand) and sets the SF, ZF, and PF status flags according to the result. The result is then discarded.

Operation

```
TEMP ← SRC1 AND SRC2;
SF ← MSB(TEMP);
IF TEMP = 0
    THEN ZF ← 0;
    ELSE ZF ← 1;
FI:
PF ← BitwiseXNOR(TEMP[0:7]);
CF ← 0;
OF ← 0;
(*AF is Undefined*)
```

Flags Affected

The OF and CF flags are cleared to 0. The SF, ZF, and PF flags are set according to the result (see "Operation" above). The state of the AF flag is undefined.

Protected Mode Exceptions

#GP(0)	If a memory operand effective address is outside the CS, DS, ES, FS, or GS segment limit.
	If the DS, ES, FS, or GS register contains a null segment selector.
#SS(0)	If a memory operand effective address is outside the SS segment limit.
#PF(fault-code)	If a page fault occurs.

#AC(0)   If alignment checking is enabled and an unaligned memory reference is made while the current privilege level is 3.

Real Address Mode Exceptions

#GP   If a memory operand effective address is outside the CS, DS, ES, FS, or GS segment limit.

#SS   If a memory operand effective address is outside the SS segment limit.

Virtual 8086 Mode Exceptions

#GP(0)   If a memory operand effective address is outside the CS, DS, ES, FS, or GS segment limit.

#SS(0)   If a memory operand effective address is outside the SS segment limit.

#PF(fault-code)   If a page fault occurs.

#AC(0)   If alignment checking is enabled and an unaligned memory reference is made.

UD2—Undefined Instruction

Opcode	Instruction	Description
0F 0B	UD2	Raise invalid opcode exception

Description

Generates an invalid opcode. This instruction is provided for software testing to explicitly generate an invalid opcode. The opcode for this instruction is reserved for this purpose.

Other than raising the invalid opcode exception, this instruction is the same as the NOP instruction.

Operation

#UD (* Generates invalid opcode exception *);

Flags Affected

None.

Exceptions (All Operating Modes)

#UD   Instruction is guaranteed to raise an invalid opcode exception in all operating modes).

VERR, VERW—Verify a Segment for Reading or Writing

Opcode	Instruction	Description
0F 00 /4	VERR *r/m16*	Set ZF=1 if segment specified with *r/m16* can be read
0F 00 /5	VERW *r/m16*	Set ZF=1 if segment specified with *r/m16* can be written

Description

Verifies whether the code or data segment specified with the source operand is readable (VERR) or writable (VERW) from the current privilege level (CPL). The source operand is a 16-bit register or a memory location that contains the segment selector for the segment to be verified. If the segment is accessible and readable (VERR) or writable (VERW), the ZF flag is set; otherwise, the ZF flag is cleared. Code segments are never verified as writable. This check cannot be performed on system segments.

To set the ZF flag, the following conditions must be met:

- The segment selector is not null.

- The selector must denote a descriptor within the bounds of the descriptor table (GDT or LDT).

- The selector must denote the descriptor of a code or data segment (not that of a system segment or gate).

- For the VERR instruction, the segment must be readable; the VERW instruction, the segment must be a writable data segment.

- If the segment is not a conforming code segment, the segment's DPL must be greater than or equal to (have less or the same privilege as) both the CPL and the segment selector's RPL.

The validation performed is the same as if the segment were loaded into the DS, ES, FS, or GS register, and the indicated access (read or write) were performed. The selector's value cannot result in a protection exception, enabling the software to anticipate possible segment access problems.

Operation

```
IF SRC(Offset) > (GDTR(Limit) OR (LDTR(Limit))
        THEN
                ZF ← 0
Read segment descriptor;
IF SegmentDescriptor(DescriptorType) = 0 (* system segment *)
    OR (SegmentDescriptor(Type) ≠ conforming code segment)
    AND (CPL > DPL) OR (RPL > DPL)
        THEN
                ZF ← 0
        ELSE
```

```
          IF ((Instruction = VERR) AND (segment = readable))
              OR ((Instruction = VERW) AND (segment = writable))
              THEN
                  ZF ← 1;
          FI;
FI;
```

Flags Affected

The ZF flag is set to 1 if the segment is accessible and readable (VERR) or writable (VERW); otherwise, it is cleared to 0.

Protected Mode Exceptions

The only exceptions generated for these instructions are those related to illegal addressing of the source operand.

#GP(0)   If a memory operand effective address is outside the CS, DS, ES, FS, or GS segment limit.

                    If the DS, ES, FS, or GS register is used to access memory and it contains a null segment selector.

#SS(0)   If a memory operand effective address is outside the SS segment limit.

#PF(fault-code)   If a page fault occurs.

#AC(0)   If alignment checking is enabled and an unaligned memory reference is made while the current privilege level is 3.

Real Address Mode Exceptions

#UD   The VERR and VERW instructions are not recognized in real address mode.

Virtual 8086 Mode Exceptions

#UD   The VERR and VERW instructions are not recognized in virtual 8086 mode.

WAIT/FWAIT—Wait

Opcode	Instruction	Description
9B	WAIT	Check pending unmasked floating-point exceptions.
9B	FWAIT	Check pending unmasked floating-point exceptions.

Description

Causes the processor to check for and handle pending unmasked floating-point exceptions before proceeding. (FWAIT is an alternate mnemonic for the WAIT).

This instruction is useful for synchronizing exceptions in critical sections of code. Coding a WAIT instruction after a floating-point instruction insures that any unmasked floating-point exceptions the instruction may raise are handled before the processor can modify the instruction's results. See Section 7.9., "Floating-Point Exception Synchronization" for more information on using the WAIT/FWAIT instruction.

Operation

CheckPendingUnmaskedFloatingPointExceptions;

FPU Flags Affected

The C0, C1, C2, and C3 flags are undefined.

Floating-Point Exceptions

None.

Protected Mode Exceptions

#NM   MP and TS in CR0 is set.

Real Address Mode Exceptions

#NM   MP and TS in CR0 is set.

Virtual 8086 Mode Exceptions

#NM   MP and TS in CR0 is set.

WBINVD—Write-Back and Invalidate Cache

Opcode	Instruction	Description
0F 09	WBINVD	Write-back and flush Internal caches; initiate writing-back and flushing of external caches.

Description

Writes back all modified cache lines in the processor's internal cache to main memory, invalidates (flushes) the internal caches, and issues a special-function bus cycle that directs external caches to also write back modified data.

After executing this instruction, the processor does not wait for the external caches to complete their write-back and flushing operations before proceeding with instruction execution. It is the responsibility of hardware to respond to the cache write-back and flush signals.

The WDINVD instruction is a privileged instruction. When the processor is running in protected mode, the CPL of a program or procedure must be 0 to execute this instruction. This instruction is also a serializing instruction (see "Serializing Instructions" in Chapter 7, *Multiple Processor Management*, of the *Pentium® Pro Family Developer's Manual, Volume 3*).

In situations where cache coherency with main memory is not a concern, software can use the INVD instruction.

Operation

```
WriteBack(InternalCaches);
Flush(InternalCaches);
SignalWriteBack(ExternalCaches);
SignalFlush(ExternalCaches);
Continue (* Continue execution);
```

Flags Affected

None.

Protected Mode Exceptions

#GP(0)   If the current privilege level is not 0.

Real Address Mode Exceptions

None.

Virtual 8086 Mode Exceptions

#GP(0)   The WBINVD instruction cannot be executed at the virtual 8086 mode.

Intel Architecture Compatibility

The WDINVD instruction implementation-dependent; its function may be implemented differently on future Intel Architecture processors. The instruction is not supported on Intel Architecture processors earlier than the Intel486 processor.

WRMSR—Write to Model Specific Register

Opcode	Instruction	Description
0F 30	WRMSR	Write the value in EDX:EAX to MSR specified by ECX

Description

Writes the contents of registers EDX:EAX into the 64-bit model specific register (MSR) specified in the ECX register. The high-order 32 bits are copied from EDX and the low-order 32 bits are copied from EAX. Always set undefined or reserved bits in an MSR to the values previously read.

This instruction must be executed at privilege level 0 or in real-address mode; otherwise, a general protection exception #GP(0) will be generated. Specifying a reserved or unimplemented MSR address in ECX will also cause a general protection exception.

When the WRMSR instruction is used to write to an MTRR, the TLBs are invalidated, including the global entries (see "Translation Lookaside Buffers (TLBs)" in Chapter 3, *Protected-Mode Memory Management*, of the *Pentium® Pro Family Developer's Manual, Volume 3*).

The MSRs control functions for testability, execution tracing, performance-monitoring and machine check errors. Appendix D in the *Pentium® Pro Family Developer's Manual, Volume 3* lists all the MSRs that can be written to with this instruction and their addresses.

The WRMSR instruction is a serializing instruction (see "Serializing Instructions" in Chapter 7, *Multiple Processor Management*, of the *Pentium® Pro Family Developer's Manual, Volume 3*).

The CPUID instruction should be used to determine whether MSRs are supported (EDX[5]=1) before using this instruction.

Operation

MSR[ECX] ← EDX:EAX;

Flags Affected

None.

Protected Mode Exceptions

#GP(0)	If the current privilege level is not 0.
	If the value in ECX specifies a reserved or unimplemented MSR address.

Real Address Mode Exceptions

#GP	If the current privilege level is not 0
	If the value in ECX specifies a reserved or unimplemented MSR address.

Virtual 8086 Mode Exceptions

#GP(0)   The WRMSR instruction is not recognized in virtual 8086 mode.

Intel Architecture Compatibility

The MSRs and the ability to read them with the WRMSR instruction were introduced into the Intel Architecture with the Pentium processor. Execution of this instruction by an Intel Architecture processor earlier than the Pentium processor results in an invalid opcode exception #UD.

XADD—Exchange and Add

Opcode	Instruction	Description
0F C0/r	XADD r/m8,r8	Exchange r8 and r/m8; load sum into r/m8.
0F C1/r	XADD r/m16,r16	Exchange r16 and r/m16; load sum into r/m16.
0F C1/r	XADD r/m32,r32	Exchange r32 and r/m32; load sum into r/m32.

Description

Exchanges the first operand (destination operand) with the second operand (source operand), then loads the sum of the two values into the destination operand. The destination operand can be a register or a memory location; the source operand is a register.

This instruction can be used with a LOCK prefix.

Operation

TEMP ← SRC + DEST
SRC ← DEST
DEST ← TEMP

Flags Affected

The CF, PF, AF, SF, ZF, and OF flags are set according to the result stored in the destination operand.

Protected Mode Exceptions

#GP(0)	If the destination is located in a nonwritable segment.
	If a memory operand effective address is outside the CS, DS, ES, FS, or GS segment limit.
	If the DS, ES, FS, or GS register contains a null segment selector.
#SS(0)	If a memory operand effective address is outside the SS segment limit.
#PF(fault-code)	If a page fault occurs.
#AC(0)	If alignment checking is enabled and an unaligned memory reference is made while the current privilege level is 3.

Real Address Mode Exceptions

#GP	If a memory operand effective address is outside the CS, DS, ES, FS, or GS segment limit.
#SS	If a memory operand effective address is outside the SS segment limit.

Virtual 8086 Mode Exceptions

#GP(0)	If a memory operand effective address is outside the CS, DS, ES, FS, or GS segment limit.
#SS(0)	If a memory operand effective address is outside the SS segment limit.
#PF(fault-code)	If a page fault occurs.
#AC(0)	If alignment checking is enabled and an unaligned memory reference is made.

Intel Architecture Compatibility

Intel Architecture processors earlier than the Intel486 processor do not recognize this instruction. If this instruction is used, you should provide an equivalent code sequence that runs on earlier processors.

XCHG—Exchange Register/Memory with Register

Opcode	Instruction	Description
90+*rw*	XCHG AX,*r16*	Exchange *r16* with AX
90+*rw*	XCHG *r16*,AX	Exchange *r16* with AX
90+*rd*	XCHG EAX,*r32*	Exchange *r32* with EAX
90+*rd*	XCHG *r32*,EAX	Exchange *r32* with EAX
86 /*r*	XCHG *r/m8*,*r8*	Exchange byte register with EA byte
86 /*r*	XCHG *r8*,*r/m8*	Exchange byte register with EA byte
87 /*r*	XCHG *r/m16*,*r16*	Exchange *r16* with EA word
87 /*r*	XCHG *r16*,*r/m16*	Exchange *r16* with EA word
87 /*r*	XCHG *r/m32*,*r32*	Exchange *r32* with EA doubleword
87 /*r*	XCHG *r32*,*r/m32*	Exchange *r32* with EA doubleword

Description

Exchanges the contents of the destination (first) and source (second) operands. The operands can be two general-purpose registers or a register and a memory location. When the operands are two registers, one of the registers must be the EAX or AX register. If a memory operand is referenced, the LOCK# signal is automatically asserted for the duration of the exchange operation, regardless of the presence or absence of the LOCK prefix or of the value of the IOPL.

This instruction is useful for implementing semaphores or similar data structures for process synchronization. (See Chapter 5, *Processor Management and Initialization*, in the *Pentium® Pro Family Developer's Manual, Volume 3* for more information on bus locking.)

The XCHG instruction can also be used instead of the BSWAP instruction for 16-bit operands.

Operation

TEMP ← DEST
DEST ← SRC
SRC ← TEMP

Flags Affected

None.

Protected Mode Exceptions

#GP(0)   If either operand is in a nonwritable segment.

If a memory operand effective address is outside the CS, DS, ES, FS, or GS segment limit.

If the DS, ES, FS, or GS register contains a null segment selector.

#SS(0)   If a memory operand effective address is outside the SS segment limit.

#PF(fault-code)   If a page fault occurs.

#AC(0)   If alignment checking is enabled and an unaligned memory reference is made while the current privilege level is 3.

Real Address Mode Exceptions

#GP   If a memory operand effective address is outside the CS, DS, ES, FS, or GS segment limit.

#SS   If a memory operand effective address is outside the SS segment limit.

Virtual 8086 Mode Exceptions

#GP(0)   If a memory operand effective address is outside the CS, DS, ES, FS, or GS segment limit.

#SS(0)   If a memory operand effective address is outside the SS segment limit.

#PF(fault-code)   If a page fault occurs.

#AC(0)   If alignment checking is enabled and an unaligned memory reference is made.

XLAT/XLATB—Table Look-up Translation

Opcode	Instruction	Description
D7	XLAT m8	Set AL to memory byte DS:[(E)BX + unsigned AL]
D7	XLATB	Set AL to memory byte DS:[(E)BX + unsigned AL]

Description

Locates a byte entry in a table in memory, using the contents of the AL register as a table index, then copies the contents of the table entry back into the AL register. The index in the AL register is treated as unsigned integer. The XLAT and XLATB instructions get the base address of the table in memory from the DS:EBX registers (or the DS:BX registers when the address-size attribute of 16 bits.) The XLAT instruction allows a different segment register to be specified with a segment override. When assembled, the XLAT and XLATB instructions produce the same machine code.

Operation

```
IF AddressSize = 16
    THEN
        AL ← (DS:BX + ZeroExtend(AL))
    ELSE (* AddressSize = 32 *)
        AL ← (DS:EBX + ZeroExtend(AL));
FI;
```

Flags Affected

None.

Protected Mode Exceptions

#GP(0)	If a memory operand effective address is outside the CS, DS, ES, FS, or GS segment limit.
	If the DS, ES, FS, or GS register contains a null segment selector.
#SS(0)	If a memory operand effective address is outside the SS segment limit.
#PF(fault-code)	If a page fault occurs.
#AC(0)	If alignment checking is enabled and an unaligned memory reference is made while the current privilege level is 3.

Real Address Mode Exceptions

#GP	If a memory operand effective address is outside the CS, DS, ES, FS, or GS segment limit.
#SS	If a memory operand effective address is outside the SS segment limit.

Virtual 8086 Mode Exceptions

#GP(0)   If a memory operand effective address is outside the CS, DS, ES, FS, or GS segment limit.

#SS(0)   If a memory operand effective address is outside the SS segment limit.

#PF(fault-code) If a page fault occurs.

#AC(0)   If alignment checking is enabled and an unaligned memory reference is made.

XOR—Logical Exclusive OR

Opcode	Instruction	Description
34 ib	XOR AL,imm8	AL XOR imm8
35 iw	XOR AX,imm16	AX XOR imm16
35 id	XOR EAX,imm32	EAX XOR imm32
80 /6 ib	XOR r/m8,imm8	r/m8 XOR imm8
81 /6 iw	XOR r/m16,imm16	r/m16 XOR imm16
81 /6 id	XOR r/m32,imm32	r/m32 XOR imm32
83 /6 ib	XOR r/m16,imm8	r/m16 XOR imm8
83 /6 ib	XOR r/m32,imm8	r/m32 XOR imm8
30 /r	XOR r/m8,r8	r/m8 XOR r8
31 /r	XOR r/m16,r16	r/m16 XOR r16
31 /r	XOR r/m32,r32	r/m32 XOR r32
32 /r	XOR r8,r/m8	r8 XOR r/m8
33 /r	XOR r16,r/m16	r8 XOR r/m8
33 /r	XOR r32,r/m32	r8 XOR r/m8

Description

Performs a bitwise exclusive-OR (XOR) operation on the destination (first) and source (second) operands and stores the result in the destination operand location. The source operand can be an immediate, a register, or a memory location; the destination operand can be a register or a memory location.

Operation

DEST ← DEST XOR SRC;

Flags Affected

The OF and CF flags are cleared; the SF, ZF, and PF flags are set according to the result. The state of the AF flag is undefined.

Protected Mode Exceptions

#GP(0)   If the destination operand points to a nonwritable segment.

If a memory operand effective address is outside the CS, DS, ES, FS, or GS segment limit.

If the DS, ES, FS, or GS register contains a null segment selector.

#SS(0)   If a memory operand effective address is outside the SS segment limit.

#PF(fault-code) If a page fault occurs.

#AC(0)   If alignment checking is enabled and an unaligned memory reference is made while the current privilege level is 3.

Real Address Mode Exceptions

#GP   If a memory operand effective address is outside the CS, DS, ES, FS, or GS segment limit.

#SS   If a memory operand effective address is outside the SS segment limit.

Virtual 8086 Mode Exceptions

#GP(0)   If a memory operand effective address is outside the CS, DS, ES, FS, or GS segment limit.

#SS(0)   If a memory operand effective address is outside the SS segment limit.

#PF(fault-code) If a page fault occurs.

#AC(0)   If alignment checking is enabled and an unaligned memory reference is made.

intel®

A

EFLAGS
Cross-Reference

APPENDIX A
EFLAGS CROSS-REFERENCE

The cross-reference in Table A-1 summarizes how the flags in the processor's EFLAGS register are affected by each instruction. For detailed information on how flags are affected, see Chapter 11, *Instruction Set Reference*. The following codes describe the how the flags are affected:

T	Instruction tests flag.
M	Instruction modifies flag (either sets or resets depending on operands).
0	Instruction resets flag.
1	Instruction sets flag.
—	Instruction's effect on flag is undefined.
R	Instruction restores prior value of flag.
Blank	Instruction does not affect flag.

Table A-1. EFLAGS Cross-Reference

Instruction	OF	SF	ZF	AF	PF	CF	TF	IF	DF	NT	RF
AAA	—	—	—	TM	—	M					
AAD	—	M	M	—	M	—					
AAM	—	M	M	—	M	—					
AAS	—	—	—	TM	—	M					
ADC	M	M	M	M	M	TM					
ADD	M	M	M	M	M	M					
AND	0	M	M	—	M	0					
ARPL			M								
BOUND											
BSF/BSR	—	—	M	—	—	—					
BSWAP											
BT/BTS/BTR/BTC	—	—	—	—	—	M					

Table A-1. EFLAGS Cross-Reference (Contd.)

Instruction	OF	SF	ZF	AF	PF	CF	TF	IF	DF	NT	RF
CALL											
CBW											
CLC						0					
CLD									0		
CLI								0			
CLTS											
CMC						M					
CMOV*cc*	T	T	T		T	T					
CMP	M	M	M	M	M	M					
CMPS	M	M	M	M	M	M			T		
CMPXCHG	M	M	M	M	M	M					
CMPXCHG8B			M								
CPUID											
CWD											
DAA	—	M	M	TM	M	TM					
DAS	—	M	M	TM	M	TM					
DEC	M	M	M	M	M						
DIV	—	—	—	—	—	—					
ENTER											
ESC											
FCMOV*cc*			T		T	T					
FCOMI, FCOMIP, FUCOMI, FUCOMIP			M		M	M					
HLT											
IDIV	—	—	—	—	—	—					
IMUL	M	—	—	—	—	M					
IN											
INC	M	M	M	M	M						
INS									T		
INT							0			0	
INTO	T						0			0	
INVD											
INVLPG											

Table A-1. EFLAGS Cross-Reference (Contd.)

Instruction	OF	SF	ZF	AF	PF	CF	TF	IF	DF	NT	RF
IRET	R	R	R	R	R	R	R	R	R	T	
Jcc	T	T	T		T	T					
JCXZ											
JMP											
LAHF											
LAR			M								
LDS/LES/LSS/LFS/LGS											
LEA											
LEAVE											
LGDT/LIDT/LLDT/LMSW											
LOCK											
LODS									T		
LOOP											
LOOPE/LOOPNE			T								
LSL			M								
LTR											
MOV											
MOV control, debug, test	—	—	—	—	—	—					
MOVS									T		
MOVSX/MOVZX											
MUL	M	—	—	—	—	M					
NEG	M	M	M	M	M	M					
NOP											
NOT											
OR	0	M	M	—	M	0					
OUT											
OUTS									T		
POP/POPA											
POPF	R	R	R	R	R	R	R	R	R	R	
PUSH/PUSHA/PUSHF											
RCL/RCR 1	M					TM					
RCL/RCR count	—					TM					

Table A-1. EFLAGS Cross-Reference (Contd.)

Instruction	OF	SF	ZF	AF	PF	CF	TF	IF	DF	NT	RF
RDMSR											
RDPMC											
RDTSC											
REP/REPE/REPNE											
RET											
ROL/ROR 1	M					M					
ROL/ROR count	—					M					
RSM	M	M	M	M	M	M	M	M	M	M	M
SAHF		R	R	R	R	R					
SAL/SAR/SHL/SHR 1	M	M	M	—	M	M					
SAL/SAR/SHL/SHR count	—	M	M	—	M	M					
SBB	M	M	M	M	M	TM					
SCAS	M	M	M	M	M	M			T		
SETcc	T	T	T		T	T					
SGDT/SIDT/SLDT/SMSW											
SHLD/SHRD	—	M	M	—	M	M					
STC						1					
STD									1		
STI								1			
STOS									T		
STR											
SUB	M	M	M	M	M	M					
TEST	0	M	M	—	M	0					
UD2											
VERR/VERRW			M								
WAIT											
WBINVD											
WRMSR											
XADD	M	M	M	M	M	M					
XCHG											
XLAT											
XOR	0	M	M	—	M	0					

intel.

B

EFLAGS
Condition Codes

APPENDIX B
EFLAGS CONDITION CODES

Table B-1 gives all the condition codes that can be tested for by the CMOV*cc*, FCMOV*cc*, J*cc* and SET*cc* instructions. The condition codes refer to the setting of one or more status flags (CF, OF, SF, ZF, and PF) in the EFLAGS register. The "Mnemonic" column gives the suffix (*cc*) added to the instruction to specific the test condition. The "Condition Tested For" column describes the condition specified in the "Status Flag Setting" column. The "Instruction Subcode" column gives the opcode suffix added to the main opcode to specify a test condition.

Table B-1. EFLAGS Condition Codes

Mnemonic (*cc*)	Condition Tested For	Instruction Subcode	Status Flags Setting
O	Overflow	0000	OF = 1
NO	No overflow	0001	OF = 0
B NAE	Below Neither above nor equal	0010	CF = 1
NB AE	Not below Above or equal	0011	CF = 0
E Z	Equal Zero	0100	ZF = 1
NE NZ	Not equal Not zero	0101	ZF = 0
BE NA	Below or equal Not above	0110	(CF OR ZF) = 1
NBE A	Neither below nor equal Above	0111	(CF OR ZF) = 0
S	Sign	1000	SF = 1
NS	No sign	1001	SF = 0
P PE	Parity Parity even	1010	PF = 1
NP PO	No parity Parity odd	1011	PF = 0
Mnemonic	Meaning	Instruction Subcode	Condition Tested
L NGE	Less Neither greater nor equal	1100	(SF xOR OF) = 1
NL GE	Not less Greater or equal	1101	(SF xOR OF) = 0

Table B-1. EFLAGS Condition Codes (Contd.)

Mnemonic (*cc*)	Condition Tested For	Instruction Subcode	Status Flags Setting
LE NG	Less or equal Not greater	1110	((SF XOR OF) OR ZF) = 1
NLE G	Neither less nor equal Greater	1111	((SF XOR OF) OR ZF) = 0

Many of the test conditions are described in two different ways. For example LE (less or equal) and NG (not greater) describe the same test condition. Alternate mnemonics are provided to make code more intelligible.

The terms "above" and "below" are associated with the CF flag and refer to the relation between two unsigned integer values. The terms "greater" and "less" are associated with the SF and OF flags and refer to the relation between two signed integer values.

intel®

C

Floating-Point
Exceptions Summary

APPENDIX C
FLOATING-POINT EXCEPTIONS SUMMARY

Table C-1 lists the floating-point instruction mnemonics in alphabetical order. For each mnemonic, it summarizes the exceptions that the instruction may cause. See Section 7.8., "Floating-Point Exception Conditions" for a detailed discussion of the floating-point exceptions. The following codes indicate the floating-point exceptions:

#IS	Invalid-operation exception for stack underflow or stack overflow.
#IA	Invalid-operation exception for invalid arithmetic operands and unsupported formats.
#D	Denormal-operand exception.
#Z	Divide-by-zero exception.
#O	Numeric-overflow exception.
#U	Numeric-underflow exception.
#P	Inexact-result (precision) exception.

Table C-1. Floating-Point Exceptions Summary

Mnemonic	Instruction	#IS	#IA	#D	#Z	#O	#U	#P
F2XM1	2^X-1	Y	Y	Y			Y	Y
FABS	Absolute value	Y						
FADD(P)	Add real	Y	Y	Y		Y	Y	Y
FBLD	BCD load	Y						
FBSTP	BCD store and pop	Y	Y					Y
FCHS	Change sign	Y						
FCLEX	Clear exceptions							
FCMOV*cc*	Floating-point conditional move	Y						
FCOM, FCOMP, FCOMPP	Compare real	Y	Y	Y				
FCOMI, FCOMIP, FUCOMI, FUCOMIP	Compare real and set EFLAGS	Y	Y					
FCOS	Cosine	Y	Y	Y			Y	Y
FDECSTP	Decrement stack pointer							
FDIV(R)(P)	Divide real	Y	Y	Y	Y	Y	Y	Y
FFREE	Free register							

Table C-1. Floating-Point Exceptions Summary (Contd.)

Mnemonic	Instruction	#IS	#IA	#D	#Z	#O	#U	#P
FIADD	Integer add	Y	Y	Y		Y	Y	Y
FICOM(P)	Integer compare	Y	Y	Y				
FIDIV	Integer divide	Y	Y	Y	Y		Y	Y
FIDIVR	Integer divide reversed	Y	Y	Y	Y	Y	Y	Y
FILD	Integer load	Y						
FIMUL	Integer multiply	Y	Y	Y		Y	Y	Y
FINCSTP	Increment stack pointer							
FINIT	Initialize processor							
FIST(P)	Integer store	Y	Y					Y
FISUB(R)	Integer subtract	Y	Y	Y		Y	Y	Y
FLD extended or stack	Load real	Y						
FLD single or double	Load real	Y	Y	Y				
FLD1	Load + 1.0	Y						
FLDCW	Load Control word	Y	Y	Y	Y	Y	Y	Y
FLDENV	Load environment	Y	Y	Y	Y	Y	Y	Y
FLDL2E	Load $\log_2 e$	Y						
FLDL2T	Load $\log_2 10$	Y						
FLDLG2	Load $\log_{10} 2$	Y						
FLDLN2	Load $\log_e 2$	Y						
FLDPI	Load π	Y						
FLDZ	Load + 0.0	Y						
FMUL(P)	Multiply real	Y	Y	Y		Y	Y	Y
FNOP	No operation							
FPATAN	Partial arctangent	Y	Y	Y			Y	Y
FPREM	Partial remainder	Y	Y	Y			Y	
FPREM1	IEEE partial remainder	Y	Y	Y			Y	
FPTAN	Partial tangent	Y	Y	Y			Y	Y
FRNDINT	Round to integer	Y	Y	Y				Y
FRSTOR	Restore state	Y	Y	Y	Y	Y	Y	Y
FSAVE	Save state							
FSCALE	Scale	Y	Y	Y		Y	Y	Y
FSIN	Sine	Y	Y	Y			Y	Y
FSINCOS	Sine and cosine	Y	Y	Y			Y	Y

Table C-1. Floating-Point Exceptions Summary (Contd.)

Mnemonic	Instruction	#IS	#IA	#D	#Z	#O	#U	#P
FSQRT	Square root	Y	Y	Y				Y
FST(P) stack or extended	Store real	Y						
FST(P) single or double	Store real	Y	Y	Y		Y	Y	Y
FSTCW	Store control word							
FSTENV	Store environment							
FSTSW (AX)	Store status word							
FSUB(R)(P)	Subtract real	Y	Y	Y		Y	Y	Y
FTST	Test	Y	Y	Y				
FUCOM(P)(P)	Unordered compare real	Y	Y	Y				
FWAIT	CPU Wait							
FXAM	Examine							
FXCH	Exchange registers	Y						
FXTRACT	Extract	Y	Y	Y	Y			
FYL2X	$Y \cdot \log_2 X$	Y	Y	Y	Y	Y	Y	Y
FYL2XP1	$Y \cdot \log_2(X + 1)$	Y	Y	Y			Y	Y

intel®

Index

intel

INDEX

NORTH AMERICAN SALES OFFICES

ARIZONA

Intel Corp.
410 North 44th Street
Suite 470
Phoenix 85008
Tel: (800) 628-8686
FAX: (602) 244-0446

CALIFORNIA

Intel Corp.
26707 W. Agoura Road
Suite 203
Calabasas, CA 91302
Tel: (800) 628-8686
FAX: (818)-880-1820

Intel Corp.
3550 Watt Avenue
Suite 140
Sacramento 95821
Tel: (800) 628-8686
FAX: (916) 979-7011

Intel Corp.
9655 Granite Ridge Drive
3rd Floor
Suite 4A
San Diego 92123
Tel: (800) 628-8686
FAX: (619) 467-2460

Intel Corp.
1781 Fox Drive
San Jose 95131
Tel: (800) 628-8686
FAX: (408) 441-9540

Intel Corp.
1551 North Tustin Avenue
Suite 800
Santa Ana 92701
Tel: (800) 628-8686
TWX: (910) 595-1114
FAX: (714) 541-9157

Intel Corp.
514 Via de la Valle
Suite 208-RCO
Solana Beach 92075

Intel Corp.
1960 E. Grand Avenue
Suite 150
El Segundo, CA 90245
Tel: (800) 628-8686
FAX: (310) 640-7133

COLORADO

Intel Corp.
600 South Cherry Street
Suite 700
Denver 80222
Tel: (800) 628-8686
TWX: 910-931-2289
FAX: (303) 322-8670

CONNECTICUT

Intel Corp.
40 Old Ridgebury Road
Suite 311
Danbury 06811
Tel: (800) 628-8686
FAX: (203) 778-2168

FLORIDA

Intel Corp.
600 West Hillsboro Blvd.
Suite 348
Deerfield Beach 33441
Tel: (800) 628-8686
FAX: (305) 421-2444

Intel Corp.
2250 Lucien Way
Suite 100
Suite 8
Maitland 32751
Tel: (800) 628-8686
FAX: (407) 660-1283

GEORGIA

Intel Corp.
20 Technology Park
Suite 150
Norcross 30092
Tel: (800) 628-8686
FAX: (404) 448-0875

IDAHO

Intel Corp.
910 W. Main Street
Suite 236
Boise 83702
Tel: (800) 628-8686
FAX: (208) 331-2295

ILLINOIS

Intel Corp.
300 North Martingale Road
Suite 400
Schaumburg 60173
Tell: (800) 628-8686
FAX: (708) 605-9762

INDIANA

Intel Corp.
8041 Knue Road
Indianapolis 46250
Tel: (800) 628-8686
FAX: (317) 577-4939

MARYLAND

Intel Corp.
131 National Bus. Pkwy
Suite 200
Annapolis Junction 20701
Tel: (800) 628-8686
FAX: (301) 206-3678

MASSACHUSETTS

Intel Corp.
Nagog Park
125 Nagog Park
Acton 01720
Tel: (800) 628-8686
FAX: (508) 266-3867

MICHIGAN

Intel Corp.
32255 North Western Hwy.
Suite 212, Tri Atria
Farmington Hills 48334
Tel: (800) 628-8686
FAX: (313) 851-8770

MINNESOTA

Intel Corp.
3500 West 80th Street
Suite 360
Bloomington 55431
Tel: (800) 628-8686
TWX: 910-576-2867
FAX: (612) 831-6497

NEW JERSEY

Intel Corp.
2001 Route 46
Suite 310
Parsippany 07054
Tel: (800) 628-8686
FAX: (201) 402-4893

Intel Corp.
Lincroft Center
125 Half Mile Road
Red Bank 07701
Tel: (800) 628-8686
FAX: (908) 747-0983

NEW YORK

Intel Corp.
850 Cross Keys Office Pk
Fairport 14450
Tel: (800) 628-8686
TWX: 510-253-7391
FAX: (716) 223-2561

Intel Corp.
2950 Expressway Drive
Islandia 11722
Tel: (800) 628-8686
TWX: 510-227-6236
FAX: (516) 348-7939

OHIO

Intel Corp.
56 Milford Drive
Suite 205
Hudson 44236
Tel: (800) 628-8686
FAX: (216) 528-1026

*†Intel Corp.
3401 Park Center Drive
Suite 220
Dayton 45414
Tel: (800) 628-8686
TWX: 810-450-2528
FAX: (513) 890-8658

OKLAHOMA

Intel Corp.
6801 North Broadway
Suite 115
Oklahoma City 73162
Tel: (800) 628-8686
FAX: (405) 840-9819

OREGON

Intel Corp.
15254 NW Greenbrier
Pkwy
Building B
Beaverton 97006
Tel: (800) 628-8686
TWX: 910-467-8741
FAX: (503) 645-8181

PENNSYLVANIA

Intel Corp.
925 Harvest Drive
Suite 200
Blue Bell 19422
Tel: (800) 628-8686
FAX: (215) 641-0785

SOUTH CAROLINA

Intel Corp.
7403 Parklane Road
Suite 4
Columbia 29223
Tel: (800) 628-8686
FAX: (803) 788-7999

Intel Corp.
100 Executive Center Dr
Suite 109, B183
Greenville 29615
Tel: (800) 628-8686
FAX: (803) 297-3401

TEXAS

Intel Corp.
8911 Capital of Texas Hwy
Suite 4230
Austin 78759
Tel: (800) 628-8686
FAX: (512) 338-9335

Intel Corp.
5000 Quorum Drive
Suite 750
Dallas 75240
Tel: (800) 628-8686
FAX: (214) 233-1325

Intel Corp.
20405 State Hwy 249
Suite 880
Houston 77070
Tel: (800) 628-8686
TWX: 910-881-2490
FAX: (713) 376-2891

UTAH

Intel Corp.
428 East 6400 South
Suite 135
Murray 84107
Tel: (800) 628-8686
FAX: (801) 268-1457

WASHINGTON

Intel Corp.
2800 156th Avenue SE
Suite 105
Bellevue 98007
Tel: (800) 628-8686
FAX: (206) 746-4495

WISCONSIN

Intel Corp.
400 North Executive Drive
Suite 401
Brookfield 53005
Tel: (800) 628-8686
FAX: (414) 789-2746

CANADA

BRITISH COLUMBIA

Intel of Canada, Ltd.
999 Canada Place
Suite 404
Suite 11
Vancouver V6C 3E2
Tel: (800) 628-8686
FAX: (604) 844-2813

ONTARIO

Intel of Canada, Ltd.
2650 Queensview Drive
Suite 250
Ottawa K2B 8H6
Tel: (800) 628-8686
FAX: (613) 820-5936

Intel of Canada, Ltd.
190 Attwell Drive
Suite 500
Rexdale M9W 6H8
Tel: (800) 628-8686
FAX: (416) 675-2438

QUEBEC

Intel of Canada, Ltd.
1 Rue Holiday, Tour West
Suite 320
Pt. Claire H9R 5N3
Tel: (800) 628-8686
FAX: 514-694-0064

NORTH AMERICAN SERVICE OFFICES

Computervision

Intel Corporation's North American Preferred Service Provider
Central Dispatch: 1-800-876-SERV (1-800-876-7378)

ALABAMA
Birmingham
Huntsville

ALASKA
Anchorage

ARIZONA
Phoenix
Tucson

ARKANSAS
North Little Rock

CALIFORNIA
Concord
Los Angeles
Ontario
Orange
Redwood City
Sacramento
San Diego
San Francisco
Van Nuys

COLORADO
Colorado Springs
Denver

CONNECTICUT
E. Windsor
Middlebury

FLORIDA
Ft. Lauderdale
Jacksonville
Miami
Orlando
Pensacola
Tampa

GEORGIA
Atlanta

HAWAII
Honolulu

ILLINOIS
Chicago
Wood Dale

INDIANA
Carmel
Evansville
Ft. Wayne
South Bend

IOWA
Cedar Rapids
Davenport
West Des Moines

KANSAS
Kansas City
Wichita

KENTUCKY
Louisville
Madisonville

LOUISIANA
Baton Rouge
New Orleans

MAINE
Auburn

MARYLAND
Baltimore

MASSACHUSETTS
Bedfoird
S. Easton

MICHIGAN
Detroit
Flint
Grand Rapids
Lansing
Troy

MINNESOTA
Minneapolis

MISSOURI
Springfield
Street Louis

MISSISSIPPI
Jackson

NEW HAMPSHIRE
Manchester*

MONTANA
Butte

NEBRASKA
Omaha

NEW JERSEY
Cherry Hill
Hamilton Township
Westfield

NEW MEXICO
Albuquerque

NEW YORK
Albany
Binghampton
Buffalo
Farmingdale
New York City
Rochester
Dryden

NORTH CAROLINA
Ashville
Charlotte
Greensboro
Raleigh
Wilmington

OHIO
Cincinnati
Cleveland
Columbus
Dayton

OKLAHOMA
Oklahoma City
Tulsa

OREGON
Beaverton

PENNSYLVANIA
Camp Hill
Erie
Pittsburgh
Wayne

SOUTH CAROLINA
Charleston
Columbia
Greenville

TENNESSEE
Chattanooga
Knoxville
Memphis
Nashville

TEXAS
Austin
Houston
Dallas
Tyler

UTAH
Salt Lake City

VERMONT
White River Junction

VIRGINIA
Charlottesville
Richmond
Roanoke
Virginia Beach

WASHINGTON
Renton
Richland

WASHINGTON D.C.*

WEST VIRGINIA
Charleston

WISCONSIN
Milwaukee

CANADA
Calgary
Edmonton
Fredericton
Halifax
Mississauga
Montreal
Ottawa
Toronto
Vancouver, BC*
Winnipeg
Quebec City
Regina
St.John's